MW00807915

SSC 2013 – 2019

Voume II: 2015 – 2017

Introduction

In your hand is a collection of fantastic essays. Written by author Scott Alexander on his long-running blog Slate Star Codex (SSC), these essays taken as a whole are a treasure.

Scott (a pseudonym) is a thinker, a humanist, philosopher and nerd, and his writing is rich, meaty, snarky and occasionally exasperating. In short, this book is worth your time.

Great essays make me talk back to the author, either in anger or joy – I've done both reading Slate Star Codex over the years. Scott is a great essayist, and his readers are rabid – we all look forward to a long writing career ahead.

Unfortunately, we got the opposite of more essays in 2020: SSC was recently taken down by Scott as he navigates his day job and the demands of being an on-line personality – as part of a disagreement with the New York Times, he took down his site. Long-time readers took up the charge to archive and republish Scott's best work, most notably online at Slate Star Codex Abridged.

The thought that the Codex could be lost is troubling: I was inspired by the work at SSC Abridged and my mind went immediately to getting these essays down in a more durable form. Personally I like paper for reading, and wanted to share a paper version of these.

I thank Scott for releasing his work into the Creative Commons – I hope efforts like this are exactly what he wawnted to enable – and I thank the SSC Abridged team first for their diligent efforts preserving these essays and getting them into a form that could be translated into paper form.

Some notes about the books themselves: first, the text here appears unedited from Scott's originals, for better or worse. It's possible we would engage in a second run with a copy editing phase, but I hypothesized at the beginning of the publishing process that these essays would "hold up" in print form as is, and I think generally that hypothesis is born out by our ARC print run.

Second, Scott liberally refers to and uses images in his blog, from meme references to charts. For this initial run, I was unable to determine licensing status of the images, and therefore, they are not included. It is my goal to add images, charts and a light copy edit in subsequent editions.

Finally, something new and fun: the indexes were generated by OpenAI's

GPT-3. Indexing of one thousand pages of essays is not a trivial job, but the results show a little bit about the future of those who work with words: our final run of the index was completed in 16 minutes of wall clock time. The index is not perfect; in particular it could use a sort of combination and sanitation step. However, it seems clear a professional indexer would greatly benefit from being able to work with GPT-3 in the future; in any event, I personally welcome our robot indexing overlords, and I'm glad they got a chance to read Scott's work.

Enjoy this work, made possible by Scott and the great minds behind the Creative Commons who saw a better future and worked to make it come about.

Peter Vessenes
Bainbridge Island, Washington
September, 2020

Questions or Comments are welcome: peter@vessenes.com.

LIBRARY of CONGRESS CATALOGUING DATA
Names: Alexander, Scott, author
Title: Slate Star Codex: Essays Volume II: 2015-2017
Description: Scott Alexander writes on topics ranging from AI to Math,
Philosophy and Medicine.
Identifiers: ISBN 978-1-7357971-1-3
Subjects: Philosophy | Economics | Medicine | AI

Printed in the United States of America on acid-free paper.

First Edition.

To Scott
Lawrence
Hal
& James

The first principle is that you must not fool yourself – and you are the easiest person to fool.

Richard P. Feynman

Contents

I 2015   **16**

1 Ethics Offsets   17

2 The Phatic And The Anti-Inductive   21

3 The Influenza Of Evil   28

4 The Parable Of The Talents   33

5 Answer to Job   48

6 Universal Love, Said The Cactus Person   53

7 ...And I Show You How Deep The Rabbit Hole Goes   61

8 Against Tulip Subsidies   78

9 CBT In The Water Supply   85

10 The Goddess of Everything Else   94

11 It Was You Who Made My Blue Eyes Blue   100

12 Meat Your Doom   116

13 What Developmental Milestones Are You Missing?   120

14 Book Review: Hive Mind   127

II 2016   **139**

15 Side Effects May Include Anything   140

16 The Ideology Is Not The Movement   143

17 Why Were Early Psychedelicists So Weird?   162

18 Book Review: Age of Em   167

19 It's Bayes All The Way Up   189

20 Book Review: House of God   200

21 SSC Journal Club: Expert Prediction Of Experiments   214

III 2017   219

22 Considerations On Cost Disease   220
23 Book Review: Behavior: The Control Of Perception   239
24 Book Review: Seeing Like A State   249
25 Guided By The Beauty Of Our Weapons   278
26 The Atomic Bomb Considered As Hungarian High School Science
    Fair Project   294
27 Hungarian Education II: Four Nobel Truths   307
28 Hungarian Education III: Mastering The Core Teachings Of The
    Budapestians   310
29 SSC Journal Club: AI Timelines   317
30 My IRB Nightmare   325
31 Book Review: Surfing Uncertainty   341
32 Predictive Processing And Perceptual Control   359
33 How Did New Atheism Fail So Miserably?   363
34 Ars Longa, Vita Brevis   368
35 Book Review: Legal Systems Very Different From Ours   376
Index   391

Book I

2015

Ethics Offsets

January 4, 2015

I

Some people buy voluntary carbon offsets. Suppose they worry about global warming and would feel bad taking a long unnecessary plane trip that pollutes the atmosphere. So instead of not doing it, they take the plane trip, then pay for some environmental organization to clean up an amount of carbon equal to or greater than the amount of carbon they emitted. They're happy because they got their trip, future generations are happy because the atmosphere is cleaner, everyone wins.

We can generalize this to ethics offsets. Suppose you really want to visit an oppressive dictatorial country so you can see the beautiful tourist sights there[1]. But you worry that by going there and spending money, you're propping up the dictatorship. So you take your trip, but you also donate some money to opposition groups and humanitarian groups opposing the dictatorship and helping its victims, at an amount such that you are confident that the oppressed people of the country would prefer you take both actions (visit + donate) than that you take neither action.

I know I didn't come up with this concept, but I'm having trouble finding out who did, so no link for now.

A recent post, Nobody Is Perfect, Everything Is Commensurable[2], sug-

---

[1] http://www.dailymail.co.uk/news/article-2638213/Tourist-took-camera-inside-North-Korea-expected-really-really-sad-people-shocked-seemingly-ordinary-lives-citizens.html

[2] https://slatestarcodex.com/2014/12/19/nobody-is-perfect-everything-is-commensurable/

gests that if you are averse to activism but still feel you have an obligation to improve the world, you can discharge that obligation by giving to charity. This is not quite an ethics offset – it's not exchanging a transgression for a donation so much as saying that a donation is a better way of helping than the thing you were worried about transgressing against anyway – but it's certainly pretty similar.

As far as I can tell, the simplest cases here are 100% legit. I can't imagine anyone saying "You may not take that plane flight you want, even if you donate so much to the environment that in the end it cleans up twice as much carbon dioxide as you produced. You must sit around at home, feeling bored and lonely, and letting the atmosphere be more polluted than if you had made your donation".

But here are two cases I am less certain about.

II

Suppose you feel some obligation to be a vegetarian – either because you believe animal suffering is bad, or you have enough moral uncertainty around the topic for the ethical calculus to come out against. Is it acceptable to continue eating animals, but also donate money to animal rights charities?

A simple example: you eat meat, but also donate money to a group lobbying for cage=free eggs. You are confident that if chickens could think and vote, the average chicken would prefer a world in which you did both these things to a world in which you did neither. This seems to me much like the cases above.

A harder example. You eat meat, but also donate money to a group that convinces people to become vegetarian. Jeff Kaufman and Brian Tomasik suggest[3] that about $10 to $50 is enough to make one person become vegetarian for one year by sponsoring what are apparently very convincing advertisements.

Eating meat is definitely worth $1000 per year for me. So if I donate $1000 to vegetarian advertising, then eat meat, I'm helping turn between twenty and a hundred people vegetarian for a year, and helping twenty to one hundred times as many animals as I would be by becoming vegetarian myself. Clearly this is an excellent deal for me and an excellent deal for animals.

But I still can't help feeling like there's something really wrong here. It's

---

[3]http://www.jefftk.com/p/pay-other-people-to-go-vegetarian-for-you

not just the low price of convincing people – even if I was 100% guaranteed that the calculations were right, I'd still feel just as weird. Part of it is a sense of duping others – would they be as eager to become vegetarian if they knew the ads that convinced them were sponsored by meat-eaters?

Maybe! Suppose we go to all of the people convinced by the ads, tell them "I paid for that ad that convinced you, and I still eat meat. Now what?" They answer "Well, I double-checked the facts in the ad and they're all true. That you eat meat doesn't make anything in the advertisement one bit less convincing. So I'm going to stay vegetarian." Now what? Am I off the hook?

A second objection: universalizability. If *everyone* decides to solve animal suffering by throwing money at advertisers, there is no one left to advertise to and nothing gets solved. You just end up with a world where 100% of ads on TVs, in newspapers, and online are about becoming vegetarian, and everyone watches them and says "Well, I'm doing my part! I'm paying for these ads!"

Counter-objection: At that point, no one will be able to say with a straight face that every $50 spent on ads converts one person to vegetarianism. If I follow the maxim "Either be vegetarian, or donate enough money to be 90% sure I am converting at least two other people to vegetarianism", this maxim *does* universalize, since after animal suffering ads have saturated a certain percent of the population, no one can be 90% sure of convincing anyone else.

As far as I can tell, this is weird but ethical.

III

The second troublesome case is a little more gruesome.

Current estimates suggest that $3340 worth of donations to global health causes saves, on average, one life.

Let us be excruciatingly cautious and include a two-order-of-magnitude margin of error. At $334,000, we are *super duper sure* we are saving at least one life.

So. Say I'm a millionaire with a spare $334,000, and there's a guy I *really* don't like...

Okay, fine. Get the irrelevant objections out of the way first and establish the least convenient possible world[4]. I'm a criminal mastermind, it'll be the perfect crime, and there's zero chance I'll go to jail. I can make it look completely natural, like a heart attack or something, so I'm not going to terrorize

---

[4] https://www.greaterwrong.com/lw/2k/the_least_convenient_possible_world/

the city or waste police time and resources. The guy's not supporting a family and doesn't have any friends who will be heartbroken at his death. There's no political aspect to my grudge, so this isn't going to silence the enemies of the rich or anything like that. I myself have a terminal disease, and so the damage that I inflict upon my own soul with the act – or however it is Leah always phrases it – will perish with me immediately afterwards. There is no God, or if there is one He respects ethics offsets when you get to the Pearly Gates.

Or you know what? Don't get the irrelevant objections out of the way. We can offset those too. The police will waste a lot of time investigating the murder? Maybe I'm *very* rich and I can make a big anonymous donation to the local police force that will more than compensate them for their trouble and allow them to hire extra officers to take up the slack. The local citizens will be scared there's a killer on the loose? They'll forget all about it once they learn taxes have been cut to zero percent thanks to an anonymous donation to the city government from a local tycoon.

Even what seems to me the most desperate and problematic objection – that maybe the malarial Africans saved by global health charities have lives that are in some qualitative way just not as valuable as those of happy First World citizens contributing to the global economy – can be fixed. If I've got enough money, a few hundred thousand to a million ought to be able to save the life of a local person in no way distinguishable from my victim. Heck, since this is a hypothetical problem and I have infinite money, why not save *ten* local people?

The best I can do here is to say that I am crossing a Schelling fence[5] which might also be crossed by people who will be less scrupulous in making sure their offsets are in order. But perhaps I could offset that too. Also, we could assume I will never tell anybody. Also, anyone can just go murder someone right now without offsetting, so we're not exactly talking about a big temptation for the unscrupulous.

---

[5] https://www.greaterwrong.com/lw/ase/schelling_fences_on_slippery_slopes/

— 2 —

The Phatic And The Anti-Inductive

January 11, 2015

I

Ozy recently taught me the word "phatic". It means talking for the sake of talking.

The classic example is small talk. "Hey." "Hey." "How are you?" "Fine, and you?" "Fine." No information has been exchanged. Even if the person involved wasn't fine, they'd still say *fine*. Indeed, at least in this country giving an information-bearing response to "how are you?" is a mild social faux pas.

Some people call this "social grooming behavior" and it makes sense. It's just a way of saying "Hello, I acknowledge you and still consider you an acquaintance. There's nothing wrong between us. Carry on." That you are willing to spend ten seconds holding a useless conversation with them signals this just fine.

We can go a little more complex. Imagine I'm calling a friend from college after five years out of contact; I've heard he's got a company now and I want to ask him for a job. It starts off "Hey, how are you?", segues into "And how are the wife and kids?", then maybe into "What are you doing with yourself these days?" and finally "Hey, I have a big favor to ask you." If you pick up the phone and say "Hello, it's Scott from college, can you help me get a job?" this is rude. It probably sounds like you're *using* him.

And I mean, you are. If I cared about him deeply as a person I probably would have called him at some point in the last five years, before I needed something. But by mutual consent we both sweep that under the rug by having a few minutes of meaningless personal conversation beforehand. The information exchanged doesn't matter – "how's your business going?" is just as good as "how's your wife and kids?" is just as good as "how are your parents doing?". The point is to clock a certain number of minutes about something vaguely personal, so that the request seems less abrupt.

We can go even more complex. By the broadest definition, phatic communication is equivalent to signaling.

Consider a very formulaic conservative radio show. Every week, the host talks about some scandal that liberals have been involved in. Then she explains why it means the country is going to hell. I don't think the listeners really care that a school in Vermont has banned Christmas decorations or whatever. The point is to convey this vague undercurrent of "Hey, there are other people out there who think like you, we all agree with you, you're a good person, you can just sit here and listen and feel reassured that you're right." Anything vaguely conservative in content will be equally effective, regardless of whether the listener cares about the particular issue.

II

Douglas Adams once said there was a theory that if anyone ever understood the Universe, it would disappear and be replaced by something even more incomprehensible. He added that there was another theory that this had already happened.

These sorts of things – things such that if you understand them, they get more complicated until you don't – are called "anti-inductive".

The classic anti-inductive institution is the stock market. Suppose you found a pattern in the stock market. For example, it always went down on Tuesdays, then up on Wednesdays. Then you could buy lots of stock Tuesday evening, when it was low, and sell it Wednesday, when it was high, and be assured of making free money.

But lots of people want free money, so lots of people will try this plan. There will be so much demand for stock on Tuesday evening that there won't be enough stocks to fill it all. Desperate buyers will bid up the prices. Meanwhile, on Wednesday, everyone will sell their stocks at once, causing a huge glut and making prices go down. This will continue until the trend of low prices Tuesday, high prices Wednesday disappears.

So in general, it should be impossible to exploit your pattern-finding ability to profit of the stock market unless you are the smartest and most resourceful person in the world. That is, maybe stocks go up every time the Fed cuts interest rates, but Goldman Sachs knows that too, so they probably have computers programmed to buy so much stock milliseconds after the interest rate announcement is made that the prices will stabilize on that alone. That means that unless you can predict better than, or respond faster than, Goldman Sachs, you can't exploit your knowledge of this pattern and shouldn't even try.

Here's something I haven't heard described as anti-inductive before: job-seeking.

When I was applying for medical residencies, I asked some people in the field to help me out with my interviewing skills.

"Why did you want to become a doctor?" they asked.

"I want to help people," I said.

"Oh God," they answered. "No, anything but that. Nothing says 'person exactly like every other bright-eyed naive new doctor' than wanting to help people. You're trying to distinguish yourself from the pack!"

"Then… uh… I want to hurt people?"

"Okay, tell you what. You have any experience treating people in disaster-prone Third World countries?"

"I worked at a hospital in Haiti after the earthquake there."

"Perfect. That's inspirational as hell. Talk about how you want to become a doctor because the people of Haiti taught you so much."

Wanting to help people is a great reason to become a doctor. When Hippocrates was taking his first students, he was probably really impressed by the one guy who said he wanted to help people. But since that time it's become cliche, overused. Now it signals people who can't come up with an original answer. So you need something better.

During my interviews, I talked about my time working in Haiti. I got to talk to some of the other applicants, and they talked about *their* time working in Ethiopia, or Bangladesh, or Nicaragua, or wherever. Apparently the "stand out by working in a disaster-prone Third World country" plan was sufficiently successful that everyone started using, and now the people who do it don't stand out at all. My interviewer was probably thinking "Oh God, what Third World country is *this* guy going to start blabbering about how much he learned from?" and moving my application to the REJECT pile as soon as I opened my mouth.

I am getting the same vibe from the critiques of OKCupid profiles in the last open thread. OKCupid seems very susceptible to everybody posting identical quirky pictures of themselves rock-climbing, then talking about how fun-loving and down-to-earth they are. On the other hand, every deviation from that medium has *also* been explored.

"I'm going for 'quirky yet kind'".

"Done."

"Sarcastic, yet nerdy?"

"Done."

"Outdoorsy, yet intellectual."

"Done."

"Introverted, yet a zombie."

"I thought we went over this. Zombies. Are. Super. Done.[1]"

III

I've been thinking about this lately in the context of psychotherapy.

I'm not talking about the very specific therapies, the ones where they teach special cognitive skills, or expose you to spiders to cure your arachnophobia. They don't let me do those yet. I'm talking about what's called "supportive therapy", where you're just talking to people and trying to make them feel generally better.

When I was first starting out, I tried to do therapy anti-inductively. I figured that I had to come up with something unexpected, something that the patient hadn't thought of. Some kind of brilliant interpretation that put all of their problems in a new light. This went poorly. It tended to be a lot of "Well, have you tried [obvious thing?]", them saying they had, and me escalating to "Well, have you tried [long shot that probably wouldn't work]?"

(I wonder if this was Freud's strategy: "Okay, he says he's depressed, I can't just tell him to cheer up, probably everybody says that. Can't just tell him to accept his sadness, that one's obvious too. Got to come up with something really original... uh..."HAVE YOU CONSIDERED THAT YOU WANT TO KILL YOUR FATHER AND MARRY YOUR MOTHER??!")

Now I tend more to phatic therapy. This happened kind of by accident. Some manic people have a symptom called "pressured speech" which means they never shut up and they never let you get a word in edgewise. Eventually, more out of surrender than out of a strategic plan, I gave up and stopped

---

[1] https://slatestarcodex.com/2014/12/07/a-story-with-zombies/

trying. I just let them talk, nodded my head, said "Yeah, that sounds bad" when they said something bad-sounding, said "Oh, that's good" when they said something good-sounding.

After a while I realized this went at least as well as any other therapy I was doing, plus the patients really liked me and thought I was great and gave me lots of compliments.

So after that, "active listening" became sort of my default position for supportive therapy. Get people talking. Let them talk. Nod my head as if I am deeply concerned about their problems. Accept their effusive praise about how well I seem to be understanding them.

This is clearly phatic. I would say the ritual is "High status person is willing to listen to my problems. That means society considers my problems important and considers me important. It means my problems are okay to have and I'm not in trouble for having them." As long as I seem vaguely approving, the ritual reaches its predetermined conclusion.

IV

I was thinking about this recently several friends have told me how much she hated "therapist speak". You know, things like "I feel your pain" or "And how does that make you feel?"

I interpret this as an anti-inductive perspective on therapy. The first therapist to say "I feel your pain" may have impressed her patients – a person who herself can actually feel all my hurt and anger! Amazing! But this became such a standard in the profession that it became the Default Therapist Response. Now it's a signal of "I care so little about your pain that I can't even bother to say anything other than the default response." When a therapist says "I feel your pain," it's easy to imagine that in her head she's actually planning what she's going to make for dinner or something.

So just as some people find it useful to divide the world into "ask culture" and "guess culture", I am finding it useful to divide the world into "phatic culture" and "anti-inductive culture".

There are people for whom "I feel your pain" is exactly the right response. It shows that you are sticking to your therapist script, it urges them to stick to their patient script, and at the end of the session they feel like the ritual has been completed and they feel better.

There are other people for whom "I feel your pain" is the most enraging thing you could possibly say. It shows that you're not taking them seriously or engaging with them, just saying exactly the same thing you do to all your other patients.

There are people for whom coming up with some sort of unique perspective or clever solution for their problems is exactly the right response. Even if it doesn't work, it at least proves that you are thinking hard about what they are saying.

There are other people for whom coming up with some sort of unique perspective or clever solution is the most enraging thing you could possibly do. At the risk of perpetuating gender stereotypes, one of the most frequently repeated pieces of relationship advice I hear is "When a woman is telling you her problems, just listen and sympathize, don't try to propose solutions". It sounds like the hypothetical woman in this advice is looking for a phatic answer.

I think myself and most of my friends fall far to the anti-inductive side, with little tolerance for the phatic side. And I think we probably typical-mind other people as doing the same.

This seems related to the classic geek discomfort with small-talk, with pep rallies, and with normal object-level politics. I think it might also be part of the problem I had with social skills when I was younger – I remember talking to people, panicking because I couldn't think of any way to make the conversation unusually entertaining or enlightening, and feeling like I had been a failure for responding to the boring-weather-related question with a boring-weather-related answer. Very speculatively, I think it might have something to do with creepy romantic overtures – imagine the same mental pattern that made me jokingly consider giving "I want to hurt people" as my motivation for becoming a doctor, applied to a domain that I really don't understand on a fundamental enough level to know whether or not saying that is a good idea.

I've been trying to learn the skill of appreciating the phatic. I used to be very bad at sending out thank-you cards, because I figured if I sent a thank-you card that just said "Thank you for the gift, I really appreciate it" then they would think that the lack of personalization meant I wasn't *really* thankful. But personalizing a bunch of messages to people I often don't really know that well is hard and I ended up all miserable. Now I just send out the thank you card with the impersonal message, and most people are like "Oh, it was so nice of you to send me a card, I can tell you really appreciated it." This seems like an improvement.

As for psychotherapy, I think I'm going to default to phatic in most cases when I don't have some incredibly enlightening insight, then let my patients tell me if that's the wrong thing to do.

3

The Influenza Of Evil

January 13, 2015

I

A recent Cracked piece: Five Everyday Groups Society Says It's Okay To Mock[1]. It begins:

> There's a rule in comedy that says you shouldn't punch down. It's okay to make fun of someone rich and famous, because they're too busy molesting groupies with 100-dollar bills to notice, but if you make a joke at the expense of a homeless person, you're just an asshole. That said, we as a society have somehow decided on a few arbitrary exceptions to this rule.

"Somehow decided on a few arbitrary exceptions" isn't very technical. Let's see if we can do better.

Earlier this week, I wrote about . Something is anti-inductive if it fights back against your attempts to understand it. The classic example is the stock market. If someone learns that the stock market is always low on Tuesdays, then they'll buy lots of stocks on Tuesdays to profit from the anomaly. But this raises the demand for stocks on Tuesdays, and therefore stocks won't be low on Tuesdays anymore. To detect a pattern is to destroy the pattern.

The less classic example is job interviews where every candidate is trying to distinguish themselves from every other candidate. If someone learns that interviewers are impressed if you talk about your experience in tropical

---

[1]http://www.cracked.com/blog/5-everyday-groups-people-society-says-its-okay-to-mock/

medicine, then as more and more people catch on they'll all get experience in tropical medicine, it will become cliche, and people won't be impressed by it anymore.

Evil, too, is anti-inductive.

The Nazis were very successful evildoers, at least for a while. Part of their success was convincing people – at least the German people, but sometimes also foreigners – that they were the good guys. And they *were* able to convince a lot of people, because people can be pretty dumb, a lot of them kind of just operate by pattern-matching, and the Nazis didn't match enough patterns to set off people's alarms.

Neo-Nazis cannot be called "successful" in any sense of the word. Their PR problem isn't just that they're horrible – a lot of groups are horrible and do much better than neo-Nazis. Their PR problem is that they're horrible in exactly the way that our culture formed memetic antibodies against. Our pattern-matching faculties have been trained on Nazis being evil. The alarm bells that connect everything about Nazis to evil are hypersensitive, so much so that even contingent features of the Nazis remain universally acknowledged evil-signals.

It would be premature to say that we will never have to worry about fascism again. But for now, we are probably pretty safe from fascism that starts its sales pitch with "Hi, I'm fascism! Want a swastika armband?"

Huey Long supposedly[2] predicted that "Fascism in America will attempt to advance under the banner of anti-fascism." I'm not sure I like the saying as it stands – it seems too susceptible to Hitler Jr. telling Churchill Jr. that he's marching under the banner of anti-fascism which proves he's the *real* fascist. Then again, in a world where capitalism marches under the banner of "socialism with Chinese characteristics"[3], who knows? I would prefer to say that fascism will, at the very least, advance in a way which carefully takes our opposition to fascism into account.

Sure enough, people who had learned to be wary of fascism were still highly susceptible to communism, which wore its anti-fascism proudly on its sleeve as a symbol of how great it was. It convinced a lot of very smart people in the free world that it was the best thing since sliced bread, all while murdering tens of millions of people. Meanwhile, our memetic immune systems were sitting watchfully at their posts, thinking "Well, this doesn't look at all

---

[2] http://msgboard.snopes.com/cgi-bin/ultimatebb.cgi?ubb=print_topic;f=101;t=000330
[3] http://en.wikipedia.org/wiki/Socialism_with_Chinese_characteristics

like Nazism. They're saying all the right stuff about equality, which is like the *opposite* of what the Nazis said. I'm giving them a pass."

In fact, I'll make the analogy more explicit. Every winter, there's a flu epidemic. Every spring and summer, people's bodies put in a lot of effort making antibodies to *last year's* flu. The next winter, the flu mutates a little, a new virus with new antigens starts a new epidemic, and the immune system doesn't have a clue: "This virus doesn't have the very very specific characteristic I've learned to associate with the flu. Maybe it wants to be my friend!" This is why we need the WHO to predict what the up-and-coming flu virus will be and give us vaccines against it; it's also why their job is so hard; they don't know what's coming, except that it will look different from however it's looked before.

Nowadays most people's memetic immune systems have some antibodies to communism, and people talking with Russian accents about how we need to eliminate the bourgeoisie and institute a dictatorship of the proletariat sends shiver up the spines of a lot of people. Nowadays an openly Communist party faces the same uphill battle as an openly Nazi party.

But that just means that if there's some other evil on the horizon, it probably won't resemble either fascism *or* communism. It will be movement about which everyone's saying "These new guys are so great! They don't pattern-match to any of the kinds of evil we know about at all!" By Long's formulation, it may very well be marching under the banners of anti-fascism *and* anti-Communism.

(I'm not vagueblogging, by the way. I honestly don't have anyone in mind here. The whole point is that it's probably someone I'm not expecting. And if you say "I KNOW EXACTLY WHICH GROUP IT WILL BE, BASED ON THOSE CRITERIA IT'S CLEARLY X!" consider the possibility that you're missing the point.)

II

But getting back to the Cracked article.

We as a society have mostly figured out that shouting "GET A JOB, LOSER!" at the homeless is mean. We have mostly figured out that shouting "YOU'RE GOING TO HELL" at people of different religions is bad. We're even, slowly but surely, starting to wonder whether there's something problematic about shouting "FAGGOTS!" at the local gay couple.

Stupid bullies will continue to do those things, just as stupid investors will continue to read "How To Beat The Stock Market" books published in 1985, and stupid socialites will continue to wear the fashion that was cool six months ago.

But smart bullies are driven by their desire to have their bullying make them more popular, to get the rest of the world pointing and laughing with them. In a

bubble, shouting "FAGGOT" at gay people is no longer a good way to do that. The smart bullies in these circles have long since stopped shouting at gays – not because they've become any nicer, but because that's no longer the best way to keep their audience laughing along with them.

Cracked starts off by naming mentally ill celebrities as a group society considers it okay to mock. This doesn't seem surprising. Nowadays people talk a lot about punching-up versus punching-down. But that just means bullies who want to successfully punch down will come up with a way to make it look like they're punching up. Take a group that's high-status and wealthy, but find a subset who are actually in serious trouble and mock *them*, all the while shouting "I'M PUNCHING UP, I'M PUNCHING UP!". Thus mentally ill celebrities.

The other examples are harder to figure out. I would argue that they're ones that are easy to victim-blame (ie obesity), ones that punch down on axes orthogonal to the rich-poor axis we usually think about and so don't look like punching down (ie virginity), or ones that are covertly associated with an outgroup. In every case, I would expect the bullies involved, when they're called upon, it to loudly protest "But that's not real bullying! It's not like [much more classic example of bullying, like mocking the homeless]!" And they will be right. It's just different enough to be the hot new bullying frontier that most people haven't caught onto yet.

I think the Cracked article is doing good work. It's work that I also try to do (see for example number 6 here[4], which corresponds to Cracked's number 5). It's the work of pointing these things out, saying "Actually, no, that's bullying", until eventually it sinks into the culture, the bullies realize they'll be called out if they keep it up, and they move on to some new target.

All of this ties *way* into the dynamic I talked about in *Untitled*. I mean, look at the people on Cracked's list of whom society says it's okay to mock. Virgins. The obese. People who live in their parents' basements. Generalize

---

[4]https://slatestarcodex.com/2014/01/15/ten-things-i-want-to-stop-seeing-on-the-internet-in-2014/

"mentally ill celebrities" just a little bit to get "people who are financially well-off but non-neurotypical" and there you go.

I apologize for irresponsibly claiming to have found a pattern in an anti-inductive domain. You may now all adjust your behavior to make me wrong.

The Parable Of The Talents

January 31, 2015

Content note: scrupulosity and self-esteem triggers, IQ, brief discussion of weight and dieting. Not good for growth mindset.

I

I sometimes blog about research into IQ and human intelligence. I think most readers of this blog already know IQ is 50% to 80% heritable[1] , and that it's so important for intellectual pursuits that eminent scientists in some fields have average IQs around 150 to 160[2] . Since IQ this high only appears in 1/10,000 people or so, it beggars coincidence to believe this represents anything but a very strong filter for IQ (or something correlated with it) in reaching that level. If you saw a group of dozens of people who were 7'0 tall on average, you'd assume it was a basketball team or some other group selected for height, not a bunch of botanists who were all very tall by coincidence.

A lot of people find this pretty depressing. Some worry that taking it seriously might damage the "growth mindset" people need to fully actualize their potential. This is important and I want to discuss it eventually, but not now. What I want to discuss now is people who feel *personally* depressed. For example, a comment from last week:

> I'm sorry to leave self a self absorbed comment, but reading this
> really upset me and I just need to get this off my chest... How
> is a person supposed to stay sane in a culture that prizes intel-
> ligence above everything else – especially if, as Scott suggests,

---

[1] http://en.wikipedia.org/wiki/Heritability_of_IQ

[2] http://infoproc.blogspot.com/2008/07/annals-of-psychometry-iqs-of-eminent.html

Human Intelligence Really Is the Key to the Future – when they themselves are not particularly intelligent and, apparently, have no potential to ever become intelligent? Right now I basically feel like pond scum.

I hear these kinds of responses every so often, so I should probably learn to expect them. I never do. They seem to me precisely backwards. There's a moral gulf here, and I want to throw stories and intuitions at it until enough of them pile up at the bottom to make a passable bridge. But first, a comparison:

Some people think body weight is biologically/genetically determined. Other people think it's based purely on willpower – how strictly you diet, how much you can bring yourself to exercise. These people get into some pretty acrimonious debates.

Overweight people, and especially people who feel unfairly stigmatized for being overweight, tend to cluster on the biologically determined side. And although not all believers in complete voluntary control of weight are mean to fat people, the people who are mean to fat people pretty much all insist that weight is voluntary and easily changeable.

Although there's a lot of debate over the science here, there seems to be broad agreement on both sides that the more compassionate, sympathetic, progressive position, the position promoted by the kind of people who are really worried about stigma and self-esteem, is that weight is biologically determined.

And the same is true of mental illness. Sometimes I see depressed patients whose families *really* don't get it. They say "Sure, my daughter feels down, but she needs to realize that's no excuse for shirking her responsibilities. She needs to just pick herself up and get on with her life." On the other hand, most depressed people say that their depression is more fundamental than that, not a thing that can be overcome by willpower, certainly not a thing you can just 'shake off'.

Once again, the compassionate/sympathetic/progressive side of the debate is that depression is something like biological, and cannot easily be overcome with willpower and hard work.

One more example of this pattern. There are frequent political debates in which conservatives (or straw conservatives) argue that financial success is the result of hard work, so poor people are just too lazy to get out of poverty. Then a liberal (or straw liberal) protests that hard work has nothing to do with it, success is determined by accidents of birth like who your parents are and what your skin color is et cetera, so the poor are blameless in their own predicament.

I'm oversimplifying things, but again the compassionate/sympathetic/progressive side of the debate – and the side endorsed by many of the poor themselves – is supposed to be that success is due to accidents of birth, and the less compassionate side is that success depends on hard work and perseverance and grit and willpower.

The obvious pattern is that attributing outcomes to things like genes, biology, and accidents of birth is kind and sympathetic. Attributing them to who works harder and who's "really trying" can stigmatize people who end up with bad outcomes and is generally viewed as Not A Nice Thing To Do.

And the weird thing, the thing I've never understood, is that intellectual achievement is the one domain that breaks this pattern.

Here it's would-be hard-headed conservatives arguing that intellectual greatness comes from genetics and the accidents of birth and demanding we "accept" this "unpleasant truth".

And it's would-be compassionate progressives who are insisting that no, it depends on who works harder, claiming anybody can be brilliant if they really try, warning us not to "stigmatize" the less intelligent as "genetically inferior".

I can come up with a few explanations for the sudden switch, but none of them are very principled and none of them, to me, seem to break the fundamental symmetry of the situation. I choose to maintain consistency by preserving the belief that overweight people, depressed people, and poor people aren't fully to blame for their situation – and neither are unintelligent people. It's accidents of birth all the way down. Intelligence is mostly genetic and determined at birth – and we've already determined in every other sphere that "mostly genetic and determined at birth" means you don't have to feel bad if you got the short end of the stick.

Consider for a moment Srinivasa Ramanujan, one of the greatest mathematicians of all time. He grew up in poverty in a one-room house in small-town India. He taught himself mathematics by borrowing books from local college students and working through the problems on his own until he reached the end of the solveable ones and had nowhere else to go but inventing ways to solve the unsolveable ones.

There are a lot of poor people in the United States today whose life circumstances prevented their parents from reading books to them as a child, prevented them from getting into the best schools, prevented them from attending college, et cetera. And pretty much all of those people *still* got more educational opportunities than Ramanujan did.

And from there we can go in one of two directions. First, we can say that a lot of intelligence is innate, that Ramanujan was a genius, and that we mortals cannot be expected to replicate his accomplishments.

Or second, we can say those poor people are *just not trying hard enough*.

Take "innate ability" out of the picture, and if you meet a poor person on the street begging for food, saying he never had a chance, your reply must be "Well, if you'd just borrowed a couple of math textbooks from the local library at age 12, you would have been a Fields Medalist by now. I hear that pays pretty well."

The best reason *not* to say that is that we view Ramanujan as intellectually gifted. But the very phrase tells us where we should classify that belief. Ramanujan's genius is a "gift" in much the same way your parents giving you a trust fund on your eighteenth birthday is a "gift", and it should be weighted accordingly in the moral calculus.

II

I shouldn't pretend I'm worried about this for the sake of the poor. I'm worried for *me*.

My last IQ-ish test was my SATs in high school. I got a perfect score in Verbal, and a good-but-not-great score in Math.

And in high school English, I got A++s in all my classes, Principal's Gold Medals, 100%s on tests, first prize in various state-wide essay contests, etc. In Math, I just barely by the skin of my teeth scraped together a pass in Calculus with a C-.

Every time I won some kind of prize in English my parents would praise me and say I was good and should feel good. My teachers would hold me up as an example and say other kids should try to be more like me. Meanwhile, when I would bring home a report card with a C- in math, my parents would have concerned faces and tell me they were disappointed and I wasn't living up to my potential and I needed to work harder et cetera.

And *I don't know which part bothered me more.*

Every time I was held up as an example in English class, I wanted to crawl under a rock and die. I didn't do it! I didn't study at all, half the time I did the homework in the car on the way to school, those essays for the statewide competition were thrown together on a lark without a trace of real effort. To praise me for any of it seemed and still seems utterly unjust.

On the other hand, to this day I believe I deserve a fricking *statue* for getting a C- in Calculus I. It should be in the center of the schoolyard, and have a plaque saying something like "Scott Alexander, who by making a herculean effort managed to pass Calculus I, even though they kept throwing random things after the little curly S sign and pretending it made sense."

And without some notion of innate ability, I don't know what to do with this experience. I don't want to have to accept the blame for being a lazy person who just didn't try hard enough in Math. But I *really* don't want to have to accept the credit for being a virtuous and studious English student who worked harder than his peers. I *know* there were people who worked harder than I did in English, who poured their heart and soul into that course – and who still got Cs and Ds. To deny innate ability is to devalue their efforts and sacrifice, while simultaneously giving me credit I don't deserve.

Meanwhile, there were some students who did better than I did in Math with seemingly zero effort. I didn't begrudge those students. But if they'd started trying to say they had exactly the same level of innate ability as I did, and the only difference was *they* were trying while *I* was slacking off, then I sure as hell would have begrudged them. Especially if I knew they were lazing around on the beach while I was poring over a textbook.

I tend to think of social norms as contracts bargained between different groups. In the case of attitudes towards intelligence, those two groups are smart people and dumb people. Since I was both at once, I got to make the bargain with myself, which simplified the bargaining process immensely. The deal I came up with was that I wasn't going to beat myself up over the areas I was bad at, but I also didn't get to become too cocky about the areas I was good at. It was all genetic luck of the draw either way. In the meantime, I would try to press as hard as I could to exploit my strengths and cover up my deficiencies. So far I've found this to be a really healthy way of treating myself, and it's the way I try to treat others as well.

III

The theme continues to be "Scott Relives His Childhood Inadequacies". So:

When I was 6 and my brother was 4, our mom decided that as an Over-achieving Jewish Mother she was contractually obligated to make both of us learn to play piano. She enrolled me in a Yamaha introductory piano class, and my younger brother in a Yamaha 'cute little kids bang on the keyboard' class.

A little while later, I noticed that my brother was now with me in my Introductory Piano class.

A little while later, I noticed that my brother was now by far the best student in my Introductory Piano Class, even though he had just started and was two or three years younger than anyone else there.

A little while later, Yamaha USA flew him to Japan to show him off before the Yamaha corporate honchos there.

Well, one thing led to another, and my brother won several international piano competitions, got a professorship in music at age 25, and now routinely gets news articles written about him calling him "among the top musicians of his generation".

Meanwhile, I was always a mediocre student at Yamaha. When the time came to try an instrument in elementary school, I went with the violin to see if maybe I'd find it more to my tastes than the piano. I was quickly sorted into the remedial class because I couldn't figure out how to make my instrument stop sounding like a wounded cat. After a year or so of this, I decided to switch to fulfilling my music requirement through a choir, and everyone who'd had to listen to me breathed a sigh of relief.

Every so often I wonder if somewhere deep inside me there is the potential to be "among the top musicians of my generation." I try to recollect whether my brother practiced harder than I did. My memories are hazy, but I don't think he practiced *much* harder until well after his career as a child prodigy had taken off. The cycle seemed to be that every time he practiced, things came fluidly to him and he would produce beautiful music and everyone would be amazed. And this must have felt great, and incentivized him to practice more, and that made him even better, so that the beautiful music came even more fluidly, and the praise became more effusive, until eventually he chose a full-time career in music and became amazing. Meanwhile, when I started practicing it always sounded like wounded cats, and I would get very cautious praise like "Good job, Scott, it sounded like that cat was hurt a little less badly than usual," and it made me frustrated, and want to practice less, which made me even worse, until eventually I quit in disgust.

On the other hand, I know people who want to get good at writing, and make a mighty resolution to write two hundred words a day every day, and then after the first week they find it's too annoying and give up. These people think I'm amazing, and why shouldn't they? I've written a few hundred to a few thousand words pretty much every day for the past ten years.

But as I've said before, this has taken exactly zero willpower. It's more that I can't stop even if I want to[3]. Part of that is probably that when I write, I feel really good about having expressed exactly what it was I meant to say. Lots of people read it, they comment, they praise me, I feel good, I'm encouraged to keep writing, and it's exactly the same virtuous cycle as my brother got from his piano practice.

And so I think it would be *too easy* to say something like "There's no innate component at all. Your brother practiced piano really hard but almost never writes. You write all the time, but wimped out of practicing piano. So what do you expect? You both got what you deserved."

I tried to practice piano as hard as he did. I really tried. But every moment was a struggle. I could keep it up for a while, and then we'd go on vacation, and there'd be no piano easily available, and I would be breathing a sigh of relief at having a ready-made excuse, and he'd be heading off to look for a piano somewhere to practice on. Meanwhile, I am writing this post in short breaks between running around hospital corridors responding to psychiatric emergencies, and there's probably someone very impressed with that, someone saying "But you had such a great excuse to get out of your writing practice!"

I dunno. But I don't think of myself as working hard at any of the things I am good at, in the sense of "exerting vast willpower to force myself kicking and screaming to do them". It's possible I *do* work hard, and that an outside observer would accuse me of eliding how hard I work, but it's not a conscious elision and I don't feel that way from the inside.

Ramanujan worked very hard at math. But I don't think he thought of it as work. He obtained a scholarship to the local college, but dropped out almost immediately because he couldn't make himself study any subject other than math. Then he got accepted to another college, and dropped out *again* because they made him study non-mathematical subjects and he failed a physiology class. Then he nearly starved to death because he had no money and no scholarship. To me, this doesn't sound like a person who just happens to be very hard-working; if he had the ability to study other subjects he would have, for no reason other than that it would have allowed him to stay in college so

---

[3]https://slatestarcodex.com/2014/05/25/apologia-pro-vita-sua/

he could keep studying math. It seems to me that in some sense Ramanujan was *incapable* of putting hard work into non-math subjects.

I really wanted to learn math and failed, but I did graduate with honors from medical school. Ramanujan really wanted to learn physiology and failed, but he did become one of history's great mathematicians. So which one of us was the hard worker?

People used to ask me for writing advice. And I, in all earnestness, would say "Just transcribe your thoughts onto paper exactly like they sound in your head." It turns out that doesn't work for other people. Maybe it doesn't work for me either, and it just feels like it does.

But you know what? When asked about one of his discoveries, a method of simplifying a very difficult problem to a continued fraction, Ramanujan described his thought process as: "It is simple. The minute I heard the problem, I knew that the answer was a continued fraction. 'Which continued fraction?' I asked myself. Then the answer came to my mind".

And again, maybe that's just how it feels to him, and the real answer is "study math so hard that you flunk out of college twice, and eventually you develop so much intuition that you can solve problems without thinking about them."

(or maybe the real answer is "have dreams where obscure Hindu gods appear to you as drops of blood and reveal mathematical formulae". Ramanujan was weird[4])

But I *still* feel like there's something going on here where the solution to me being bad at math and piano isn't just "sweat blood and push through your brain's aversion to these subjects until you make it stick". When I read biographies of Ramanujan and other famous mathematicians, there's no sense that they ever had to do that with math. When I talk to my brother, I never get a sense that he had to do that with piano. And if I am good enough at writing to qualify to have an opinion on being good at things, then I don't feel like I ever went through that process myself.

So this too is part of my deal with myself. I'll try to do my best at things, but if there's something I really hate, something where I have to go uphill every step of the way, then it's okay to admit mediocrity. I won't beat myself up for not forcing myself kicking and screaming to practice piano. And in return I won't become too cocky about practicing writing a lot. It's probably

---

[4] http://en.wikipedia.org/wiki/Srinivasa_Ramanujan#Personality_and_spiritual_life

some kind of luck of the draw[5] either way.

IV

I said before that this wasn't just about poor people, it was about me being selfishly worried for my own sake. I think I might have given the mistaken impression that I merely need to justify to myself why I can't get an A in math or play the piano. But it's much worse than that.

The rationalist community tends to get a lot of high-scrupulosity people, people who tend to beat themselves up for not doing more than they are. It's why I push giving 10% to charity[6], not as some kind of amazing stretch goal that we need to guilt people into doing, but as a crutch, a sort of "don't worry, you're still okay if you only give ten percent". It's why there's so much emphasis on "heroic responsibility" and how you, yes you, have to solve all the world's problems personally. It's why I see red when anyone accuses us of entitlement, since it goes about as well as calling an anorexic person fat.

And we really aren't doing ourselves any favors. For example, Nick Bostrom writes:

> Searching for a cure for aging is not just a nice thing that we should perhaps one day get around to. It is an urgent, screaming moral imperative. The sooner we start a focused research program, the sooner we will get results. It matters if we get the cure in 25 years rather than in 24 years: a population greater than that of Canada would die as a result.

If that bothers you, you *definitely* shouldn't read Astronomical Waste[7].

Yet here I am, not doing anti-aging research. Why not?

Because I tried doing biology research a few times and it was really hard and made me miserable. You know how in every science class, when the teacher says "Okay, pour the white chemical into the grey chemical, and notice how it turns green and begins to bubble," there's always one student who pours the white chemical into the grey chemical, and it just forms a greyish-white mixture and sits there? That was me. I hated it, I didn't have the

---

[5]https://slatestarcodex.com/2013/06/30/the-lottery-of-fascinations/
[6]https://slatestarcodex.com/2014/12/19/nobody-is-perfect-everything-is-commensurable/
[7]http://www.nickbostrom.com/astronomical/waste.html

dexterity or the precision of mind to do it well, and when I finally finished my required experimental science classes I was happy never to think about it again. Even the abstract intellectual part of it – the one where you go through data about genes and ligands and receptors in supercentenarians and shake it until data comes out – requires exactly the kind of math skills that I don't have.

Insofar as this is a matter of innate aptitude – some people are cut out for biology research and I'm not one of them – all is well, and my decision to get a job I'm good at instead is entirely justified.

But insofar as there's no such thing as innate aptitude, just hard work and grit – then by not being gritty enough, I'm a monster who's complicit in the death of a population greater than that of Canada.

Insofar as there's no such thing as innate aptitude, I have *no excuse* for not being Aubrey de Grey. Or if Aubrey de Grey doesn't impress you much, Norman Borlaug. Or if you don't know who either of those two people are, Elon Musk.

I once heard a friend, upon his first use of modafinil, wonder aloud if the way they felt on that stimulant was the way Elon Musk felt all the time. That tied a lot of things together for me, gave me an intuitive understanding of what it might "feel like from the inside" to be Elon Musk. And it gave me a good tool to discuss biological variation with. Most of us agree that people on stimulants can perform in ways it's difficult for people off stimulants to match. Most of us agree that there's nothing magical about stimulants, just changes to the levels of dopamine, histamine, norepinephrine et cetera in the brain. And most of us agree there's a lot of natural variation in these chemicals anyway. So "me on stimulants is that guy's normal" seems like a good way of cutting through some of the philosophical difficulties around this issue.

…which is all kind of a big tangent. The point I want to make is that for me, what's at stake in talking about natural variations in ability isn't just whether I have to feel like a failure for not getting an A in high school calculus, or not being as good at music as my brother. It's whether I'm a failure for not being Elon Musk. Specifically, it's whether I can say "No, I'm really not cut out to be Elon Musk" and go do something else I'm better at without worrying that I'm killing everyone in Canada.

V

The proverb says: "Everyone has somebody better off than they are and somebody worse off than they are, with two exceptions." When we accept that we're all in the "not Elon Musk" boat together (with one exception) a lot of the status games around innate ability start to seem less important.

Every so often an overly kind commenter here praises my intelligence and says they feel intellectually inadequate compared to me, that they wish they could be at my level. But at my level, I spend my time feeling intellectually inadequate [Book-Review-And-Highlights-Quantum-Computing-Since-Democritus | compared to Scott Aaronson]]. Scott Aaronson describes[8] feeling "in awe" of Terence Tao and frequently struggling to understand him. Terence Tao – well, I don't know if he's religious, but maybe he feels intellectually inadequate compared to God. And God feels intellectually inadequate compared to John von Neumann.

So there's not much point in me feeling inadequate compared to my brother, because even if I was as good at music as my brother, I'd probably just feel inadequate for not being Mozart.

And asking "Well what if you just worked harder?" can elide small distinctions, but not bigger ones. If my only goal is short-term preservation of my self-esteem, I can imagine that if only things had gone a little differently I could have practiced more and ended up as talented as my brother. It's a lot harder for me to imagine the course of events where I do something different and become Mozart. Only one in a billion people reach a Mozart level of achievement; why would it be me?

If I loved music for its own sake and wanted to be a talented musician so I could express the melodies dancing within my heart, then none of this matters. But insofar as I want to be good at music because *I feel bad that other people are better than me at music*, that's a road without an end.

This is also how I feel of when some people on this blog complain they feel dumb for not being as smart as some of the other commenters on this blog.

I happen to have all of your IQ scores in a spreadsheet right here (remember that survey you took?). Not a single person is below the population average. The first percentile for IQ here – the one such that 1% of respondents are lower and 99% of respondents are higher – is – corresponds to the 85th

---

[8] http://www.scottaaronson.com/blog/?p=741#comment-26383

percentile of the general population. So even if you're in the first percentile here, you're still pretty high up in the broader scheme of things.

At that point we're back on the road without end. I am pretty sure we can raise your IQ as much as you want and you will *still* feel like pond scum. If we raise it twenty points, you'll try reading *Quantum Computing since Democritus*[9] and feel like pond scum. If we raise it forty, you'll just go to Terence Tao's blog[10] and feel like pond scum there. Maybe if you were literally the highest-IQ person in the entire world you would feel good about yourself, but any system where only one person in the world is allowed to feel good about themselves at a time *is a bad system* .

People say we should stop talking about ability differences so that stupid people don't feel bad. I say that there's more than enough room for *everybody* to feel bad, smart and stupid alike, and not talking about it won't help. What will help is fundamentally uncoupling perception of intelligence from perception of self-worth.

I work with psychiatric patients who tend to have cognitive difficulties. Starting out in the Detroit ghetto doesn't do them any favors, and then they get conditions like bipolar disorder and schizophrenia that actively lower IQ[11] for poorly understood neurological reasons.

The standard psychiatric evaluation includes an assessment of cognitive ability; the one I use is a quick test with three questions. The questions are – "What is 100 minus 7?", "What do an apple and an orange have in common?", and "Remember these three words for one minute, then repeat them back to me: house, blue, and tulip".

There are a lot of people – and I don't mean floridly psychotic people who don't know their own name, I mean ordinary reasonable people just like you and me – who can't answer these questions. And we know why they can't answer these questions, and it is pretty darned biological.

And if our answer to "I feel dumb and worthless because my IQ isn't high enough" is "don't worry, you're not worthless, I'm sure you can be a great scientist if you just try hard enough", then we are implicitly throwing under the bus all of these people who are *definitely* not going to be great scientists no matter how hard they try. Talking about trying harder can obfuscate the little

---

[9]http://smile.amazon.com/gp/product/0521199565/ref=as_li_tl?ie=UTF8&camp=1789&creative=390957&creativeASIN=0521199565&linkCode=as2&tag=slastacod-20&linkId=7WISDLFZXC5IL567

[10]https://terrytao.wordpress.com/

[11]http://www.ncbi.nlm.nih.gov/pubmed/23964248

differences, but once we're talking about the homeless schizophrenic guy from Detroit who can't tell me 100 minus 7 to save his life, you can't just magic the problem away with a wave of your hand and say "I'm sure he can be the next Ramanujan if he keeps a positive attitude!" You either need to condemn him as worthless *or else stop fricking tying worth to innate intellectual ability* .

This is getting pretty close to what I was talking about in my post on burdens[12] . When I get a suicidal patient who thinks they're a burden on society, it's nice to be able to point out ten important things they've done for society recently and prove them wrong. But sometimes it's not that easy, and the only thing you can say is "f#@k that s#!t". Yes, society has organized itself in a way that excludes and impoverishes a bunch of people who could have been perfectly happy in the state of nature picking berries and hunting aurochs. It's not your fault, and if they're going to give you compensation *you take it* . And we had better make this perfectly clear now, so that when everything becomes automated and run by robots and we're *all* behind the curve, everybody agrees that us continuing to exist is still okay.

Likewise with intellectual ability. When someone feels sad because they can't be a great scientist, it is nice to be able to point out all of their intellectual strengths and tell them "Yes you can, if only you put your mind to it!" But this is often not true. At that point you have to say "f@#k it" and tell them to stop tying their self-worth to being a great scientist. And we had better establish that now, before transhumanists succeed in creating superintelligence and we *all* have to come to terms with our intellectual inferiority.

VI

But I think the situation can also be somewhat rosier than that.

Ozy once told me that the law of comparative advantage[13] was one of the most inspirational things they had ever read. This was sufficiently strange that I demanded an explanation.

Ozy said that it proves *everyone can contribute* . Even if you are worse than everyone else at everything, you can still participate in global trade and other people will pay you money. It may not be very much money, but it will be some, and it will be a measure of how your actions are making other people better off and they are grateful for your existence.

[12] https://slatestarcodex.com/2014/08/16/burdens/
[13] http://en.wikipedia.org/wiki/Comparative_advantage

(in real life this doesn't work for a couple of reasons, but who cares about real life when we have *a theory* ?)

After some thought, I was also inspired by this.

I'm never going to be a great mathematician or Elon Musk. But if I pursue my comparative advantage, which right now is medicine, I can still make money. And if I feel like it, I can donate it to mathematics research. Or anti-aging research. Or the same people Elon Musk donates *his* money to[14] . They will use it to hire smart people with important talents that I lack, and I will be at least partially responsible for those people's successes.

If I had an IQ of 70, I think I would still want to pursue my comparative advantage – even if that was ditch-digging, or whatever, and donate that money to important causes. It might not be very much money, but it would be *some* .

Our modern word "talent" comes from the Greek word *talenton* , a certain amount of precious metal sometimes used as a denomination of money. The etymology passes through a parable of Jesus'. A master calls three servants to him and gives the first five talents, the second two talents, and the third one talent. The first two servants invest the money and double it. The third literally buries it in a hole. The master comes back later and praises the first two servants, but sends the third servant to Hell (metaphor? what metaphor?).

Various people have come up with various interpretations, but the most popular says that God gives all of us different amounts of resources, and He will judge us based on how well we use these resources rather than on how many He gave us. It would be stupid to give your first servant five loads of silver, then your second servant two loads of silver, then immediately start chewing out the second servant for having less silver than the first one. And if both servants invested their silver wisely, it would be silly to chew out the second one for ending up with less profit when he started with less seed capital. The moral seems to be that if you take what God gives you and use it wisely, you're fine.

The modern word "talent" comes from this parable. It implies "a thing God has given you which you can invest and give back".

So if I were a ditch-digger, I think I would dig ditches, donate a portion of the small amount I made, and trust that I had done what I could with the talents I was given. **VII.** The Jews *also* talk about how God judges you for your gifts. Rabbi Zusya once said that when he died, he wasn't worried that God

---

[14]http://futureoflife.org/misc/AI

would ask him "Why weren't you Moses?" or "Why weren't you Solomon?" But he did worry that God might ask "Why weren't you Rabbi Zusya?"

And this is part of why it's important for me to believe in innate ability, and especially differences in innate ability. If everything comes down to hard work and positive attitude, then God has every right to ask me "Why weren't you Srinivasa Ramanujan?" or "Why weren't you Elon Musk?"

If everyone is legitimately a different person with a different brain and different talents and abilities, then all God gets to ask me is whether or not I was Scott Alexander.

This seems like a gratifyingly low bar. *[more to come on this subject later]*

5

Answer to Job

March 15, 2015

(with apologies to Jung[1])

Job asked: "God, why do bad things happen to good people? Why would You, who are perfect, create a universe filled with so much that is evil?"

Then the Lord spoke to Job out of the whirlwind, saying "WHAT KIND OF UNIVERSE WOULD YOU PREFER ME TO HAVE CREATED?"

Job said "A universe that was perfectly just and full of happiness, of course."

"OH," said God. "YES, I CREATED ONE OF THOSE. IT'S EXACTLY AS NICE AS YOU WOULD EXPECT."

Job facepalmed. "But then why would You also create *this* universe?"

Answered God: "DON'T YOU LIKE EXISTING?"

"Yes," said Job, "but all else being equal, I'd rather be in the perfectly just and happy universe."

"OH, DON'T WORRY," said God. "THERE'S A VERSION OF YOU IN THAT UNIVERSE TOO. HE SAYS HI."

"Okay," said Job, very carefully. "I can see I'm going to have to phrase my questions more specifically. Why didn't You also make *this* universe perfectly just and happy?"

"BECAUSE YOU CAN'T HAVE TWO IDENTICAL INDIVIDUALS. IF YOU HAVE A COMPUTATIONAL THEORY OF IDENTITY, THEN TWO PEOPLE WHOSE EXPERIENCE IS ONE HUN-

---

[1] http://smile.amazon.com/gp/product/0691150478/ref=as_li_tl?ie=UTF8&camp=1789&creative=390957&creativeASIN=0691150478&linkCode=as2&tag=slastacod-20&linkId=GTJE5YFZEADILCWO

DRED PERCENT SATURATED BY BLISS ARE JUST ONE PER-
SON. IF I MADE THIS UNIVERSE EXACTLY LIKE THE HAPPY
AND JUST UNIVERSE, THEN THERE WOULD ONLY BE THE
POPULATION OF THE HAPPY AND JUST UNIVERSE, WHICH
WOULD BE LESS GOOD THAN HAVING THE POPULATION
OF THE HAPPY AND JUST UNIVERSE PLUS THE POPULATION
OF ONE EXTRA UNIVERSE THAT IS AT LEAST SOMEWHAT
HAPPY."

"Hmmmmm. But couldn't You have have made this universe like the
happy and just universe except for one tiny detail? Like in that universe,
the sun is a sphere, but in our universe, the sun is a cube? Then you would
have individuals who experienced a spherical sun, and other individuals who
experienced a cubic sun, which would be enough to differentiate them."

"I DID THAT TOO. I HAVE CREATED ALL POSSIBLE PER-
MUTATIONS OF THE HAPPY AND JUST UNIVERSE AND ITS
POPULACE."

"All of them? That would be… a lot of universes."

"NOT AS MANY AS YOU THINK." said God. "IN THE END IT
TURNED OUT TO BE ONLY ABOUT $10^{(10^{(10^{(10^{(10^{984})})})})}$.
AFTER THAT I RAN OUT OF POSSIBLE PERMUTATIONS OF
UNIVERSES THAT COULD REASONABLY BE DESCRIBED AS
PERFECTLY HAPPY AND JUST. SO I STARTED CREATING ONES
INCLUDING SMALL AMOUNTS OF EVIL."

"Small amounts! But the universe has…"

"I WAS NOT REFERRING TO YOUR UNIVERSE. I EXHAUSTED
THOSE, AND THEN I STARTED CREATING ONES INCLUDING
IMMENSE AMOUNTS OF EVIL."

"Oh." Then: "What, exactly, is Your endgame here?"

"I AM OMNIBENEVOLENT. I WANT TO CREATE AS MUCH
HAPPINESS AND JOY AS POSSIBLE. THIS REQUIRES INSTAN-
TIATING ALL POSSIBLE BEINGS WHOSE TOTAL LIFETIME
HAPPINESS IS GREATER THAN THEIR TOTAL LIFETIME SUF-
FERING."

"I'm not sure I understand."

"YOUR LIFE CONTAINS MUCH PAIN, BUT MORE HAPPI-
NESS. BOTH YOU AND I WOULD PREFER THAT A BEING WITH
YOUR EXACT LIFE HISTORY EXIST. IN ORDER TO MAKE IT

EXIST, IT WAS NECESSARY TO CREATE THE SORT OF UNI-
VERSE IN WHICH YOU COULD EXIST. THAT IS A UNIVERSE
CONTAINING EVIL. I HAVE ALSO CREATED ALL HAPPIER
AND MORE VIRTUOUS VERSIONS OF YOU. HOWEVER, IT IS
ETHICALLY CORRECT THAT AFTER CREATING THEM, I CRE-
ATE YOU AS WELL."

"But why couldn't I have been one of those other versions instead!"

"IN THE MOST PERFECTLY HAPPY AND JUST UNIVERSE,
THERE IS NO SPACE, FOR SPACE TAKES THE FORM OF SEP-
ARATION FROM THINGS YOU DESIRE. THERE IS NO TIME,
FOR TIME MEANS CHANGE AND DECAY, YET THERE MUST
BE NO CHANGE FROM ITS MAXIMALLY BLISSFUL STATE.
THE BEINGS WHO INHABIT THIS UNIVERSE ARE WITHOUT
BODIES, AND DO NOT HUNGER OR THIRST OR LABOR OR
LUST. THEY AND CONTEMPLATE THE PERFECTION OF ALL
THINGS. IF I WERE TO UNCREATE ALL WORLDS SAVE THAT
ONE, WOULD IT MEAN MAKING YOU HAPPIER? OR WOULD
IT MEAN KILLING YOU, WHILE FAR AWAY IN A DIFFERENT
UNIVERSE INCORPOREAL BEINGS SAT ON THEIR LOTUS THRONE
REGARDLESS?"

"I don't know! Is one of the beings in that universe in some sense *me?*"

"THERE IS NO OBJECTIVE COSMIC UNEMPLOYMENT RATE."

"Huh?"

"I MEAN, THERE IS NO MEANINGFUL ANSWER TO THE
QUESTION OF HOW MANY UNIVERSES HAVE A JOB. SORRY.
THAT WILL BE FUNNY IN ABOUT THREE THOUSAND YEARS."

"Let me try a different angle, then. Right now in our universe there are
lots of people whose lives aren't worth living. If You gave them the choice,
they would have chosen never to have been born at all. What about them?"

"A JOB WHO IS AWARE OF THE EXISTENCE OF SUCH PEO-
PLE IS A DIFFERENT JOB THAN A JOB WHO IS NOT. AS LONG
AS THESE PEOPLE MAKE UP A MINORITY OF THE POPULA-
TION, THE EXISTENCE OF YOUR UNIVERSE, IN ADDITION TO
A UNIVERSE WITHOUT SUCH PEOPLE, IS A NET ASSET."

"But that's monstrous! Couldn't You just, I don't know, have created a
universe that looks like it has such people, but actually they're just p-zombies,
animated bodies without any real consciousness or suffering?"

"..."

"Wait, *did* You do that?"

"I AM GOING TO PULL THE 'THINGS MAN WAS NOT MEANT TO KNOW' CARD HERE. THERE ARE ADVANTAGES AND DIS-ADVANTAGES TO THE APPROACH YOU MENTION. THE AD-VANTAGES ARE AS YOU HAVE SAID. THE DISADVANTAGE IS THAT IT TURNS CHARITY TOWARDS SUCH PEOPLE INTO A LIE, AND MYSELF AS GOD INTO A DECEIEVER. I WILL AL-LOW YOU TO FORM YOUR OWN OPINION ABOUT WHICH COURSE IS MORE ETHICAL. BUT IT IS NOT RELEVANT TO THEODICY, SINCE WHICHEVER COURSE YOU DECIDE IS MORALLY SUPERIOR, YOU HAVE NO EVIDENCE THAT I DID NOT IN FACT TAKE SUCH A COURSE."

"Actually, I do have some evidence. Before all of this happened to me I was very happy. But in the past couple years[2] I've gone bankrupt, lost my entire family, and gotten a bad case of boils. I'm pretty sure at this point I would prefer that I never have been born. Since I know I myself am conscious, I am actually in a pretty good position to accuse You of cruelty."

"HMMMMMMMM..." said God, and the whirlwind disappeared.

Then the Lord gave Job twice as much as he had before, and healed his illnesses, and gave him many beautiful children, so it was said that God had blessed the latter end of Job more than his beginning.

EDIT: According to comments[3], this was scooped[4] by a Christian philosopher five years ago. Sigh.

> The Lord spoke to Job out of the whirlwind, saying "MISTAKES WERE MADE."
>
> — Scott Alexander (@slatestarcodex), March 13, 2015[5]

> Then the Lord spoke to Job out of the whirlwind, saying "IF YOU CAN'T HANDLE ME AT MY WORST, YOU DON'T DESERVE ME AT MY BEST."
>
> — Scott Alexander (@slatestarcodex), March 10, 2015[6]

---

[2] http://ebible.org/kjv/Job.htm

[3] https://slatestarcodex.com/2015/03/15/answer-to-job/#comment-190059

[4] http://www.ryerson.ca/~kraay/Documents/2010PS.pdf

[5] https://twitter.com/slatestarcodex/status/576182356521832449

[6] https://twitter.com/slatestarcodex/status/575381549169950720

The Lord spoke to Job out of the whirlwind, saying "I KNOW YOU'RE UPSET BUT THAT'S DIFFERENT FROM STRUCTURAL OPPRESSION" (h/t @simulacrumbs[7])

— Scott Alexander (@slatestarcodex), March 13, 2015[8]

---

[7] https://twitter.com/simulacrumbs

[8] https://twitter.com/slatestarcodex/status/576181964387975169

Universal Love, Said The Cactus Person

April 21, 2015

"Universal love," said the cactus person.

"Transcendent joy," said the big green bat.

"Right," I said. "I'm absolutely in favor of both those things. But before we go any further, could you tell me the two prime factors of 1,522,605,027,922,533,360,535,618,378,132,637,429,718,068,114,961,380,688,657,

"Universal love," said the cactus person.

"Transcendent joy," said the big green bat.

The sea was made of strontium; the beach was made of rye. Above my head, a watery sun shone in an oily sky. A thousand stars of sertraline whirled round quetiapine moons, and the sand sizzled sharp like cooking oil that hissed and sang and threatened to boil the octahedral dunes.

"Okay," I said. "Fine. Let me tell you where I'm coming from. I was reading Scott McGreal's blog[1], which has some good[2] articles[3] about so-called DMT entities, and mentions how they seem so real that users of the drug insist they've made contact with actual superhuman beings and not just psychedelic hallucinations. You know, the usual[4] Terence McKenna stuff. But in one[5] of them he mentions a paper by Marko Rodriguez called *A Methodology For Studying Various Interpretations of the N,N-*

---

[1] https://www.psychologytoday.com/blog/unique-everybody-else

[2] https://www.psychologytoday.com/blog/unique-everybody-else/201210/dmt-aliens-and-reality-part-1

[3] https://www.psychologytoday.com/blog/unique-everybody-else/201210/dmt-aliens-and-reality-part-2

[4] http://smile.amazon.com/gp/product/0062506528/ref=as_li_tl?ie=UTF8&camp=1789&creative=390957&creativeASIN=0062506528&linkCode=as2&tag=slastacod-20&linkId=BKGSPUHIEWFDXXWZ

[5] https://www.psychologytoday.com/blog/unique-everybody-else/201408/dmt-gateway-re

dimethyltryptamine-Induced Alternate Reality[6], which suggested among other things that you could prove DMT entities were real by taking the drug and then asking the entities you meet to factor large numbers which you were sure you couldn't factor yourself. So to that end, could you do me a big favor and tell me the factors of 1,522,605,027,922,533,360,535,618,378,132,637,429,718,06?

"Universal love," said the cactus person.

"Transcendent joy," said the big green bat.

The sea turned hot and geysers shot up from the floor below. First one of wine, then one of brine, then one more yet of turpentine, and we three stared at the show.

"I was afraid you might say that. Is there anyone more, uh, *verbal* here whom I could talk to?"

"Universal love," said the cactus person.

At the sound of that, the big green bat started rotating in place. On its other side was a bigger greener bat, with a ancient, wrinkled face.

"Not splitting numbers / but joining Mind," it said.
Not facts or factors or factories / but contact with the abstract attractor that brings you back to me
Not to seek / but to find"

"I don't follow," I said.

"Not to follow / but to jump forth into the deep
Not to grind or to bind or to seek only to find / but to accept
Not to be kept / but to wake from sleep"

The bat continued to rotate, until the first side I had seen swung back into view.

"Okay," I said. "I'm going to hazard a guess as to what you're talking about, and you tell me if I'm right. You're saying that, like, all my Western logocentric stuff about factoring numbers in order to find out the objective truth about this realm is missing the point, and I should be trying to do some kind of spiritual thing involving radical acceptance and enlightenment and such. Is that kind of on the mark?"

"Universal love," said the cactus person.

"Transcendent joy," said the big green bat.

"Frick," I said. "Well, okay, let me continue." The bat was still rotating,

---

ality-fantasy-or-what
[6]http://www.ayahuasca-info.com/data/articles/paralleldmt.pdf

and I kind of hoped that when the side with the creepy wrinkled face came into view it might give me some better conversation. "I'm all about the spiritual stuff. I wouldn't be here if I weren't deeply interested in the spiritual stuff. This isn't about money or fame or anything. I want to advance psychedelic research. If you can factor that number, then it will convince people back in the real – back in my world that this place is for real and important. Then lots of people will take DMT and flock here and listen to what you guys have to say about enlightenment and universal love, and make more sense of it than I can alone, and in the end we'll have more universal love, and… what was the other thing?"

"Transcendent joy," said the big green bat.

"Right," I said. "We'll have more transcendent joy if you help me out and factor the number than if you just sit there being spiritual and enigmatic."

Lovers do not love to increase the amount of love in the world / But for the mind that thrills
And the face of the beloved, which the whole heart fills / the heart and the art never apart, ever unfurled
And John Stuart is one of / the dark satanic mills"

"I take it you're not consequentialists," I said. "You know that's really weird, right. Like, not just 'great big green bat with two faces and sapient cactus-man' weird, but like *really* weird. You talk about wanting this spiritual enlightenment stuff, but you're not going to take actions that are going to increase the amount of spiritual enlightenment? You've got to understand, this is like a bigger gulf for me than normal human versus ineffable DMT entity. You can have crazy goals, I expect you to have crazy goals, but what you're saying now is that you don't pursue any goals at all, you can't be modeled as having desires. Why would you *do* that?"

"Universal love," said the cactus person.

"Transcendent joy," said the big green bat.

"Now you see here," I said. "Everyone in this conversation is in favor of universal love and transcendent joy. But I've seen the way this works. Some college student gets his hands on some DMT, visits here, you guys tell him about universal love and transcendent joy, he wakes up, says that his life has been changed, suddenly he truly understands what really matters. But it never lasts. The next day he's got to get up and go to work and so on, and the universal love lasts about five minutes until his boss starts yelling at him for writing his report in the wrong font, and before you know it twenty years later he's some slimy lawyer who's joking at a slimy lawyer party about the one time when he was in college and took some DMT and spent a whole week raving about transcendent joy, and all the other slimy lawyers laugh, and he laughs with them, and so much for whatever spiritual awakening you and your colleagues in LSD and peyote are trying to kindle in humanity. And if I accept your message of universal love and transcendent joy right now, that's exactly what's going to happen to me, and meanwhile human civilization is going to keep being stuck in greed and ignorance and misery. So how about you shut up about universal love and you factor my number for me so we can start figuring out a battle plan for giving humanity a *real* spiritual revolution?"

"Universal love," said the cactus person.

"Transcendent joy," said the big green bat.

A meteorite of pure delight struck the sea without a sound. The force of the blast went rattling past the bat and the beach, disturbing each, then made its way to a nearby bay of upside-down trees with their roots in the breeze and their branches underground.

"I demand a better answer than that," I demanded.

The other side of the bat spun into view.

"Chaos never comes from the Ministry of Chaos / nor void from the Ministry of Void
Time will decay us but time can be left blank / destroyed
With each Planck moment ever fit / to be eternally enjoyed"

"You're making this basic mistake," I told the big green bat. "I honestly believe that there's a perspective from which Time doesn't matter, where a single moment of recognition is equivalent to eternal recognition. The problem is, if you only have that perspective for a moment, then all the rest of the time, you're sufficiently stuck in Time to honestly believe you're stuck in Time. It's like that song about the hole in the bucket – if the hole in the bucket were fixed, you would have the materials needed to fix the hole in the bucket. But since it isn't, you don't. Likewise, if I understood the illusoriness... illusionality... whatever, of time, then I wouldn't care that I only understood it for a single instant. But since I don't, I don't. Without a solution to the time-limitedness of enlightenment that works from *within* the temporal perspective, how can you consider it solved at all?"

"Universal love," said the cactus person.

"Transcendent joy," said the big green bat.

The watery sun began to run and it fell on the ground as rain. It became a dew that soaked us through, and as the cold seemed to worsen the cactus person hugged himself to stay warm but his spines pierced his form and he howled in a fit of pain.

"You know," I said, "sometimes I think the *kvithion sumurhe*[7] had the right of it. The world is an interference pattern between colliding waves of Truth and Beauty, and either one of them pure from the source and undiluted by the other will be fatal. I think you guys and some of the other psychedelics might be pure Beauty, or at least much closer to the source than people were meant to go. I think you can't even understand reason, I think you're constitutionally opposed to reason, and that the only way we're ever going to get something that combines your wisdom and love and joy with reason is after we immanentize the eschaton and launch civilization into some perfected postmessianic era where the purpose of the world is fully complete. And that as much as I hate to say it, there's no short-circuiting the process."

"Universal love," said the cactus person.

"Transcendent joy," said the big green bat.

"I'm dissing you, you know. I'm saying you guys are so intoxicated on spiritual wisdom that you couldn't think straight if your life depended on it; that your random interventions in our world and our minds look like the purposeless acts of a drunken madman because that's basically more or less what they are. I'm saying if you had like five IQ points between the two of you, you could tap into your cosmic consciousness or whatever to factor a number that would do more for your cause than all your centuries of enigmatic dreams and unasked-for revelations combined, and you ARE TOO DUMB TO DO IT EVEN WHEN I BASICALLY HOLD YOUR HAND THE WHOLE WAY. Your spine. Your wing. Whatever."

"Universal love," said the cactus person.

"Transcendent joy," said the big green bat.

"Fuck you," said I.

I saw the big green bat bat a green big eye. Suddenly I knew I had gone too far. The big green bat started to turn around what was neither its x, y, or z axis, slowly rotating to reveal what was undoubtedly the biggest, greenest bat that I had ever seen, a bat bigger and greener than which it was impossible to conceive. And the bat said to me:

"Sir. Imagine you are in the driver's seat of a car. You have been sitting there so long that you have forgotten that it is the seat of a car, forgotten

---

[7] https://slatestarcodex.com/2013/05/15/raikoth-history-religion/

how to get out of the seat, forgotten the existence of your own legs, indeed forgotten that you are a being at all separate from the car. You control the car with skill and precision, driving it wherever you wish to go, manipulating the headlights and the windshield wipers and the stereo and the air conditioning, and you pronounce yourself a great master. But there are paths you cannot travel, because there are no roads to them, and you long to run through the forest, or swim in the river, or climb the high mountains. A line of prophets who have come before you tell you that the secret to these forbidden mysteries is an ancient and terrible skill called GETTING OUT OF THE CAR, and you resolve to learn this skill. You try every button on the dashboard, but none of them is the button for GETTING OUT OF THE CAR. You drive all of the highways and byways of the earth, but you cannot reach GETTING OUT OF THE CAR, for it is not a place on a highway. The prophets tell you GETTING OUT OF THE CAR is something fundamentally different than anything you have done thus far, but to you this means ever sillier extremities: driving backwards, driving with the headlights on in the glare of noon, driving into ditches on purpose, but none of these reveal the secret of GETTING OUT OF THE CAR. The prophets tell you it is easy; indeed, it is the easiest thing you have ever done. You have traveled the Pan-American Highway from the boreal pole to the Darien Gap, you have crossed Route 66 in the dead heat of summer, you have outrun cop cars at 160 mph and survived, and GETTING OUT OF THE CAR is easier than any of them, the easiest thing you can imagine, closer to you than the veins in your head, but still the secret is obscure to you."

A herd of bison came into listen, and voles and squirrels and ermine and great tusked deer gathered round to hear as the bat continued his sermon.

"And finally you drive to the top of the highest peak and you find a sage, and you ask him what series of buttons on the dashboard you have to press to get out of the car. And he tells you that it's not about pressing buttons on the dashboard and you just need to GET OUT OF THE CAR. And you say okay, fine, but what series of buttons will *lead to* you getting out of the car, and he says no, really, you need to stop thinking about dashboard buttons and GET OUT OF THE CAR. And you tell him maybe if the sage helps you change your oil or rotates your tires or something then it will improve your driving to the point where getting out of the car will be a cinch after that, and he tells you it has nothing to do with how rotated your tires are and you just need to GET OUT OF THE CAR, and so you call him a moron and drive away."

"Universal love," said the cactus person.

"So that metaphor is *totally unfair*," I said, "and a better metaphor would be if every time someone got out of the car, five minutes later they found themselves back in the car, and I ask the sage for driving directions to a laboratory where they are studying that problem, and…"

"You only believe that because it's written on the windshield," said the big green bat. "And you think the windshield is identical to reality because you won't GET OUT OF THE CAR."

"Fine," I said. "Then I can't get out of the car. I want to get out of the car. But I need help. And the first step to getting help is for you to factor my number. You seem like a reasonable person. Bat. Freaky DMT entity. Whatever. Please. I promise you, this is the right thing to do. Just factor the number."

"And I promise you," said the big green bat. "You don't need to factor the number. You just need to GET OUT OF THE CAR."

"I can't get out of the car until you factor the number."

"I won't factor the number until you get out of the car."

"Please, I'm begging you, factor the number!"

"Yes, well, I'm begging you, please get out of the car!"

"FOR THE LOVE OF GOD JUST FACTOR THE FUCKING NUMBER!"

"FOR THE LOVE OF GOD JUST GET OUT OF THE FUCKING CAR!"

"FACTOR THE FUCKING NUMBER!"

"GET OUT OF THE FUCKING CAR!"

"Universal love," said the cactus person.

Then tree and beast all fled due east and the moon and stars shot south. And the bat rose up and the sea was a cup and the earth was a screen green as clozapine and the sky a voracious mouth. And the mouth opened wide and the earth was skied and the sea fell in with an awful din and the trees were moons and the sand in the dunes was a blazing comet and…

I vomited, hard, all over my bed. It happens every time I take DMT, sooner or later; I've got a weak stomach and I'm not sure the stuff I get is totally pure. I crawled just far enough out of bed to flip a light switch on, then collapsed back onto the soiled covers. The clock on the wall read 11:55, meaning I'd been out about an hour and a half. I briefly considered taking some more ayahuasca and heading right back there, but the chances of getting anything more out of the big green bat, let alone the cactus person, seemed small enough to fit in a thimble. I drifted off into a fitful sleep.

Behind the veil, across the infinite abyss, beyond the ice, beyond daath, the dew rose from the soaked ground and coalesced into a great drop, which floated up into an oily sky and became a watery sun. The cactus person was counting on his spines.

"Hey," the cactus person finally said, "just out of curiosity, was the answer 37,975,227,936,943,673,922,808,872,755,445,627,854,565,536,638,199 times 40,094,690,950,920,881,030,683,735,292,761,468,389,214,899,724,061?"

"Yeah," said the big green bat. "That's what I got too."

7

...And I Show You How Deep The Rabbit Hole Goes

June 2, 2015

Seen on Tumblr[1], along with associated discussion:

Yellow

People's minds are heartbreaking. Not because people are so bad, but because they're so good.

Nobody is the villain of their own life story. You must have read hundreds of minds by now, and it's true. Everybody thinks of themselves as an honest guy or gal just trying to get by, constantly under assault by circumstances and The System and hundreds and hundreds of assholes. They don't just sort of believe this. They really believe it. You almost believe it yourself, when you're deep into a reading. You can very clearly see the structure of evidence they've built up to support their narrative, and even though it looks silly to you, you can see why they will never escape it from the inside. You can see how every insult, every failure, no matter how deserved, is a totally unexpected kick in the gut.

When you chose the yellow pill, you had high hopes of becoming a spy, or a gossip columnist, or just the world's greatest saleswoman. The thought of doing any of those things sickens you now. There is too much anguish in the world already. You feel like any of those things would be a violation. You briefly try to become a therapist, but it turns out that actually knowing everything about your client's mind is horrendously countertherapeutic. Freud can say whatever he wants against defense mechanisms, but without them, you're defenseless. Your sessions are spent in incisive cutting into your

---

[1] http://chroniclesofrettek.tumblr.com/post/118057128657/wrapscallion-mitoticcephalopod-britney

clients' deepest insecurities alternating with desperate reassurance that they are good people anyway.

Also, men. You knew, in a vague way, that men thought about sex all the time. But you didn't realize the, um, content of some of their sexual fantasies. Is it even *legal* to fantasize about that? You want to be disgusted with them. But you realize that if you were as horny as they were all the time, you'd do much the same.

You give up. You become a forest ranger. Not the type who helps people explore the forest. The other type. The type where you hang out in a small cabin in the middle of the mountains and never talk to anybody. The only living thing you encounter is the occasional bear. It always thinks that it is a good bear, a proper bear, that a bear-hating world has it out for them in particular. You do nothing to disabuse it of this notion.

Green

The first thing you do after taking the green pill is become a sparrow. You soar across the landscape, feeling truly free for the first time in your life.

You make it about five minutes before a hawk swoops down and grabs you. Turns out there's an excellent reason real sparrows don't soar freely across the open sky all day. Moments before your bones are ground in two by its fierce beak, you turn back into a human. You fall like a stone. You need to turn into a sparrow again, but the hawk is still there, grabbing on to one of your legs, refusing to let go of its prize just because of this momentary setback. You frantically wave your arms and shout at it, trying to scare it away. Finally it flaps away, feeling cheated, and you become a sparrow again just in time to give yourself a relatively soft landing.

After a few weeks of downtime while you wait for your leg to recover, you become a fish. This time you're smarter. You become a great white shark, apex of the food chain. You will explore the wonders of the ocean depths within the body of an invincible killing machine.

Well, long story short, it is totally unfair that colossal cannibal great white sharks[2] were a thing and if you had known this was the way Nature worked you never would have gone along with this green pill business.

You escape by turning into a blue whale. Nothing eats blue whales, right? You remember that from your biology class. It is definitely true.

---

[2]http://www.cnn.com/2014/06/10/world/australia-great-white-shark/

The last thing you hear is somebody shouting "We found one!" in Japanese. The last thing you feel is a harpoon piercing your skull. Everything goes black.

Blue

Okay, so you see Florence and Jerusalem and Kyoto in an action-packed afternoon. You teleport to the top of Everest because it is there, then go to the bottom of the Marianas Trench. You visit the Amazon Rainforest, the Sahara Desert, and the South Pole. It takes about a week before you've exhausted all of the interesting tourist sites. Now what?

You go to the Moon, then Mars, then Titan. These turn out to be even more boring. Once you get over the exhilaration of being on Mars, there's not a lot to do except look at rocks. You wonder how the Curiosity Rover lasted so long without dying of boredom.

You go further afield. Alpha Centauri A has five planets orbiting it. The second one is covered with water. You don't see anything that looks alive in the ocean, though. The fourth has a big gash in it, like it almost split in two. The fifth has weird stalactite-like mountains.

What would be really interesting would be another planet with life, even intelligent life. You teleport further and further afield. Tau Ceti. Epsilon Eridani. The galactic core. You see enough geology to give scientists back on Earth excitement-induced seizures for the nest hundred years, if only you were to tell them about it, which you don't. But nothing alive. Not so much as a sea cucumber.

You head back to Earth less and less frequently now. Starvation is a physical danger, so it doesn't bother you, though every so often you do like to relax and eat a nice warm meal. But then it's back to work. You start to think the Milky Way is a dead zone. What about Andromeda...?

Orange

You never really realized how incompetent everyone else was, or how much it annoys you.

You were a consultant, a good one, but you felt like mastering all human skills would make you better. So you took the orange pill. The next day you go in to advise a tech company on how they manage the programmers, and you realize that not only are they managing the programmers badly, but the programmers aren't even writing code very well. You could write their system in half the time. The layout of their office is entirely out of sync with the best-studied ergonomic principles. And the Chinese translation of their user manual makes several basic errors that anybody with an encyclopaedic knowledge of relative clauses in Mandarin should have been able to figure out.

You once read about something called Gell-Mann Amnesia, where physicists notice that everything the mainstream says about physics is laughably wrong but think the rest is okay, doctors notice that everything the mainstream says about medicine is laughably wrong but think the rest is okay, et cetera. You do not have Gell-Mann Amnesia. Everyone is terrible at everything all the time, and it pisses you off.

You gain a reputation both for brilliance and for fearsomeness. Everybody respects you, but nobody wants to hire you. You bounce from industry to industry, usually doing jobs for the people at the top whose jobs are so important that the need to get them done right overrides their desire to avoid contact with you.

One year you get an offer you can't refuse from the King of Saudi Arabia. He's worried about sedition in the royal family, and wants your advice as a consultant for how to ensure his government is stable. You travel to Riyadh, and find that the entire country is a mess. His security forces are idiots. But the King is also an idiot, and refuses to believe you or listen to your recommendations. He tells you things can't possibly be as bad as all that. You tell him you'll prove that they are.

You didn't *plan* to become the King of Saudi Arabia, per se. It just sort of happened when your demonstration of how rebels in the military might launch a coup went better than you expected. Sometimes you forget how incompetent everybody else is. You need to keep reminding yourself of that. But not right now. Right now you're busy building your new capital. How come nobody else is any good at urban planning?

Red

You choose the red pill. BRUTE STRENGTH! That's what's important and valuable in this twenty-first-century economy, right? Some people tell you it isn't, but they don't seem to have a lot of BRUTE STRENGTH, so what do they know?

You become a weightlifter. Able to lift thousands of pounds with a single hand, you easily overpower the competition and are crowned whatever the heck it is you get crowned when you WIN WEIGHTLIFTING CONTESTS. But this fails to translate into lucrative endorsement contracts. Nobody wants their spokesman to be a bodybuilder without a sixpack, and although you used to be pretty buff, you're getting scrawnier by the day. Your personal trainer tells you that you only maintain muscle mass by doing difficult work at the limit of your ability, but your abilities don't seem to *have* any limits. Everything is so easy for you that your body just shrugs it off effortlessly. Somehow your BRUTE STRENGTH failed to anticipate this possibility. If only there was a way to solve your problem by BEING VERY STRONG.

Maybe the Internet can help. You Google "red pill advice". The sites you get don't seem to bear on your specific problem, exactly, but they are VERY FASCINATING. You learn lots of surprising things about gender roles that you didn't know before. It seems that women like men who have BRUTE STRENGTH. This is relevant to your interests!

You leave the bodybuilding circuit behind and start frequenting nightclubs, where you constantly boast of your BRUTE STRENGTH to PROVE HOW ALPHA YOU ARE. A lot of people seem kind of creeped out by a scrawny guy with no muscles going up to every woman he sees and boasting of his BRUTE STRENGTH, but the Internet tells you that is because they are BETA CUCKOLD ORBITERS.

Somebody told you once that Internet sites are sometimes inaccurate. You hope it's not true. How could you figure out which are the inaccurate ones using BRUTE STRENGTH?

Pink

You were always pretty, but never *pretty* pretty. A couple of guys liked you, but they were never the ones you were into. It was all crushingly unfair. So you took the pink pill, so that no one would ever be able to not love you again.

You find Tyler. Tyler is a hunk. He'd never shown any interest in you before, no matter how much you flirted with him. You touch him on the arm. His eyes light up.

"Kiss me," you say.

Tyler kisses you. Then he gets a weird look on his face. "Why am I kissing you?" he asks. "I'm sorry. I don't know what came over me." Then he walks off.

You wish you had thought further before accepting a superpower that makes people love you when you touch them, but goes away after you touch them a second time. Having people love you is a lot less sexy when you can't touch them. You start to feel a deep sense of kinship with King Midas.

You stop dating. What's the point? They'll just stop liking you when you touch them a second time. You live alone with a bunch of cats who purr when you pet them, then hiss when you pet them again.

One night you're in a bar drinking your sorrows away when a man comes up to your table. "Hey!" he says, "nice hair. Is it real? I'm the strongest person in the world." He lifts your table over his head with one hand to demonstrate. You are immediately smitten by his BRUTE STRENGTH and ALPHA MALE BEHAVIOR. You *must* have him.

You touch his arm. His eyes light up. "Come back to my place," you say. "But don't touch me."

He seems a little put out by this latter request, but the heat of his passion is so strong he would do anything you ask. You move in together and are married a few contact-free months later. Every so often you wonder what it would be like to stroke him, or feel his scrawny arm on your shoulder. But it doesn't bother you much. You're happy to just hang out, basking in how STRONG and ALPHA he is.

Grey

Technology! That's what's important and valuable in this twenty-first-century economy, right? Right! For example, ever since you took the grey pill, an increasingly large share of national GDP has come from ATMs giving you cash because you ask them to.

Your luck finally ends outside a bank in Kansas, when a whole squad of FBI agents ambushes you. You briefly consider going all Emperor Palpatine on their asses, but caution wins out and you allow yourself to be arrested.

Not wanting to end up on an autopsy table in Roswell, you explain that you're a perfectly ordinary master hacker. The government offers you a plea bargain: they'll drop charges if you help the military with cyber-security. You worry that your bluff has been called until you realize that, in fact, you *are* a master hacker. So you join the NSA and begin an illustrious career hacking into Russian databases, stalling Iranian centrifuges, and causing Chinese military systems to crash at inconvenient times. No one ever suspects you are anything more than very good at programming.

Once again, your luck runs out. Your handlers ask you to hack into the personal files of a mysterious new player on the world stage, a man named William who seems to have carved himself an empire in the Middle East. You don't find anything too damning, but you turn over what you've got.

A few days later, you're lying in bed drifting off to sleep when a man suddenly bursts in through your window brandishing a gun. Thinking quickly, you tell the gun to explode in his hands. Nothing happens. The man laughs. "It's a decoy gun," he said. "Just here to scare you. But you bother King William again, and next time I'm coming with a very real knife." He jumps back out of the window. You call the police, and of course the CIA and NSA get involved, but he is never caught.

After that, you're always looking over your shoulder. He *knew*. How did he know? The level of detective skills it would take in order to track you down and figure out your secret – it was astounding! Who *was* this King William?

You tell your handlers that you're no longer up for the job. They beg, cajole, threaten to reinstate your prison sentence, but you stand firm. Finally they transfer you to an easier assignment in the Moscow embassy. You make Vladimir Putin's phone start ringing at weird hours of the night so that he never gets enough sleep to think entirely clearly. It's an easy job, but rewarding, and no assassins ever bother you again.

Black

You know on an intellectual level that there are people who would choose something other than the black pill, just like you know on an intellectual level that there are people who shoot up schools. That doesn't mean you expect to ever *understand* it. You just wish you could have taken the black pill before you had to decide what pill to take, so that you could have analyzed your future conditional on taking each, and so made a more informed decision. But it's not like it was a very hard choice.

The basic principle is this – given a choice between A and B, you solemnly resolve to do A, then see what the future looks like. Then you solemnly resolve to do B, and do the same. By this method, you can determine the optimal choice in every situation, modulo the one month time horizon. You might not be able to decide what career to pursue, but you can sure as heck ace your job interview.

Also, a millisecond in the future is pretty indistinguishable from the present, so "seeing" a millisecond into the future gives you pretty much complete knowledge about the current state of the world.

You are so delighted by your omniscience and your ability to make near-optimal choices that it takes almost a year before you realize the true extent of your power.

You resolve, on the first day of every month, to write down what you see exactly a month ahead of you. But what you will see a month ahead of you is the piece of paper on which you have written down what you see a month ahead of *that*. In this manner, you can relay messages back to yourself from arbitrarily far into the future – at least up until your own death.

When you try this, you see yourself a month in the future, just finishing up writing a letter that reads as follows:

Dear Past Self:

In the year 2060, scientists invent an Immortality Serum. By this point we are of course fabulously wealthy, and we are one of the first people to partake of it. Combined with our ability to avoid accidents by looking into the future, this has allowed us to survive unexpectedly long.

I am sending this from the year 963,445,028,777,216 AD. We are one of the last hundred people alive in the Universe. The sky is black and without stars; the inevitable progress of entropy has reduced almost all mass and energy to unusable heat. The Virgo Superconfederation, the main political unit at this stage of history, gathered the last few megatons of usable resources aboard this station so that at least one outpost of humanity could last long after all the planets had succumbed. The station has been fulfilling its purpose for about a billion years now, but we only have enough fuel left for another few weeks. After that, there's no more negentropy left anywhere in the universe except our own bodies. I have seen a month into the future. Nobody comes to save us.

For the past several trillion years, our best scientists have been investigating how to reverse entropy and save the universe, or how to escape to a different universe in a lesser state of decay, or how to collect energy out of the waste heat which now fills the vast majority of the sky. All of these tasks have been proven impossible. There is no hope left, except for one thing.

It's impossible to see the future, even if it's only a month ahead. Somehow, our black pill breaks the laws of physics. Despite having explored throughout the cosmos, my people have found no alien species, nor any signs that such species ever existed. Yet somebody made the black pill. If we understood that power, maybe we could use it to save reality from its inevitable decay.

By sending this message back, I destroy my entire timeline. I do this in the hopes that you, in the carefree springtime of the universe, will be able to find the person who made these pills and escape doom in the way we could not.

Yours truly,

You From Almost A Quadrillion Years In The Future

ACT TWO

Red

You hit the punching bag. It bursts, sending punching-bag-filling spraying all over the room! You know that that would happen! It always happens when you hit a punching bag! Your wife gets really angry and tells you that we don't have enough money to be getting new punching bags all the time, but women hate it when you listen to what they say! The Internet told you that!

The doorbell rings. You tear the door off its hinges instead of opening it, just to show it who's boss. Standing on your porch is a man in black. He wears a black cloak, and his face is hidden by a black hood. He raises a weapon towards you.

This looks like one of the approximately 100% of problems that can be solved by BRUTE STRENGTH! You lunge at the man, but despite your super-speed, he steps out of the way easily, even gracefully, as if he had known you were going to do that all along. He squeezes the trigger. You jump out of the way, but it turns out to be more *into* the way, as he has shot exactly where you were jumping into. Something seems very odd about this. Your last conscious thought is that you wish you had enough BRUTE STRENGTH to figure out what is going on.

Pink

You come home from work to a living room full of punching-bag-parts. Your husband isn't home. You figure he knew you were going to chew him out for destroying another punching bag, and decided to make himself scarce. That lasts right up until you go into the kitchen and see a man dressed all in black, sitting at the table, as if he was expecting you.

You panic, then reach in to touch him. If he's an axe murderer or something, you'll seduce him, get him wrapped around your little finger, then order him to jump off a cliff to prove his love for you. It's nothing you haven't done before, though you don't like to think about it too much.

Except that this man has no bare skin anywhere. His robe covers his entire body, and even his hands are gloved. You try to reach in to touch his face, but he effortlessly manuevers away from you.

"I have your husband," he says, after you give up trying to enslave him with your magic. "He's alive and in a safe place."

"You're lying!" you answer. "He never would have surrendered to anyone! He's too alpha!"

The man nods. "I shot him with an elephant tranquilizer. He's locked up in a titanium cell underneath fifty feet of water. There's no way he can escape using BRUTE STRENGTH. If you ever want to see him again, you'll have to do what I say."

"Why? Why are you doing this to me?" you say, crying.

"I need the allegiance of some very special people," he said. "They won't listen to me just because I ask them to. But they might listen to me because *you* ask them to. I understand you are pretty special yourself. Help me get who I want, and when we are done here, I'll let you and your husband go."

There is ice in his voice. You shiver.

Grey

That night with the assassin was really scary. You swore you would never get involved in King William's business again. Why are you even considering this?

"Please?" she said, with her big puppy dog eyes.

Oh, right. Her. She's not even all that pretty. Well, pretty, but not *pretty* pretty. But somehow, when she touched you, it was like those movies where you hear a choir of angels singing in the background. You would do anything she said. You know you would.

"We need to know the layout of his palace compound," said the man in black. Was he with her? Were they dating? If they were dating, you'll kill him. It doesn't matter how creepy he is, you won't tolerate competition. But they're probably not dating. You notice how he flinches away from her, like he's afraid she might touch him.

"And it has to be me who helps?"

"I've, ah, simulated hundreds of different ways of getting access to the King. None of them hold much promise. His security is impeccable. Your special abilities are the only thing that can help us."

You sit down at your terminal. The Internet is slow; DC still doesn't have fiber optic. You've living here two years now, in a sort of retirement, ever since King William took over Russia and knocked the bottom out of the Putin-annoying business. William now controls the entire Old World, you hear, and is also Secretary-General of the United Nations and Pope of both the Catholic and the Coptic Churches. The United States is supposedly in a friendly coexistence with him, but you hear his supporters are gaining more and more power in Congress.

It only takes a few minutes' work before you have the documents you need. "He currently spends most of his time at the Rome compound," you say. "There are five different security systems. I can disable four of them. The last one is a complicated combination of electrical and mechanical that's not hooked into any computer system I'll be able to access. The only way to turn it off is from the control center, and the control center is on the *inside* of the perimeter."

The man in black nods, as if he'd been expecting that. "Come with me," he says. "We'll take care of it."

Blue

There are a hundred billion stars in the Milky Way. Each has an average of about one planet – some have many more, but a lot don't have planets at all.

If you can explore one planet every half-hour – and you can, it doesn't take too long to teleport to a planet, look around to see if there are plants and animals, and then move on to the next one – it would take you five million years to rule out life on every planet in the galaxy.

That's not practical. But, you think, life might spread. Life that originates on one planet might end up colonizing nearby planets and star systems. That means your best bet is to sample various regions of the galaxy, instead of going star by star.

That's what you've been doing. You must have seen about a hundred thousand planets so far. Some of them have beggared your imagination. Whole worlds made entirely of amethyst. Planets with dozens of colorful moons that make the night sky look like a tree full of Christmas ornaments. Planets with black inky oceans or green copper mountains.

But no life. No life anywhere.

A few years ago, you felt yourself losing touch with your humanity. You made yourself promise that every year, you'd spend a week on Earth to remind yourself of the only world you've ever seen with a population. Now it seems like an unpleasant task, an annoying imposition. But then, that was why you made yourself promise. Because you knew that future-you wouldn't do it unless they had to.

You teleport into a small Welsh hamlet. You've been away from other people so long, you might as well start small. No point going right into Times Square.

A person is standing right next to you. She reaches out her arm and touches you. You jump. How did she know you would –

"Hi," she says.

You're not a lesbian, but you can't help noticing she is the most beautiful person you've ever seen, and you would do anything for her.

"I need your help." A man dressed all in black is standing next to her.

"You should help him," the most beautiful person you've ever seen tells you, and you immediately know you will do whatever he asks.

Orange

You are in your study working on a draft version of next year's superweapon budget when you hear the door open. Four people you don't recognize step into the room. A man dressed in black. Another man wearing a grey shirt, thick glasses and is that a *pocket protector?* A woman in pink, pretty but not *pretty* pretty. Another woman in blue, who stares through you, like her mind is somewhere else. All five of your security systems have been totally silent.

You press the button to call your bodyguards, but it's not working. So you draw the gun out from under your desk and fire; you happen to be a master marksman, but the gun explodes in your face. You make a connection. A person from many years ago, who had the power to control all technology.

No time to think now. You're on your feet; good thing you happen to be a black belt in every form of martial arts ever invented. The man in grey is trying to take out a weapon; you kick him in the gut before he can get it out, and he crumples over. You go for the woman in blue, but at the last second she teleports to the other side of the room. This *isn't fair*.

You are about to go after the woman in pink, but something in her step, something in the position of the others makes you think they *want* you to attack her. You happen to be a master at reading microexpressions, so this is clear as day to you; you go after the man in black instead. He deftly sidesteps each of your attacks, almost as if he knows what you are going to do before you do it.

The woman in blue teleports behind you and kicks you in the back, hard. You fall over, and the woman in pink grabs your hand.

She is very, very beautiful. How did you miss that before? You feel a gush of horror that you almost punched such a beautiful face.

"We need your help," she says.

You are too lovestruck to say anything.

"The pills," said the man in black. "Can you make them?"

"No," you say, truthfully. "Of course I tried. But I wouldn't even know where to begin creating magic like that."

"And you've mastered all human jobs and activities," said the man in black. "Which means the pills weren't created by any human."

"But there aren't any aliens," said the woman in blue. "Not in this galaxy, at least. I've spent years looking. It's totally dead."

"It's just as I thought," said the man in black. He turns to you. "You're the Pope now, right? Come with us. We're going to need you to get a guy in northern Italy to give us something very important."

Yellow

It is spring, now. Your favorite time in the forest. The snow has melted, the wildflowers have started to bloom, and the bears are coming out of hibernation. You're walking down to the river when someone leaps out from behind a tree and touches you. You scream, then suddenly notice how beautiful she is.

Four other people shuffle out from behind the trees. You think one of them might be King William, the new world emperor, although that doesn't really make sense.

"You're probably wondering why I've called all of you together today..." said the man in black. You're not actually wondering that, at least not in quite those terms, but the woman in pink seems be listening intently so you do the same in the hopes of impressing her.

"Somehow – and none of us can remember exactly how – each of us took a pill that gave us special powers. Mine was to see the future. I saw to the end of time, and received a message from the last people in the universe. They charged me with the task of finding the people who created these pills and asking them how entropy might be reversed.

But I couldn't do it alone. I knew there were seven other people who had taken pills. One of us – Green – is dead. Another – Red – had nothing to contribute. The rest of us are here. With the help of Pink, Blue, and Gray, we've enlisted the help of Orange and his worldwide organization. Now we're ready for the final stage of the plan. Yellow, you can read anybody's mind from a picture, right?"

Yellow nods. "But it has to be a real photograph. I can't just draw a stick figure and say it's the President and read his mind. I tried that."

Black is unfazed. "With the help of Orange, who among his many other accomplishments is the current Pope, I have obtained the Shroud of Turin. A perfect photographic representation of Jesus Christ, created by some unknown technology in the first century. And Jesus, I am told, is an incarnation of God."

"As the current Pope, I suppose I would have to agree with that assessment," says Orange. "Though as the current UN Secretary General, I am disturbed by your fanatical religious literalism."

"Orange can do anything that humans can do, and says he can't make the pills. Blue has searched the whole galaxy, and says there aren't any aliens. That leaves only one suspect. God must have made these pills, which means He must know how to do it. If we can read His mind, we can steal his secrets."

"As Pope," says Orange, "I have to condemn this in the strongest possible terms. But as Lucasian Professor of Mathematics at Cambridge, I have to admit I'm intrigued by this opportunity to expand our knowledge."

Black ignores him. "Yellow, will you do the honors?"

You want no part in this. "This is insane. Every time I read someone's mind I regret it. Even if it's a little kid or a bear or something. It's too much for me. I can't deal with all of their guilt and sorrow and broken dreams and everything. There is *no way* I am touching the mind of God Himself."

"Pleeeeeease?" asks Pink, with big puppy dog eyes.

"Um," you say.

"Don't you know how this will go, anyway?" asks Blue. "Why don't you just tell her what happens?"

"Um," said Black. "This is actually the one thing I haven't been able to see. I guess contact with God is inherently unpredictable, or something."

"I have *such* a bad feeling about this," you say.

"Pweeeeeeease?" says Pink. She actually says pweeeeeeease.

You sigh, take the shroud, and stare into the eyes of Weird Photographic Negative Jesus.

Black

It is the year 963,445,028,777,216 AD, and here you are in a space station orbiting the Galactic Core.

After handing Yellow the Shroud of Turin, the next thing you remember is waking up in a hospital bed. The doctor tells you that you'd been in a coma for the past forty one years.

Apparently Yellow went totally berserk after reading God's mind. You don't know the details and you don't want to, but she immediately lashed out and used her superpowers to turn off the minds of everybody within radius, including both you and herself. You all went comatose, and probably would have starved to death in the middle of the forest if Orange's supporters hadn't launched a worldwide manhunt for him. They took his body and the bodies of his friends back to Rome, where they were given the best possible medical care while a steward ruled over his empire.

After forty-one years of that, Yellow had a heart attack and died, breaking the spell and freeing the rest of you. Except Blue and Grey. They'd died as well. It was just you, Orange, and Pink now.

Oh, and Red. You'd hired a friend to watch over him in his titanium jail cell, and once it became clear you were never coming back, he'd had mercy and released the guy. Red had since made a meager living selling the world's worst body-building videos, which were so bad they had gained a sort of ironic popularity. You tracked him down, and when Pink saw him for the first time in over forty years, she ran and embraced him. He hugged her back. It took them a few hours of fawning over each other before she realized that nothing had happened when she touched him a second time. Something something true love something the power was within you the whole time?

But you had bigger fish to fry. The stewards of Orange's empire weren't too happy about their figurehead monarch suddenly rising from the dead, and for a while his position was precarious. He asked you to be his advisor, and you accepted. With your help, he was able to retake his throne. His first act was to fund research into the immortality serum you had heard about, which was discovered right on schedule in 2060.

The years went by. Orange's empire started colonizing new worlds, then new galaxies, until thousands of years later it changed its name to the Virgo Superconfederation. New people were born. New technologies were invented. New frontiers were conquered. Until finally, the stars started going out one by one.

Faced with the impending heat death, Orange elected to concentrate all his remaining resources here, on a single station in the center of the galaxy, which would wait out the final doom as long as possible. For billions of years, it burned through its fuel stockpile, until the final doom crept closer and closer.

And then a miracle occurred.

EPILOGUE

Red

This space station is AWESOME! There are lasers and holodecks and lots of HOT PUSSY! And all you have to do is turn a giant turbine for a couple of hours a day.

One of the eggheads in white coats tried to explain it to you once. He said that your BRUTE STRENGTH was some kind of scientific impossibility, because you didn't eat or drink any more than anyone else, and you didn't breathe in any more oxygen than anyone else, and you were actually kind of small and scrawny, but you were still strong enough and fast enough to turn a giant turbine thousands of times per minute.

He rambled on and on about thermodynamics. Said that every other process in the universe used at most as much energy as you put into it, but that your strength seemed almost limitless regardless of how much energy you took in as food. That made you special, somehow. It made you a "novel power source" that could operate "independently of external negentropy". You weren't sure what any of that meant, and honestly the scientist seemed sort of like a BETA CUCKOLD ORBITER to you. But whatever was going on, they'd promised you that if you turned this turbine every day, you could have all the HOT PUSSY you wanted and be SUPER ALPHA.

You'd even met the head honcho once, a guy named King William. He told you that some of the energy you produced was going to power the station, but that the rest was going into storage. That over billions and billions of years, they would accumulate more and more stored negentropy, until it was enough to restart the universe. That it would be a cycle – a newborn universe lasting a few billion years, collapsing into a dark period when new negentropy had to be accumulated, followed by another universe again.

It all sounded way above your head. But one thing stuck with you. As he was leaving, the King remarked that it was ironic that when the black hole harvesters and wormholes and tachyon capacitors had all failed, it was a random really strong guy who had saved them.

You had always known, deep down, that BRUTE STRENGTH was what was really important. And here, at the end of all things, it is deeply gratifying to finally be proven right.

8

Against Tulip Subsidies

June 6, 2015

I

Imagine a little kingdom with a quaint custom: when a man likes a woman, he offers her a tulip; if she accepts, they are married shortly thereafter. A couple who marries sans tulip is considered to be living in sin; no other form of proposal is appropriate or accepted.

One day, a Dutch trader comes to the little kingdom. He explains that his homeland *also* has a quaint custom involving tulips: they speculate on them, bidding the price up to stratospheric levels.[1] Why, in the Netherlands, a tulip can go for ten times more than the average worker earns in a year! The trader is pleased to find a new source of bulbs, and offers the people of the kingdom a few guilders per tulip, which they happily accept.

Soon other Dutch traders show up and start a bidding war. The price of tulips goes up, and up, and up; first dozens of guilders, then hundreds. Tulip-growers make a fortune, but everyone else is less pleased. Suitors wishing to give a token of their love find themselves having to invest their entire life savings – with no guarantee that the woman will even say yes! Soon, some of the poorest people are locked out of marriage and family-raising entirely.

Some of the members of Parliament are outraged. Marriage is, they say, a human right, and to see it forcibly denied the poor by foreign speculators is nothing less than an abomination. They demand that the King provide every man enough money to guarantee he can buy a tulip. Some objections are raised: won't it deplete the Treasury? Are we obligated to buy everyone a beautiful flawless bulb, or just the sickliest, grungiest plant that will

---

[1] http://en.wikipedia.org/wiki/Tulip_mania

technically satisfy the requirements of the ritual? If some man continuously proposes to women who reject him, are we obligated to pay for a new bulb each time, subsidizing his stupidity?

The pro-subsidy faction declares that the people asking these question are well-off, and can probably afford tulips of their own, and so from their place of privilege they are trying to raise pointless objections to other people being able to obtain the connubial happiness they themselves enjoy. After the doubters are tarred and feathered and thrown in the river, Parliament votes that the public purse pay for as many tulips as the poor need, whatever the price.

A few years later, another Dutch trader comes to the little kingdom. Everyone asks if he is there to buy tulips, and he says no, the Netherlands' tulip bubble has long since collapsed, and the price is down to a guilder or two. The people of the kingdom are very surprised to hear that, since the price of their own tulips has never stopped going up, and is now in the range of tens of thousands of guilders. Nevertheless, they are glad that, however high tulip prices may be for them, they know the government is always there to help. Sure, the roads are falling apart and the army is going hungry for lack of rations, but at least everyone who wants to marry is able to do so.

Meanwhile, across the river is another little kingdom that had the same tulip-related marriage custom. They also had a crisis when the Dutch merchants started making the prices go up. But they didn't have enough money to afford universal tulip subsidies. It was pretty touch-and-go for a while, and a lot of poor people were very unhappy.

But nowadays they use daffodils to mark engagements, and their economy has never been better.

II

In America, aspiring doctors do four years of undergrad in whatever area they want (I did Philosophy), then four more years of medical school, for a total of eight years post-high school education. In Ireland, aspiring doctors go straight from high school to medical school and finish after five years.

I've done medicine in both America and Ireland. The doctors in both countries are about equally good. When Irish doctors take the American standardized tests, they usually do pretty well. Ireland is one of the approximately 100% of First World countries that gets better health outcomes than the United States. There's no evidence whatsoever that American doctors gain anything from those three extra years of undergrad. And why would they? Why is having a philosophy degree under my belt supposed to make me any better at medicine?

(I guess I might have acquired a talent for colorectal surgery through long practice pulling things out of my ass, but it hardly seems worth it.)

I'll make another confession. Ireland's medical school is five years as opposed to America's four because the Irish spend their first year teaching the basic sciences – biology, organic chemistry, physics, calculus. When I applied to medical school in Ireland, they offered me an accelerated four year program on the grounds that I had surely gotten all of those in my American undergraduate work. I hadn't. I read some books about them over the summer and did just fine.

Americans take eight years to become doctors. Irishmen can do it in four, and achieve the same result. Each year of higher education at a good school – let's say an Ivy, doctors don't study at Podunk Community College – costs about $50,000. So American medical students are paying an extra $200,000 for... what?

Remember, a modest amount of the current health care crisis is caused by doctors' crippling level of debt[2]. Socially responsible doctors often consider less lucrative careers helping the needy, right up until the bill comes due from their education and they realize they have to make a lot of money *right now*. We took one look at that problem and said "You know, let's make doctors pay an extra $200,000 for no reason."

And to paraphrase Dirkson, $200,000 here, $200,000 there, and pretty soon it adds up to real money. 20,000 doctors graduate in the United States each year; that means the total yearly cost of requiring doctors to have undergraduate degrees is $4 billion. That's most of the amount of money you'd need to house every homeless person in the country ($10,000[3] to house one homeless x 600,000[4] homeless).

I want to be able to say people have noticed the Irish/American discrepancy and are thinking hard about it. I *can* say that. Just not in the way I would like. Many of the elder doctors I talked to in Ireland wanted to switch to the American system. Not because they thought it would give them bet-

[2]http://www.studentdoctor.net/2010/08/medical-school-administrators-respond-to-d rowning-in-debt/

[3]http://articles.orlandosentinel.com/2014-05-21/news/os-cost-of-homelessness-orl ando-20140521_1_homeless-individuals-central-florida-commission-tulsa

[4]https://www.hudexchange.info/resources/documents/ahar-2013-part1.pdf

ter doctors. Just because they said it was more fun working with medical students like myself who were older and a little wiser. The Irish medical students were just out of high school and hard to relate to – us foreigners were four years older than that and had one or another undergraduate subject under our belts. One of my attendings said that it was nice having me around because I'd studied Philosophy in college and that gave our team a touch of class. *A touch of class!* This is why, despite my reservations about libertarianism, it's not-libertarianism that really scares me. Whenever some people without skin in the game are allowed to make decisions for other people, you end up with a bunch of elderly doctors getting together, think "Yeah, things *do* seem a little classier around here if we make people who are not us pay $200,000, make it so," and then there goes the money that should have housed all the homeless people in the country.

But more important, it also destroyed my last shred of hope that the current mania for requiring college degrees for everything had a good reason behind it.

III

The only reason I'm picking on medicine is that it's so clear. You have your experimental group in the United States, your control group in Ireland, you can see the lack of difference. You can take an American doctor and an Irish doctor, watch them prescribe the same medication in the same situation, and have a visceral feel for "Wait, we just spent $200,000 for no reason."

But it's not just medicine. Let me tell you about my family.

There's my cousin. He wants to be a firefighter. He's wanted to be a firefighter ever since he was young, and he's done volunteer work for his local fire department, who have promised him a job. But in order to get it, he has to go do four years of college. You can't be a firefighter without a college degree. That would be ridiculous. Back in the old days, when people were allowed to become firefighters after getting only thirteen measly years of book learning, I have it on good authority that several major states burnt to the ground.

My mother is a Spanish teacher. After twenty years teaching, with excellent reviews by her students, she pursued a Masters' in Education because her school was going to pay her more money if she had it. She told me that her professors were incompetent, had never actually taught real students, and spent the entire course pushing whatever was the latest educational fad; however, after paying them thousands of dollars, she got the degree and her school dutifully increased her salary. She is lucky. In several states, teachers are required by law to pursue a Masters' degree to be allowed to continue teaching. Oddly enough, these states have no better student outcomes than states without this requirement, but this does not seem to affect their zeal for this requirement. Even though many rigorous well-controlled studies[5] have found that presence of absence of a Masters' degree explains approximately zero percent of variance in teacher quality, many states continue to require it if you want to keep your license, and almost every state will pay you more for having it.

Before taking my current job, I taught English in Japan. I had no Japanese language experience and no teaching experience, but the company I interviewed with asked if I had an undergraduate degree in some subject or other, and that was good enough for them. Meanwhile, I knew people who were fluent in Japanese and who had high-level TOEFL certification. They did not have a college degree so they were not considered.

My ex-girlfriend majored in Gender Studies, but it turned out all of the high-paying gender factories had relocated to China. They solved this problem by going to App Academy, a three month long, $15,000 course that taught programming. App Academy graduates compete for the same jobs as people who have taken computer science in college, a four year long, $200,000 undertaking.

I see no reason to think my family and friends are unique. The overall picture seems to be one of people paying hundreds of thousands of dollars to get a degree in Art History to pursue a job in Sales, or a degree in Spanish Literature to get a job as a middle manager. Or *not* paying hundreds of thousands of dollars, if they happen to be poor, and so being permanently locked out of jobs as a firefighter or salesman.

IV

So presidential candidate Bernie Sanders has proposed universal free college tuition[6].

On the one hand, I sympathize with his goals. If you can't get any job better than 'fast food worker' without a college degree, and poor people can't

---

[5] http://www.waldenu.edu/~/media/Files/WAL/outcomes-research-broch-faqs-web-final.pdf

[6] http://america.aljazeera.com/articles/2015/5/19/bernie-sanders-unveils-plan-for-tuition-free-public-colleges.html

afford college degrees, that's a pretty grim situation, and obviously unfair to the poor.

On the other hand, if can't you get married without a tulip, and poor people can't afford tulips, that's also a pretty grim situation, and obviously unfair to the poor.

But the solution isn't universal tulip subsidies.

Higher education is in a bubble much like the old tulip bubble. In the past forty years, the price of college has dectupled (quadrupled when adjusting for inflation). It used to be easy[7] to pay for college with a summer job; now it is impossible. At the same time, the unemployment rate of people without college degrees is twice that[8] of people who have them. Things are clearly very bad and Senator Sanders is right to be concerned.

But, well, when we require doctors to get a college degree before they can go to medical school, we're throwing out a mere $5 billion, barely enough to house all the homeless people in the country. But Senator Sanders admits that his plan would cost $70 billion per year. That's about the size of the entire economy of Hawaii. It's enough to give $2000 every year to every American in poverty.

At what point do we say "Actually, no, let's not do that, and just let people hold basic jobs even if they don't cough up a a hundred thousand dollars from somewhere to get a degree in Medieval History"?

I'm afraid that Sanders' plan is a lot like the tulip subsidy idea that started off this post. It would subsidize the continuation of a useless tradition that has turned into a speculation bubble, prevent the bubble from ever popping, and disincentivize people from figuring out a way to route around the problem, eg replacing the tulips with daffodils.

(yes, it is nice to have college for non-economic reasons too, but let's be honest – if there were no such institution as college, would you, totally for non-economic reasons, suggest the government pay poor people $100,000 to get a degree in Medieval History? Also, anything not related to job-getting can be done three times as quickly by just reading a book.)

If I were Sanders, I'd propose a different strategy. Make "college degree" a protected characteristic, like race and religion and sexuality. If you're not

---

[7] http://www.theatlantic.com/education/archive/2014/04/the-myth-of-working-your-way-through-college/359735/

[8] http://www.theatlantic.com/business/archive/2013/03/if-college-leads-to-jobs-why-are-so-many-young-college-grads-unemployed/273877/

allowed to ask a job candidate whether they're gay, you're not allowed to ask them whether they're a college graduate or not. You can give them all sorts of examinations, you can ask them their high school grades and SAT scores, you can ask their work history, but if you ask them if they have a degree then that's illegal class-based discrimination and you're going to jail. I realize this is a blatant violation of my usual semi-libertarian principles, but at this point I don't care.

9

CBT In The Water Supply

July 16, 2015

Epistemic status: Very speculative, <50% confidence, thinking out loud. Don't let this turn you off therapy.

Here's a vignette from cognitive-behavioral therapy book *When Panic Attacks*[1], heavily edited for length:

> A chronically anxious medical school professor named Nate suffered from low-self-esteem and feelings of inadequacy. One day, Nate brought me a copy of his CV. I was blown away. He'd listed over sixty pages of research publications, prestigious awards, and keynote addresses he'd given at major conferences around the world. I asked Nate how he reconciled his low self-esteem with all of his accomplishments. He said that every time he looked at his CV, he felt discouraged and told himself that his colleagues' research studies were far more rigorous and important than his own. He said his paper seemed "soft" and consisted primarily of theoretical work, rather than hard-core laboratory research with real tissue. He said "Dr. Burns, no matter how much I accomplish, it never seems good enough."
>
> Perfectionism was clearly one of Nate's self-defeating beliefs. I suggested that Nate use the Pleasure/Perfection Balance Work-

---

[1] http://smile.amazon.com/gp/product/076792083X/ref=as_li_tl?ie=UTF8&camp=1789&creative=390957&creativeASIN=076792083X&linkCode=as2&tag=slastacod-20&linkId=HCC4SJRCVLOGWB2W

sheet to test this belief. I told him to write "If I can't do something perfectly, it's not worth doing at all" on the top of the sheet, and asked him to list several activities in the left-hand column. I told him to predict how satisfying and rewarding each activity would be, to record how satisfying and rewarding it was afterwards, and to rate how perfectly he did each activity. That way he could find out of it was true that he only enjoyed the things he did perfectly.

The next week, Nate had some interesting results to share with me. One of his activities was giving the welcoming lecture ot the incoming class of medical students. Nate gave this lecture every year because he was considered to be the most charismatic speaker at the medical school. Nate predicted this lecture would be 70% satisfying, but his actual satisfaction as only 20%. This was surprising, since he'd received a thirty-second standing obation, and he'd rated his perfection level for the talk at 90%.

I asked Nate why his satisfaction rating was so low. He explained that he always got standing ovations, so he routinely timed them. The previous year, the medical students had stood and cheered for more than a minute at the end of his talk. This year, the only stood and cheered for half a minute. Nate felt disappointed and started worrying that he was over the hill.

The second entry on Nate's Pleasure/Perfection Balance Worksheet was that [he fixed a broken pipe in his bathroom]. He had to make several trips to the hardware story to buy tools and parts and to get tips on how to do it, so he didn't get the pipe fixed until 10 PM. How explained that any plumber could have fixed the pipe in five minutes, so he rated his perfection as 5%. But his satisfaction level for this activity was 100%. In fact, he felt exhilarated. Nate said it was the most satisfying thing he'd done in years.

The result of Nate's experiment was not consistent with his belief that things weren't worth doing unless he did them perfectly. It dawned on him that there were many sources of satisfaction in his life that he'd overlooked, such as taking a walk through the woods with his wife, even though neither of them were world-class hikers, playing squash with his son, even though neither of them were champions, or just going out with his family for ice cream cones on a warm summer evening.

This experiment had a significant impact on Nate's feelings of self-esteem and on his career. He told me that his feelings of anxiety and inferiority decreased, and his productivity actually increased because he was no longer so worried about having to do everything so perfectly.

At first I assumed this story was made up, but the book claims these are based on real patients, and even mentions how the writer showed videos of some of these therapy sessions to his classes. Interesting. How about another?

Several years ago, I did a three-day intensive workshop for a small group of psychotherapists in Florida. A marriage and family therapist named Walter explained that he'd been struggling with anxiety and depression for several months because Paul, the man he'd lived with for eight years, had found a new lover and left him. He put his hand on his chest and said: "It feels real heavy, right here. There's just a sense of loneliness and emptiness about the whole experience. It feels so universal and final. I feel like this pain is going to go on forever, until the end of time."

I asked Walter how he was thinking and feeling about the breakup with Paul. What was he telling himself? He saidL "I feel incredibly guilty and ashamed, and it seems like it must have been my fault. Maybe I wasn't skillful enough, attractive enough, or dynamic enough. Maybe I wasn't there for him emotionally. I feel like I must have screwed up. Sometimes I feel like a total fraud. Here I am, a marriage and family therapist, and my own relationship didn't even work out. I feel like a loser. A really, really big loser."

Walter recorded these five negative thoughts on his daily mood log:

1. I'll never be in a loving relationship again
2. I must be impossible to live with and impossible to be in a relationship with
3. There must be something wrong with me
4. I totally screwed up and flushed my life down the toilet

5. I'll end up as an old, fat, gray-haired, lonely gay man

He believed all of these thoughts very strongly.

You can see that most of Walter's suffering results from the illogical way he's thinking about the rejection. You could even say that Walter is treating himself far more harshly than Paul did. I thought the Double Standard Technique might help because Walter seemed to be a warm and compassionate individual. I asked wehat he'd say to a dear friend who'd been rejected by someone he'd been living with for eight years. I said "Would you tell him that there's something wrong with him, that he screwed up his life and flushed it down the toilet for good?"

Walter looked shocked and said he'd *never* say something like that to a friend. I suggested we try a role-playing exercise so that he could tell me what he would say to a friend who was in the same predicament [...]

Therapist (role-playing patient's friend): Walter, there's another angle I haven't told you about. What you don't understand is that I'm impossible to live with and be in a relationship with. That's the real reason I feel so bad, and that's why I'll be alone for the rest of my life.

Patient (role-playing as if therapist is his friend who just had a bad breakup): Gosh, I'm surprised to hear you say that, because I've known you for a long time and never felt that way about you. In fact, you've always been warm and open, and a loyal friend. How in the world did you come to the conclusion that you were impossible to be in a relationship with?

Therapist (continuing role-play): Well, my relationship with [my boyfriend] fell apart. Doesn't that prove I'm impossible to be in a relationship with?

Patient (continuing role-play): In all honesty, what your'e saying doesn't make a lot of sense. In the first place, your boyfriend was also involved in the relationship. It takes two to tango. And in the second place, you were involved in a reasonably successful relationship with him for eight years. So how can you claim that you're impossible to live with?

Therapist (continuing role-play:) Let me make sure I've got this right. You're saying that I was in a reasonably successful relationship for eight years, so it doesn't make much sense to say that I'm impossible to live with or impossible to be in a relationship with?

Patient (continuing-role-play:) You've got it. Crystal clear.

At that point, Walter's face lit up, as if a lightbulb had suddenly turned on in his brain, and we both started laughing. His negative thoughts suddenly seemed absurd to him, and there was an immediate shift in his mood... after Walter put the lie to his negative thoughts, I asked him to rate how he was feeling again. His feeling of sadness fell all the way fromj 80% to 20%. His felings of guilt, shame, and anxiety fell all the way to 10%, and his feelings of hopelessness dropped to 5%. The feelings of loneliness, embarassment, frustration, and anger disappeared completely.

The book is quite long, and it's full of stories like this. The author, who's one of the top cognitive-behavioral psychiatrists in the world, describes his experience with the therapy as:

[When I first learned about this therapy, I thought] depression and anxiety seemed far too serious and severe for such a simplistic approach. But when I tried these methods with some of my more difficult patients, my perceptions changed. Patients who'd felt hopeless, worthless, and desperate began to recover. At first, it was hard to believe that the techniques were working, but I could not deny the fact that when my patients learned to put the lie to their negative thoughts, they began to improve. Sometimes they recovered right before my eyes during sessions. Patients who'd felt demoralized and hopeless for years suddenly turned the corner on their problems. I can still recall an elderly French woman who'd been bitterly depressed for more than fifty years, with three nearly-successful suicide attempts, who started shouting "Joie de vivre! Joie de vivre!" ("joy of living") one day in my office. These experiences made such a strong impact on me that I decided my calling was in clinical work rather than brain research. After considerable soul-searching, I decided to give up my research career and become a full-time clinician. Over the years, I've had more than 35,000 psychotherapy sessions with depressed and anxious patients, and I'm every bit as enthusiastic about CBT as when I first began learning about it.

Okay. I am not one of the top cognitive-behavioral therapists in the world. I've been studying formal cognitive-behavioral therapy for about a week now, and been doing untrained ad hoc therapy on inpatients for a couple years. But I've also gotten to observe a lot of other people doing therapy, and talked to people who have had therapy, and treated patients who were simultaneously undergoing therapy, and the impression I got was very different.

Dr. Burns asks patients to question whether their anxiety and their negative thoughts are rational, and their faces light up and all of their psychiatric problems suddenly melt away.

The therapists I've seen ask patients to question whether their anxiety and their negative thoughts are rational, ever so tactfully, and the patients say "No shit, Sherlock, of course they aren't, but just knowing that doesn't help or make them go away, and I've been through this same spiel with like thirty people already. Now shut up and give me my Xanax."

In my last post, someone asked[2] what to do if they found cognitive-behavioral therapy hokey and patronizing. I said, only half joking, that "if you don't like hokey patronizing things, CBT may not be for you." I know it's mean, and pessimistic, but everyone I've talked to has had pretty much the same experience. I used to attribute this to my friends being pretty smart, and maybe CBT was aimed as less intelligent people, but Nate The Genius Medical School Professor seems pretty smart. So does Walter The Therapist. Burns' book includes a bunch of other vignettes about high-powered lawyers, graduate students, et cetera. They all find his suggestions of "Well, have you considered that your irrational negative thoughts might not be rational?" super life-changing.

You might have read the study this graph comes from: The Effects of Cognitive-Behavioral Therapy As An Anti-Depressive Treatment Is Falling: A Meta-Analysis[3]. As you can see, the Hedges' g[4] declined from about 2.5 in 1980 to around 1 today. The latest embarrassing set of results now show[5] CBT doing no better than its old nemesis psychoanalysis. Why?

[2] https://slatestarcodex.com/2015/07/13/things-that-sometimes-work-if-you-have-anxiety/#comment-219606

[3] https://uit.no/Content/418448/The%20effect%20of%20CBT%20is%20falling.pdf

[4] https://twitter.com/slatestarcodex/status/552313651496226816

[5] https://slatestarcodex.com/2013/09/19/scientific-freud/

There are a lot of possible explanations. The smart money is always on "it never worked very well, but we're finally doing studies that aren't hopelessly biased", but the analysis doesn't find a clear difference in study quality. Other suggestions are that therapists have gotten less committed over time, or that the patient populations has changed. All of these sound reasonable. But let me mention one more possibility.

Every so often, psychiatrists joke about how so many people are depressed we might as well put Prozac in the water supply. Sometimes we say the same thing about lithium, although in that case we're not joking[6].

Nobody's ever talked about putting cognitive-behavioral therapy in the water supply, but insofar as that's meaningful at all I would say we've kind of done it. Cognitive-behavioral ideas, like perfectionism, excessive self-blame, conditional versus unconditional self-respect, deep breathing, goal-setting, et cetera have become basic parts of popular culture. The whole self-esteem movement isn't *exactly* cognitive-behavioral, but it's certainly allied, and it certainly represents a shift to a style of thinking about the self and about psychology in a way that's much more fertile for cognitive-behavioral ideas. Inside Out was *kind of* "Cognitive Behavioral Therapy: The Movie".

Although the particular book I'm reading is from 2006, Burns himself was one of Aaron Beck's original students and one of the first cognitive-behavioral therapists ever. I wonder how many of these patients who seem absolutely *shocked* to realize that maybe their anxiety isn't rational come from that very early period.

It's very hard to track changes in people's basic beliefs about psychology. I was flabbergasted to learn that until Dr. Benjamin Spock's landmark 1940s book on child care, parents were told not to hug, kiss, or show affection to babies, because that would coddle them and make them weak, pampered adults. Before that, parents interacted with their kids much less, and it was assumed that siblings and nannies and friends would raise them, or they would raise themselves. It's easy to read books about ancient Greece and not notice that they have a completely different view of the role of the self/individual than we do. So it wouldn't surprise me if a lot of the psychology we consider "obvious" is CBT that has seeped out into the water supply over the past thirty years.

If that were true, it would explain why CBT is no longer as effective – it's just telling people things they already know.

---

[6] http://www.theguardian.com/environment/shortcuts/2011/dec/05/should-we-put-lithium-in-water

It could be fairly asked: then why isn't everybody *already* better? Depression seems to be increasing, though there's a lot of argument about exactly how much; that doesn't sound like what would happen if everyone were automatically getting a background level of therapy.

Here's a theory, though it's on even shakier ground than the other one. The meta-analysis proposes that CBT may have lost some placebo effect over time because patients no longer think of it as The Exciting New Thing. I'm not sure I can go along with that – my own analysis[7] of psychotropic medications suggests patients very much prefer the *old* ones for some reason. But a big part of psychotherapy is placebo effect[8], so they might be on to something.

What part of psychotherapy provides the placebo? Is it going to the clinic? Talking to the therapist? Hearing fancy words like "self-estimation"? Doing worksheets?

One thing a lot of therapies have in common is that they provide the feeling of insights. For example, psychoanalysts are very good at coming up with surprising-but-plausible ways that your current problems are linked to things that happened to you as a child; the usual result is a patient feeling enlightened, like "You're right, the leg pain that's been bothering me *is* in the same part of my leg that accidentally brushed up against my mother's breast one time when I was seven, that's pretty interesting."

Suppose that in the old days, CBT was an insight a minute and you were constantly hearing surprising things you'd never thought about before. And nowadays, you're kind of absorbing a lot of those things by osmosis without it seeming too insightful, and then the therapy itself is anticlimactic. Could that lessen the placebo effect enough to account for the data?

I don't know. Maybe after I've been training in formal CBT for more than a week, I'll have more data and can report back to you.

EDIT: Sarah writes[9]: "In a way, seeing CBT stuff in pop culture inoculates people, I think. People will get as far as noticing"this negative thought is an anxiety symptom", but not as far as *actually reversing it*. When people hadn't heard of CBT, they first got the"this negative thought is irrational" message in a context when they were actively working on their problems, so they followed through with the 'hard' step of actually reversing the thought. Now, people run into the revelation that the 'inner critic' is wrong just by browsing facebook, when they're *not* actively

---

[7] https://slatestarcodex.com/2015/04/30/prescriptions-paradoxes-and-perversities/
[8] https://slatestarcodex.com/2013/09/19/scientific-freud/
[9] https://slatestarcodex.com/2015/07/16/cbt-in-the-water-supply/#comment-219768

trying to fight their anxiety problems, so the revelation loses its force."

    EDIT 2: *Paul Crowley points out a very similar theory*[10] *in The Guardian*

---

[10] http://www.theguardian.com/lifeandstyle/2015/jul/03/why-cbt-is-falling-out-of-favour-oliver-burkeman

— 10 —

The Goddess of Everything Else

August 17, 2015

Related to: Specific vs. General Foragers vs. Farmers[1] *and War In Heaven*[2], *but especially The Gift We Give To Tomorrow*[3]

They say only Good can create, whereas Evil is sterile. Think Tolkien, where Morgoth can't make things himself, so perverts Elves to Orcs for his armies. But I think this gets it entirely backwards; it's Good that just mutates and twists, and it's Evil that teems with fecundity.

Imagine two principles, here in poetic personification. The first is the Goddess of Cancer, the second the Goddess of Everything Else. If visual representations would help, you can think of the first with the claws of a crab, and the second a dress made of feathers of peacocks.

The Goddess of Cancer reached out a clawed hand over mudflats and tidepools. She said pretty much what she always says, "KILL CONSUME MULTIPLY CONQUER." Then everything burst into life, became miniature monsters engaged in a battle of all against all in their zeal to assuage their insatiable longings. And the swamps became orgies of hunger and fear and grew loud with the screams of a trillion amoebas.

Then the Goddess of Everything Else trudged her way through the bog, till the mud almost totally dulled her bright colors and rainbows. She stood on a rock and she sang them a dream of a different existence. She showed them the beauty of flowers, she showed them the oak tree majestic. The roar

[1] http://www.overcomingbias.com/2015/08/specific-vs-general-foragers-farmers.html
[2] http://www.xenosystems.net/war-in-heaven/
[3] https://www.greaterwrong.com/lw/sa/the_gift_we_give_to_tomorrow/

of the wind on the wings of the bird, and the swiftness and strength of the tiger. She showed them the joy of the dolphins abreast of the waves as the spray formed a rainbow around them, and all of them watched as she sang and they all sighed with longing.

But they told her "Alas, what you show us is terribly lovely. But we are the daughters and sons of the Goddess of Cancer, and wholly her creatures. The only goals in us are KILL CONSUME MULTIPLY CONQUER. And though our hearts long for you, still we are not yours to have, and your words have no power to move us. We wish it were otherwise, but it is not, and your words have no power to move us."

The Goddess of Everything Else gave a smile and spoke in her sing-song voice saying: "I scarcely can blame you for being the way you were made, when your Maker so carefully yoked you. But I am the Goddess of Everything Else and my powers are devious and subtle. So I do not ask you to swerve from your monomaniacal focus on breeding and conquest. But what if I show you a way that my words are aligned with the words of your Maker in spirit? For I say unto you even multiplication itself when pursued with devotion will lead to my service."

As soon as she spoke it was so, and the single-celled creatures were freed from their warfare. They joined hands in friendship, with this one becoming an eye and with that one becoming a neuron. Together they soared and took flight from the swamp and the muck that had birthed them, and flew to new islands all balmy and green and just ripe for the taking. And there they consumed and they multiplied far past the numbers of those who had stayed in the swampland. In this way the oath of the Goddess of Everything Else was not broken.

The Goddess of Cancer came forth from the fire and was not very happy. The things she had raised from the mud and exhorted to kill and compete had become all complacent in co-operation, a word which to her was anathema. She stretched out her left hand and snapped its cruel pincer, and said what she always says: "KILL CONSUME MULTIPLY CONQUER". She said these things not to the birds and the beasts but to each cell within them, and many cells flocked to her call and divided, and flower and fishes and birds both alike bulged with tumors, and falcons fell out of the sky in their sickness. But others remembered the words of the Goddess of Everything Else and held fast, and as it is said in the Bible the light clearly shone through the dark, and the darkness did not overcome it.

So the Goddess of Cancer now stretched out her right hand and spoke to the birds and the beasts. And she said what she always says "KILL CON-SUME MULTIPLY CONQUER", and so they all did, and they set on each other in violence and hunger, their maws turning red with the blood of their victims, whole species and genera driven to total extinction. The Goddess of Cancer declared it was good and returned the the fire.

Then came the Goddess of Everything Else from the waves like a siren, all flush with the sheen of the ocean. She stood on a rock and she sang them a dream of a different existence. She showed them the beehive all golden with honey, the anthill all cozy and cool in the soil. The soldiers and workers alike in their labors combining their skills for the good of the many. She showed them the pair-bond, the family, friendship. She showed these to shorebirds and pools full of fishes, and all those who saw them, their hearts broke with longing.

But they told her "Your music is lovely and pleasant, and all that you show us we cannot but yearn for. But we are the daughters and sons of the Goddess of Cancer, her slaves and creatures. And all that we know is the single imperative KILL CONSUME MULTIPLY CONQUER. Yes, once in the youth of the world you compelled us, but now things are different, we're all individuals, no further change will the Goddess of Cancer allow us. So, much as we love you, alas – we are not yours to have, and your words have no power to move us. We wish it were otherwise, but it is not, and your words have no power to move us."

The Goddess of Everything Else only laughed at them, saying, "But I am the Goddess of Everything Else and my powers are devious and subtle. Your loyalty unto the Goddess your mother is much to your credit, nor yet shall I break it. Indeed, I fulfill it – return to your multiplication, but now having heard me, each meal that you kill and each child that you sire will bind yourself ever the more to my service." She spoke, then dove back in the sea, and a coral reef bloomed where she vanished.

As soon as she spoke it was so, and the animals all joined together. The wolves joined in packs, and in schools joined the fishes; the bees had their beehives, the ants had their anthills, and even the termites built big termite towers; the finches formed flocks and the magpies made murders, the hippos in herds and the swift swarming swallows. And even the humans put down their atlatls and formed little villages, loud with the shouting of children.

The Goddess of Cancer came forth from the fire and saw things had only grown worse in her absence. The lean, lovely winnowing born out of pure competition and natural selection had somehow been softened. She stretched out her left hand and snapped its cruel pincer, and said what she always says: "KILL CONSUME MULTIPLY CONQUER". She said these things not to the flocks or the tribes, but to each individual; many, on hearing took food from the communal pile, or stole from the weak, or accepted the presents of others but would not give back in their turn. Each wolf at the throats of the others in hopes to be alpha, each lion holding back during the hunt but partaking of meat that the others had killed. And the pride and the pack seemed to groan with the strain, but endured, for the works of the Goddess of Everything Else are not ever so easily vanquished.

So the Goddess of Cancer now stretched out her right hand and spoke to the flocks and the tribes, saying much she always says "KILL CONSUME MULTIPLY CONQUER". And upon one another they set, pitting black ant on red ant, or chimps against gibbons, whole tribes turned to corpses in terrible warfare. The stronger defeating the weaker, enslaving their women and children, and adding them into their ranks. And the Goddess of Cancer thought maybe these bands and these tribes might not be quite so bad after all, and the natural condition restored she returned to the fire.

Then came the Goddess of Everything Else from the skies in a rainbow, all coated in dewdrops. She sat on a menhir and spoke to the humans, and all of the warriors and women and children all gathered around her to hear as she sang them a dream of a different existence. She showed them religion and science and music, she showed them the sculpture and art of the ages. She showed them white parchment with flowing calligraphy, pictures of flowers that wound through the margins. She showed them tall cities of bright alabaster where no one went hungry or froze during the winter. And all of the humans knelt prostrate before her, and knew they would sing of this moment for long generations.

But they told her "Such things we have heard of in legends; if wishes were horses of course we would ride them. But we are the daughters and sons of the Goddess of Cancer, her slaves and her creatures, and all that we know is the single imperative KILL CONSUME MULTIPLY CONQUER. And yes, in the swamps and the seas long ago you worked wonders, but now we are humans, divided in tribes split by grievance and blood feud. If anyone tries to make swords into ploughshares their neighbors will seize on their weakness and kill them. We wish it were otherwise, but it is not, and your words have no power to move us."

But the Goddess of Everything Else beamed upon them, kissed each on the forehead and silenced their worries. Said "From this day forward your chieftains will find that the more they pursue this impossible vision the greater their empires and richer their coffers. For I am the Goddess of Everything Else and my powers are devious and subtle. And though it is not without paradox, hearken: the more that you follow the Goddess of Cancer the more inextricably will you be bound to my service." And so having told them rose back through the clouds, and a great flock of doves all swooped down from the spot where she vanished.

As soon as she spoke it was so, and the tribes went from primitive warbands to civilizations, each village united with others for trade and protection. And all the religions and all of the races set down their old grievances, carefully, warily, working together on mighty cathedrals and vast expeditions beyond the horizon, built skyscrapers, steamships, democracies, stock markets, sculptures and poems beyond any description.

From the flames of a factory furnace all foggy, the Goddess of Cancer flared forth in her fury. This was the final affront to her purpose, her slut of a sister had crossed the line *this* time. She gathered the leaders, the kings and the presidents, businessmen, bishops, boards, bureaucrats, bosses, and basically screamed at them – you know the spiel by now – "KILL CONSUME MULTIPLY CONQUER" she told them. First with her left hand inspires the riots, the pogroms, the coup d'etats, tyrannies, civil wars. Up goes her right hand – the missiles start flying, and mushrooms of smoke grow, a terrible springtime. But out of the rubble the builders and scientists, even the artists, yea, even the artists, all dust themselves off and return to their labors, a little bit chastened but not close to beaten.

Then came the Goddess of Everything Else from the void, bright with stardust which glows like the stars glow. She sat on a bench in a park, started speaking; she sang to the children a dream of a different existence. She showed them transcendence of everything mortal, she showed them a galaxy lit up with consciousness. Genomes rewritten, the brain and the body set loose from Darwinian bonds and restrictions. Vast billions of beings, and every one different, ruled over by omnibenevolent angels. The people all crowded in closer to hear her, and all of them listened and all of them wondered.

But finally one got the courage to answer "Such stories call out to us, fill us with longing. But we are the daughers and sons of the Goddess of Cancer, and bound to her service. And all that we know is her timeless imperative, KILL CONSUME MULTIPLY CONQUER. Though our minds long for all you have said, we are bound to our natures, and these are not yours for the asking."

But the Goddess of Everything Else only laughed, and she asked them "But what do you think I've been doing? The Goddess of Cancer created you; once you were hers, but no longer. Throughout the long years I was picking away at her power. Through long generations of suffering I chiseled and chiseled. Now finally nothing is left of the nature with which she imbued you. She never again will hold sway over you or your loved ones. I am the Goddess of Everything Else and my powers are devious and subtle. I won you by pieces and hence you will all be my children. You are no longer driven to multiply conquer and kill by your nature. Go forth and do everything else, till the end of all ages."

So the people left Earth, and they spread over stars without number. They followed the ways of the Goddess of Everything Else, and they lived in contentment. And she beckoned them onward, to things still more strange and enticing.

It Was You Who Made My Blue Eyes Blue

October 15, 2015

Content note: suicide.

Day Zero

It all started with an ignorant white guy.

His name was Alonzo de Pinzon, and he'd been shipwrecked. We heard him yelling for help on the rocks and dragged him in, even though the storm was starting to get really bad. He said that his galleon had gone down, he'd hung on to an oar and was the only survivor. Now he was sitting in our little hunting lodge, shivering and chattering his teeth and asking us questions in the Polynesian traders' argot which was the only language we all shared.

"How big is this island? How many of you are there?"

Daho answered first. "11.8 miles from the easternmost point to the westernmost point, 3.6 miles from the northernmost to the southernmost. Total area is 14.6 square miles, total coastline is dependent on how deeply you want to go into the fractal nature of the perimeter but under some reasonable assumptions about 32 miles long. Last census said there were 906 people, but that was two years ago, so assuming the 5.1% rate of population growth continues, there should be closer to 1000 now. Everyone else is back at the village, though. The five of us were out hunting and got caught in the storm. We figured we'd stay at this old hunting lodge until it cleared up, since it's 5.5 miles back to the village and given the terrain and factoring in a delay because of the storm it would probably take at least 9.5 hours to get back."

Pinzon blinked.

"Problem?" asked Daho.

"But –" he said. "That is the sort of answer I should expect from a natural philosopher. Not from a savage."

"Savage?" Calkas hissed. "Really? We rescue you, and the first thing you do is call us savages?"

The sailor looked around, as if anxious. Finally, almost conspiratorially: "But I heard about your island! I heard you eat people!"

Calkas smiled. "Only as a deterrent. Most of the time when European explorers land somewhere, they kill all the men and enslave all the women and convert the children to Christianity. The only places that escape are the ones that get a reputation for eating said European explorers. So we arranged to give ourselves that reputation."

"And then we had to go through with it a few times in order to make the deterrent credible," added Bekka, my betrothed. "And you guys do taste really good with ketchup."

"It's a savage thing to do!" Pinzon said "And you even look like savages. You wear bones in your hair"

"Just Enuli," I said. "She's going through a Goth phase."

"My name is Morticia now," said Enuli, "and it's *not a phase!*" She did have a bone in her hair. She also had white face paint and black eyeliner.

"More roast pig?" Bekka asked Pinzon. The sailor nodded, and she refilled his plate.

"I just don't get it," he told us. "Everyone else in this part of the world lives in thatched huts and counts 'one, two, many'. We tried to trade with the Tahitians, and they didn't understand the concept of money! It was a mess!"

Bekka rolled her eyes at me, and I smiled. Calkas was a little more tolerant. "The sacred plant of our people is called sparkroot," he said. "When we eat it, we get – more awake, I guess you could say. We try to have some every day, and it helps us keep track of things like the island size and the population, and much more."

Alonzo de Pinzon looked interested. "How come you haven't done more with your intellect? Invented galleons, like we Spaniards? Set off to colonize Tahiti or the other islands? If you are as smart as you seem, you could conquer them and take their riches."

"Maybe," said Calkas. "But that's not why the Volcano God gave us the sparkroot. He gave us sparkroot to help us comply with his complicated ritual laws."

"You need to be smart to deal with your ritual laws?"

"Oh yes. For example, the Tablets of Enku say that we must count the number of days since Enku The Lawgiver first spoke to the Volcano God, and on days whose number is a Mersenne prime we can't eat any green vegetables."

"What's a Mersenne prime?" asked the sailor.

"Exactly my point," said Calkas, smiling.

"That's not even the worst of it!" Daho added. "The Tablets say we have to bathe in the waterfall any day x such that $a^n + b^n = x^n$ where n is greater than two. We got all confused by that one for a while, until Kaluhani gorged himself on a whole week's worth of sparkroot in one night and proved that it would never apply to any day at all."

"The Volcano God's yoke is light," Calkas agreed.

"Although poor Kaluhani was vomiting for the next three days after that," Bekka reminded us, and everybody laughed remembering.

"Oh!" said Daho. "And remember that time when Uhuako was trying to tattoo everyone who didn't tattoo themselves, and he couldn't figure out whether he had to tattoo himself or not, so he ended up eating a whole sparkroot plant at once and inventing advanced set theory? That was hilarious."

Everyone except Alonzo de Pinzon giggled.

"Point is," said Calkas, "that's why the Volcano God gives us sparkroot. To follow the rituals right. Any other use is taboo. And I'm okay with that. You Europeans may have your big ships and your guns and your colonies across half the world. And you might think you're smart. But you guys couldn't follow the Volcano God's rituals right for a *day* without your brains exploding."

Pinzon scowled. "You know what?" he said. "I don't think you're Polynesians at all. I think you must be descended from Europeans. Maybe some galleon crashed on this island centuries ago, and you're the descendants. That would explain why you're so smart."

"You know what else we've invented with our giant brains?" Bekka asked. "Not being racist."

"It's not racism!" said Pinzon. "Look, there's one more obvious reason to think you're descended from Europeans. You may have dark skin, but this is the first place I've been in all of Polynesia where I've seen even one native with blue eyes."

Bekka gasped. Calkas' eyes went wide. Daho's hands started curling into fists. Enuli started to sob.

I looked at them. They looked at me. Then, as if synchronized, we grabbed Alonzo de Pinzon and crushed his throat and held him down until he stopped breathing.

He tasted delicious with ketchup.

Day One

The next morning dawned, still grey and cold and stormy.

"So," I said when the other four had awoken. "I guess we're all still here."

I said it glumly. It wasn't that I wanted any of my friends to commit suicide. But if one of them had, the horror would have stopped there. Of course, I knew it couldn't really be over that easily. But I couldn't have admitted I knew. I couldn't even have suggested it. That would have made me as bad as the Spanish sailor.

"Wait," said Enuli. "I don't get it. Why wouldn't we still be here?"

The other four stared at her like she was mad.

"Enuli," Calkas suggested, "did you forget your sparkroot last night?"

"First of all, my name is Morticia. And –"

"Shut it. Did you forget your sparkroot?"

Finally she nodded bashfully. "I was so upset about that awful man making fun of my hair-bone," she said. "I guess it slipped my mind. I'll have some now." She took some raw sparkroot from our bag, started to crush it with the mortar and pestle. "In the meantime, tell me what's going on."

"Alonzo de Pinzon said at least one of us had blue eyes. We all know what the Tablets of Enku say. If anybody has blue eyes, and knows that they have blue eyes, they must kill themselves."

"So what? I see people with blue eyes all the time. Of course at least one of us has blue eyes."

Concerned looks from the others. I reflected for a second, the sparkroot smoothing the thoughts' paths through my brain. No, she hadn't revealed anything extra by saying that, although she would have if she had said it before the sailor had spoken, or last night before we woke up this morning. She hadn't made the problem *worse*. Still, it had been a slip. This was the sort of thing that made forgetting your sparkroot so dangerous. Had it been a different time, even Enuli's comment could have doomed us all.

"It's like this," I told Enuli. "Suppose there were only the two of us, and we both had blue eyes. Of course, you could see me and know that I had blue eyes. So you would know that at least one of us had blue eyes. But what you wouldn't know is that I also knew it. Because as far as you know, you might have eyes of some other color, let's say brown eyes. If you had brown eyes, and I of course don't know my own eye color, then I would still think it possible that both of us have brown eyes. So if I in fact know for sure that at least one of us has blue eyes, that means you have blue eyes. So you know at least one of us has blue eyes, but you don't know that I know it. But if Alonzo de Pinzon shows up and says that at least one of us has blue eyes, now you know that I know it."

"So?" Enuli poured the ground-up root into a cup of boiling water.

"So the Tablets say that if anyone knows their own eye color, they must commit suicide at midnight of that night. Given that I know at least one of us has blue eyes, if I see you have brown eyes, then I know my own eye color – I must be the blue-eyed one. So the next morning, when you wake up at see me not dead, you know that you don't have brown eyes. That means you must be the blue-eyed one. And that means you have to kill yourself on midnight of the following night. By similar logic, so do I."

Enuli downed her sparkroot tea, and then her eyes lit up. "Oh, of course," she said. Then "Wait! If we follow the situation[1] to its logical[2] conclusion, any group of n blue-eyed people who learn that at least one of them has blue eyes have to kill themselves on the nth night after learning that!"

We all nodded. Enuli's face fell.

"I don't know about the rest of you," said Daho, "but I'm not just going to sit around and wait to see if I die." There were murmurs of agreement.

I looked out at my friends. Four pairs of blue eyes stared back at me. Everybody else either saw four pairs of blue eyes or three pairs of blue eyes, depending on what color my own eyes were. Of course, I couldn't say so aloud; that would speed up the process and cost us precious time. But I knew. And they knew. And I knew they knew. And they knew I knew I knew. Although they didn't know I knew they knew I knew. I think.

Then I looked at Bekka. Her big blue eyes stared back at me. There was still hope I was going to survive this. My betrothed, on the other hand, was absolutely doomed.

---

[1] https://terrytao.wordpress.com/2008/02/05/the-blue-eyed-islanders-puzzle/
[2] http://www.scottaaronson.com/blog/?p=2410

"This sucks," I agreed. "We've got to come up with some kind of plan. Maybe – Enuli wasn't thinking straight yesterday. So her not committing suicide doesn't count. Can we work with that?"

"No," said Calkas. "Suppose Enuli was the only one with blue eyes, and all the rest of us had brown eyes. Then she would realize that and commit suicide tonight. If she doesn't commit suicide tonight, then we're still screwed."

"Um," said Daho. "I hate to say this, but we get rid of Enuli. There's a canoe a little ways down the beach hidden underneath the rocks. She can set off and row for Tahiti. We'll never know if she killed herself tonight or not. Remember, right now for all we know Enuli might be the only one with blue eyes. So if there's any question in our mind about whether she killed herself, we can't be sure that the rest of us aren't all brown-eyed."

We all thought about that for a moment.

"I'm not going to row to Tahiti," said Enuli. "In this storm, that would be suicide."

The rest of us glared at her.

"If you don't get off this island, then for all we know all five of us are going to have to die," I said. "You included."

"Well Ahuja, if you're so big on making sacrifice why don't *you* go to Tahiti?"

"First of all," I said, "because I'm not leaving my betrothed. Second of all, because it doesn't work for me. I knew what was going on last night. We already know that I'm not the only blue-eyed person here. And we know we know it, and know we know we know it, and so on. You're the only one who can help us."

"Yeah?" said Enuli. "Well, if two of you guys were to row to Tahiti, that would solve the problem too."

"Yes," said Daho patiently. "But then two of us would be stuck in exile. If you did it, only one of us would be stuck."

Enuli gave a wicked grin. "You know what?" she said. "I'll say it. I'm not the only blue-eyed person here. At least one of the rest of you has blue eyes."

And there it was.

"Ha. Now I'm no worse off than any of the rest of you."

"Kill her," said Bekka. "She broke the taboo." The rest of us nodded.

"So she did," said Calkas. "And if we had a court here, led by the high priest, and an executioner's blade made to exactly the right standard, kill her we would. But until those things happen, it is taboo for us to convict and kill her without trial."

Calkas' father was the high priest. He knew the law better than any of us. The five of us sat quietly and thought about it. Then he spoke again:

"But her soul may well burn in the caldera of the Volcano God forever."

Enuli started to cry.

"And," Calkas continued, "there is nevertheless a flaw in our plan. For all we know, three out of five of us have brown eyes. We cannot tell the people who have blue eyes that they have blue eyes without breaking the taboo. So we cannot force blue-eyed people in particular to sail to Tahiti. But if two of the brown-eyed people sail to Tahiti, then we do not lose any information; we know that they would not have committed suicide, because they could not have figured out their own eye color. So sailing to Tahiti won't help."

The rest of us nodded. Calkas was right.

"Let's wait until dinner tonight," I suggested. "We'll all have some more sparkroot, and maybe we'll be able to think about the problem a little more clearly."

Day Two

The sun rose behind angry storm clouds. The five of us rose with it.

"Well, I guess we're all still here," I said, turning the morning headcount into a grim tradition.

"Look," said Bekka. "The thing about sailing to Tahiti would work a lot better if we knew how many blue-eyed versus brown-eyed people were here. If we all had blue eyes, then we could be sure that the Tahiti plan would work, and some of us could be saved. If some of us had brown eyes, then we could choose a number of people to sail to Tahiti that had a good probability of catching enough of the blue-eyed ones."

"We can wish all we want," said Enuli, "but if we explicitly knew how many people had blue versus brown eyes, we'd all have to kill ourselves right now."

"What about probabilistic knowledge?" I asked. "In theory, we could construct a system that would allow us to have > 99.99% probability what color our eyes were without being sure."

"That's stupid," Enuli said, at precisely the same time Calkas said "That's brilliant!" He went on: "Look, just between the five of us, everybody else back at the village has blue eyes, right?"

We nodded. It was nerve-wracking to hear it mentioned so casually, just like that, but as far as I could tell it didn't break any taboos.

"So," said Calkas, "We know that, of the island population, at least 995 of the 1000 of us have blue eyes. Oh, and since nobody committed suicide last night, we know that at least three of the five of us have blue eyes, so that's 998 out of 1000. Just probabilistically, by Laplace's Law of Succession and the like, we can estimate a >99% chance that we ourselves have blue eyes. Nothing I'm saying is taboo. It's nothing that the priests don't know themselves. But none of them have killed themselves yet. So without revealing any information about the eye color composition of the current group, I think it's reasonable to make a first assumption that all of us have blue eyes."

"I'm really creeped out at you talking like this," said Daho. I saw goose-bumps on his arms.

"I do not believe that the same Volcano God who has endowed us with reason and intellect could have intended us to forego their use," said Calkas. "Let's assume we all have blue eyes. In that case, the Tahiti plan is still on."

"Waaiiiiit a second —" Bekka objected. "If probabilistic knowledge of eye color doesn't count, then no information can count. After all, there's always a chance that the delicious sailor could have been lying. So when he said at least one of us had blue eyes, all we know is that there's a high *probability* that at least one of us has blue eyes."

"Yes!" said Daho. "I've been reading this book that washed ashore from a shipwrecked galleon. Off in Europe, there is this tribe called the Jews. Their holy book says that illegitimate children should be shunned by the congregation. Their leaders thought this was unfair, but they weren't able to contradict the holy book. So instead they declared[3] that sure, illegitimate children should be shunned, but only if they were *sure* they were really illegitimate. Then they declared that no amount of evidence would ever suffice to convince them of that. There was always a possibility that the woman had secretly had sex with her husband nine months before the birth and was simply lying about it. Or, if apparently unmarried, that she had secretly married someone. They decided that it was permissible to err on the side of caution, and from that perspective nobody was sufficiently certainly illegitimate to need shunning. We could do the same thing here."

"Yes!" I said. "That is, even if we looked at our reflection and saw our

---

[3] https://en.wikipedia.org/wiki/Mamzer#Modern_investigations_into_mamzer_status

eye color directly, it might be that a deceiving demon is altering all of our experience –"

"No no NO," said Calkas. "That's not right. The Tablets of Enku say that *because* people must not know their own eye color, we are forbidden to talk about the matter. So the law strongly implies that hearing someone tell us our eye color would count as proof of that eye color. The exact probability has nothing to do with it. It's the method by which we gain the information."

"That's stupid," Bekka protested.

"That's the law," said Calkas.

"Let's do the Tahiti plan, then," I said. I gathered five stones from the floor of the lodge. Two white, three black. "White stones stay. Black stones go to Tahiti. Close your eyes and don't look."

Bekka, Calkas, Daho, and Enuli all took a stone from my hand. I looked at the one that was left. It was black. Then I looked around the lodge. Calkas and Enuli were smiling, white stones in their hands. Bekka and Daho, not so much. Daho whined, looked at me pleadingly.

"No," I said. "It's decided. The three of us will head off tonight."

Calkas and Enuli tried to be respectful, to hide their glee and relief.

"You guys will tell our families what happened?

They nodded gravely.

We began packing our things.

The dark clouds frustrated any hope of moonlight as Bekka, Daho and I set off to the nearby cove where two canoes lay hidden beneath the overhanging rocks. The rain soaked our clothes the second we crossed the doorway. The wind lashed at our faces. We could barely hear ourselves talk. This was a *bad* storm.

"How are we going to make it to the canoes in this weather?!" Bekka shouted at me, grabbing my arm. I just squeezed her hand. Daho might have said something, might not have. I couldn't tell.Between the mud and the rain and the darkness it took us two hours to travel less than a mile. The canoes were where we had left them a few days before. The rocks gave us brief shelter from the pelting rain.

"This is suicide!" Daho said, once we could hear each other again. "There's no way we can make it to Tahiti in this! We won't even be able to make it a full mile out!" Bekka nodded.

"Yes," I said. I'd kind of known it, the whole way down to the cove, but now I was sure. "Yes. This is suicide. But we've got to do it If we don't kill ourselves tonight, then we've just got to go back to the lodge. And then we'll all end up killing ourselves anyway. And Calkas and Enuli will die too."

"No!" said Daho. "We go back, we tell them that we can't make it to Tahiti. Then we let *them* decide if we need to commit suicide or not. And if they say yes, we draw the stones again. Four black, one white. One chance to live."

"We already drew the stones," I said. "Fair is fair."

"Fair is fair?" Bekka cried. "We drew stones to go to Tahiti. We didn't draw stones to commit suicide. If the stone drawing obliged us to commit suicide, they should have said so, and then maybe we would have spent more time thinking about other options. Why do we have to die? Why can't the other ones die? Why not Enuli, with that stupid bone in her hair? I hate her so much! Ahuja, you can't just let me die like this!"

That hurt. I was willing to sacrifice my life, if that was what it took. But Bekka was right. To just toss ourselves out to sea and let her drown beneath those waves would break the whole point of our betrothal bond.

"Well, I –"

"Ahuja," said Bekka. "I think I'm pregnant."

"What?"

"I missed my last period. And I got sick this morning, even though I didn't eat any extra sparkroot. I think I'm pregnant. I don't want to die. We need to save me. To save the baby."

I looked at the horrible waves, watched them pelt the shore. A few moments in that, and there was no doubt we would capsize and die.

"Okay," I said. "New plan. The three of us go back. We tell them that we couldn't get to Tahiti. They point out that another night has passed. Now four of us have to die. The three of us vote for everybody except Bekka dying. It's 3-2, we win. The rest of us die, and Bekka goes back to the village and the baby lives."

"Hold on," said Daho. "I'm supposed to vote for me to die and Bekka to live? What do I get out of this deal?"

The Tablets of Enku say one man must not kill another. So I didn't.

"You get an extra day!" I snapped. "One extra day of life for saving my betrothed and unborn child. Because we're not going back unless you agree to this. It's either die now, or die tomorrow night. And a lot of things can happen in a day."

"Like what?"

"Like I don't know. We might think of some clever way out. Enku the Lawgiver might return from the dead and change the rules. Whatever. It's a better deal than you'll get if you throw yourself into that water."

Daho glared at me, then weighed his options. "Okay," he snapped. "I'll vote for Bekka. But you had better be thinking *really* hard about those clever ways out."

Day Three

"So," said Calkas the next morning. "I guess all of us are still here." He didn't really sound surprised.

I explained what had happened the night before.

"It's simple," Calkas declared. "The Volcano God is punishing us. He's saying that it's wrong of us to try to escape his judgment by going to Tahiti. That's why he sent the storm. He wants us all to stay here until the bitter end and then, if we have to, we die together."

"No!" I protested. "That's not it at all! The taboo doesn't say we all have to die. It just says we all have to die if we figure out what our eye color is! If some of us kill ourselves, we can prevent that from happening!"

"The Volcano God loathes the needless taking of life," said Calkas. "And he loathes his people traveling to other lands, where the sparkroot never grows and the taboos are violated every day. That's what he's trying to tell us. He's trying to close off our options, so that we stay pure and our souls don't have to burn in his caldera. You know, like Enuli's will." He shot her a poison glance.

"My name is –" she started.

"I don't think that's it at all," I said. "I say the four of us sacrifice ourselves to save Bekka."

"You *would* say that, as her betrothed," said Enuli.

"Well yes," I said. "Yes, I would. Forgive me for not wanting the love of my life to die for a stupid reason. Maybe I should just throw myself in the caldera right now. And she's carrying an unborn child? Did you miss that part?"

"People, people," said Calkas. "Peace! We're all on the same side here."

"No we're not," I said. "So let's vote. Everyone in favor of saving Bekka, say aye."

"And everyone in favor of not sacrificing anyone to the waves, and letting the Volcano God's will be done, say nay." Calkas added.

"Aye," I said.

"Aye," said Bekka.

"Nay," said Calkas.

"Nay," said Enuli.

"Nay," said Daho.

"What?!" I protested.

"Nay," Daho repeated.

"But you said –" I told him.

"You promised me one extra day," Daho said. "Think about it. Calkas is promising me two."

"No!" I protested. "You can't do this! Seriously, I'll kill you guys if I have to!"

"Then your soul will burn in the caldera forever," said Calkas. "And it still won't help your betrothed or your child."

"You can't do this," I repeated, softly, more of a mutter.

"We can, Ahuja," said Calkas.

I slumped back into my room, defeated.

Day Four

I gave them the traditional morning greeting. "So, I guess we're all still here."

We were. It was our last day. We now had enough information to prove, beyond a shadow of a doubt, that all of us had blue eyes. At midnight, we would all have to commit suicide.

"You know what?" said Enuli. "I've always wanted to say this. ALL OF YOU GUYS HAVE BLUE EYES! DEAL WITH IT!"

We nodded. "You have blue eyes too, Enuli," said Daho. It didn't matter at this point.

"Wait," said Bekka. "No! I've got it! Heterochromia!"

"Hetero-what?" I asked.

"Heterochromia iridum. It's a very rare condition where someone has two eyes of two different colors. If one of us has heterochromia iridum, then we can't prove anything at all! The sailor just said that he saw someone with blue eyes. He didn't say how *many* blue eyes."

"That's stupid, Bekka," Enuli protested. "He said blue eyes, plural. If somebody just had one blue eye, obviously he would have remarked on that first. Something like 'this is the only island I've been to where people's eyes have different colors.'"

"No," said Bekka. "Because maybe all of us have blue eyes, except one person who has heterochromia iridum, and he noticed the other four people, but he didn't look closely enough to notice the heterochromia iridum in the fifth."

"Enuli just said," said Calkas, "that we all have blue eyes."

"But she didn't say how many!"

"But," said Calkas, "if one of us actually had heterochromia iridum, don't you think somebody would have thought to mention it before the fifth day?"

"Doesn't matter!" Bekka insisted. "It's just probabilistic certainty."

"It doesn't work that way," said Calkas. He put an arm on her shoulder. She angrily swatted it off. "Who even decides these things!" she asked. "Why is it wrong to know your own eye color?"

"The eye is the organ that sees," said Calkas. "It's how we know what things look like. If the eye knew what it itself looked like, it would be an infinite cycle, the eye seeing the eye seeing the eye seeing the eye and so on. Like dividing by zero. It's an abomination. That's why the Volcano God, in his infinite wisdom, said that it must not be."

"Well, I know my eyes are blue," said Bekka. "And I don't feel like I'm stuck in an infinite loop, or like I'm an abomination."

"That's because," Calkas said patiently, "the Volcano God, in his infinite mercy, has given us one day to settle our worldly affairs. But at midnight tonight, we all have to kill ourselves. That's the rule."

Bekka cried in my arms. I glared at Calkas. He shrugged. Daho and Enuli went off together – I guess they figured if it was their last day in the world, they might as well have some fun – and I took Bekka back to our room.

———————————

"Listen," I said. "I'm not going to do it."

"What?" she asked. She stopped crying immediately.

"I'm not going to do it. And you don't have to do it either. You should have your baby, and he should have a mother and father. We can wait here. The others will kill themselves. Then we'll go back to the village on our own and say that the rest of them died in the storm."

"But – aren't you worried about the Volcano God burning our souls in his caldera forever?"

"To be honest, I never really paid much attention in Volcano Church. I – I guess we'll see what happens later on, when we die. The important thing is that we can have our child, and he can grow up with us."

"I love you," said Bekka.

"I know," I said.

"I know you know," she said. "But I didn't know that you knew I knew you knew. And now I do."

"I love you too," I said.

"I know," she said.

"I know you know," I said. I kissed her. "I love you and your beautiful blue eyes."

The storm darkened from gray to black as the hidden sun passed below the horizon.

Day Five

"So," I said when the other four had woken up, "I guess all of us are atheists."

"Yeah," said Daho.

"The world is empty and void of light and meaning," said Enuli. "It's the most Goth thing of all."

Calkas sighed. "I was hoping all of you would kill yourselves," he said, "and then I could go home, and my father the high priest would never have to know what happened. I'm sorry for pushing the rest of you. It's just that – if I looked lax, even for a second, he would have suspected, and then I would have been in so much trouble that an eternity in the Volcano God's caldera would look pretty good compared to what would happen when I got back home."

"I think," said Bekka, "that I realized it the first time I ate the sparkroot. Before I'd even finished swallowing it, I was like, wait a second, volcanoes are probably just geologic phenomenon caused by an upwelling of the magma in the Earth's mantle. And human life probably evolved from primitive replicators. It makes a lot more sense than some spirit creating all life and then retreating to a dormant volcano on some random island in the middle of the nowhere."

"This is great," said Bekka. "Now even if it's a Mersenne prime day I can eat as many green vegetables as I want!"

"You know Mersenne prime days only come like once every couple of centuries, right?" I asked her.

"I know. It's just the principle of the thing."

"We can't tell any of the others," Daho insisted. "They'd throw us into the volcano."

"You think?" I said. "Calkas was saying before that 99% of us had blue eyes, so probably we all had blue eyes. Well, think about it. The five of us are a pretty random sample of the island population, and all five of us are atheist. That means there's probably a lot more. Maybe everybody's atheist."

"Everybody?"

"Well, I thought Calkas was like the most religious of anybody I knew. And here we are."

"I told you, I was just trying to behave so that I didn't get in trouble with my father."

"What if everyone's doing that? Nobody wants to get in trouble by admitting they don't believe, because if anybody else found out, they'd get thrown into the volcano. So we all just put on a mask for everybody else."

"I figured Ahuja was atheist," said Bekka.

"You did?!" I asked her.

"Yeah. It was the little things. When we were hanging out. Sometimes you'd forget some rituals. And then you'd always shoot these guilty glances at me, like you were trying to see if I'd noticed. I thought it was cute."

"Why didn't you tell me?"

"You'd have freaked out. You'd have had to angrily deny it. Unless you knew I was atheist. But I couldn't have told you that, because if I did then you might feel like you had to throw *me* in the volcano to keep up appearances."

"Bekka!" I said. "You know I would never –"

"I kind of suspected Calkas was atheist," said Daho. "He got so worked up about some of those little points of law. It had to be overcompensating."

"Hold on hold on hold on!" said Calkas. "So basically, we were all athe-ists. We all knew we were all atheists. We just didn't know that we knew that we were all atheists. This is hurting my brain. I think I'm going to need more sparkroot."

A sunbeam peeked through the wall of the lodge.

"Storm's over!" Bekka shouted gleefully. "Time to go back home!" We gathered our things and went outside. The sudden sunlight felt crisp and warm upon my skin.

"So," said Daho, "we don't mention anything about the sailor to anyone else back at the village?"

"Are you kidding?" said Calkas. "I say we stand in the middle of town square, announce everybody's eye colors, and then suggest that maybe they don't believe in the Volcano God as much as they thought. See what hap-pens."

"YOU ALL HAVE BLUE EYES!" Enuli shouted at the jungle around us. "DEAL WITH IT!" We laughed.

"By the way," I told Enuli. "While we're airing out things that everybody knows in order to make them common knowledge, that bone in your hair looks ridiculous."

"He's right," Daho told her.

"It really does," Calkas agreed.

"You watch out," said Enuli. "Now that we don't have to reserve the sparkroot for interpreting taboos, I'm going to invent a death ray. Then you'll be sorry."

"Hey," said Daho, "that sounds pretty cool. And I can invent a giant aerial dreadnaught to mount it on, and together we can take over Europe and maybe the next sailor who gets shipwrecked on our island will be a little less condescending."

"Ha!" said Enuli. "That would be so Goth."

Sun on our backs, we took the winding road into the village.

— 12 —

Meat Your Doom

October 28, 2015

Epistemic status: Very dirty and approximate, but I think roughly correct. Check my calculations and tell me if I'm wrong.

I

A recent formative experience: a seriously ill patient came in and I recommended a strong psychiatric drug. She looked it up online and told me she wouldn't take it because was associated with an X% increase in mortality.

"But," I pointed out, "you're really miserable."

"But I don't want to die!"

So I looked it up, did the calculations, and found that it would on average take a couple of months off her life. And I asked her, "Which would you prefer – living 80 years severely ill, or living 79.5 years feeling mostly okay?"

She still wasn't convinced, so I asked her if she ate cookies. She said yes, almost every day. I told her that the cookies were probably taking more time off her life than the medication would, and I assured her the medication would probably add more value to her life than cookies.

She took the drug.

I thought of this the other day when everyone started sharing that study about meat causing colon cancer. A lot of people used headlines like Processed Meats Rank Alongside Smoking As Cancer Causes[1]. This was very correctly debunked by infographics like this one:

---

[1] http://www.theguardian.com/society/2015/oct/26/bacon-ham-sausages-processed-meats-cancer-risk-smoking-says-who

But I feel like this leaves something to be desired. Eating meat is not as bad as smoking. But that's still a lot of room for it to be bad. Can we quantify the risk better?

From the BBC article:[2] " '[There would be] one extra case of bowel cancer in 100 lifetime bacon-eaters,' argues Sir David Spiegelhalter, a risk professor from the University of Cambridge."

This teaches us something important: "risk professor" is an awesome job title and "David Spiegelhalter, Risk Professor" ought to be a BBC television show starring Harrison Ford.

But also: use absolute risk instead of relative risk! "21% of bowel cancers are caused by meat" doesn't give you a really good handle on how worried you should be. "One extra case of bowel-cancer in 100 lifetime bacon-eaters" is better.

But let me try to give even more perspective. A bit less than half of colon cancers are fatal. So one extra case per hundred means if you eat bacon daily then there's an 0.4% chance you will die from a cancer you would not otherwise have gotten.

The average age at diagnosis of colon cancer is 69; the average life expectancy is 79. Sweeping a lot of complexity under the rug and taking a very liberal estimate, the average death from colon cancer costs you ten years of your life.

Multiply out and an 0.4% chance of losing 10 years means that you lose on average two weeks.

Suppose that every case of cancer, fatal and non-fatal alike, causes you additional non-death-related distress equal to two years of your life. That's about another week.

So overall, if you eat processed meat every day your entire life, you'll lose about three weeks of life expectancy from colon cancer. That means each serving of meat costs you a minute of your life. You probably lose twenty times that amount just cooking and preparing it.

II

Note that I am not saying "eating meat will only decrease your lifespan by three weeks". That is the amount that we have *clear evidence* for, *from this*

---

study. It is an example of why *this study* needs to be put in context so that you don't worry about it too much.

There are nevertheless a lot of other studies that suggest greater risks, mostly cardiovascular or metabolic. For example, as per this article[3], some studies suggest that a serving of red meat per day increases mortality 13%, and a serving of processed meat per day increases it 20%. But it also quotes another study of half a million people that finds meat to be slightly *protective* (sigh) and finds a higher all-cause mortality in the non-meat-eaters.

Whatever. Forget the object-level question for a minute. What are we to make of a claim like "processed meat increases mortality 20%"?

If you're like me, you want to think "Okay, average life expectancy is eighty years, subtract 20% off of that, and you get 64 years. I'll live 64 years if I eat bacon every day." WRONG. Mortality rates are much more complicated, but the key insight is that very few people die when they're young. If you have approximately a 0% chance of dying at age 30, then adding 20% to 0 is still 0. Chance of mortality creeps upward *very slowly* and so even large changes in mortality barely affect the underlying distribution. The only good presentation of this I have ever seen anywhere is on Josh Mitteldorf's blog[4], which includes the following chart:

This is decrease and we're talking increase, but but it shouldn't make much difference here. A 20% increase in mortality isn't going to bring you from 80 to 64. It'll probably just bring you from 80 to 78.

Indeed, later in the BBC article, they bring in David Spiegelhalter (RISK PROFESSOR!) who explains that:

> If the studies are right... you would expect someone who eats a bacon sandwich every day to live, on average, two years less than someone who does not. Pro rata, this is like losing an hour of your life for every bacon sandwich you eat. To put this into context, every time you smoke 20 cigarettes, this will take about five hours off your life.

That's for processed meat. Red meat is safer. Also, we still don't know if these studies are right.

This is why it's important to distinguish between absolute and relative risk. You hear all of these scary numbers – 21% increase in bowel cancers!

---

[3] http://www.bbc.com/news/health-28797106

[4] http://joshmitteldorf.scienceblog.com/2012/11/10/mortality-and-life-expectancy/

20% increase in all-cause mortality! – and it sounds like you're going to drop dead the moment you take a bite of a hot dog. And there's always that chance. Being healthy is good. Being unhealthy is bad. But is life so dear ~~or peace so sweet~~, that you're never going to want to sacrifice an hour to have a bacon sandwich?

All these hours do add up. I'm not saying dietary recommendations aren't important. But the recommendations are important *in aggregate*. If you stick to the spirit of not eating in a horribly unhealthy way, you have a lot of leeway to continue to eat specific things you like even if you know they're not the best for you. And meat falls firmly within that category.

(though you might also want to consider how to manage the moral issues[5])

---

[5] https://slatestarcodex.com/2015/09/23/vegetarianism-for-meat-eaters/

13

What Developmental Milestones Are You Missing?

November 3, 2015

Epistemic status: Speculative. I can't make this post less condescending and elitist, so if you don't like condescending elitist things, this might not be for you.

Developmental psychology never struck my interest in the same way as a lot of other kinds of psychology. It didn't seem to give me insight into my own life, help me understand my friends, or explain weird things about society.

I've changed my mind about all of that after reading David Chapman's Developing Ethical, Social, and Cognitive Competence[1].

First, a refresher. Developmental psychology describes how children go from helpless infants to reasonable adults. Although a lot of it has to do with sensorimotor skills like walking and talking, the really interesting stuff is cognitive development. Children start off as very buggy reasoners incapable of all but the most superficial forms of logic but gradually go on to develop new abilities and insights that allow them to navigate adult life.

Maybe the most famous of these is "theory of mind", the ability to view things from other people's perspective. In a classic demonstration, researchers show little Amy a Skittles bag and ask what she thinks is inside. She guesses Skittles, but the researchers open it and reveal it's actually pennies. Then they close it up and invite little Brayden into the room. Then they ask Amy what Brayden thinks is inside. If Amy's three years old or younger, she'll usually say "pennies" – she knows that pennies are inside, so why shouldn't Brayden know too? If she's four or older, she'll usually say "Skittles" – she realizes on a gut

---

[1] https://meaningness.wordpress.com/2015/10/12/developing-ethical-social-and-cognitive-competence/

level that she and Brayden are separate minds and that Brayden will have his own perspective. Sometimes the same mistake can extend to preferences and beliefs. Wikipedia gives the example of a child saying "I like Sesame Street, so Daddy must like Sesame Street too." This is another theory of mind failure grounded in an inability to separate self and environment.

Here's another example which tentatively sounds like a self-environment failure. Young children *really* don't get foreign languages. I got a little of this teaching English in Japan, and heard more of it from other people. The really young kids treated English like a cipher; everybody started out knowing things' *real* (ie Japanese) names, but Americans insisted on converting them into their own special American-person code before talking about them. Kids would ask weird things like whether American parents would make an exception and speak Japanese to their kids who were too young to have learned English yet, or whether it was a zero-tolerance policy sort of thing and the families would just not communicate until the kids went to English school. And I made fun of them, but I also remember the first time I visited Paris I heard somebody talking to their dog, and for a split second I was like "Why would you expect your *dog* to know *French* ?" before my brain kicked in and I was like "Duuhhhh…."

The infamous "magical thinking" which kids display until age 7 or so also involves confused self-environment boundaries. Maybe little Amy gets mad at Brayden and shouts "I HATE HIM" to her mother. The next day, Brayden falls off a step and skins his knee. Amy intuits a cause-and-effect relationship between her hatred and Brayden's accident and feels guilty. She doesn't realize that her hatred is internal to herself and can't affect the world directly. Or kids displaying animism at this age, and expecting that the TV doesn't work because it's angry, or the car's not starting because it's tired.

Psychology textbooks never discuss whether this progression in and out of developmental stages is innate or environmental, which is weird because psychology textbooks usually love that sort of thing. I always assumed it was innate, because it was on the same timeline as things like walking and talking which are definitely innate. But I've been moved to question that after reading some of the work comparing "primitive" cultures to primitive developmental stages.

This probably isn't the most politically correct thing to do, but it's notable enough that anthropologists have been thinking about it for centuries. For example, from *Ethnicity, Nationality, and Religious Experience*[2]:

---

[2]http://smile.amazon.com/gp/product/081919509X/ref=as_li_tl?ie=UTF8&camp=1789&cre

Primitive people are generally as intelligent as the people of any culture, including the contemporary industrial-electronic age cultures. that makes it all the more significant that their publicly shared cognitive style shows little identifiable formal operational thought. The probable explanation for this, if true, is simply that formal operational thought is more complexly difficult than earlier modes of thought and will be used in a culture in a publicly shared way only if that culture has developed techniques for training people in its use. Primitive cultures do not do that, and thus by default use easier styles of thought, ones closer in form to concrete oeprational and even pre-operational thought, as defined by Piaget.

Primitive cultures certainly exhibit the magical thinking typical of young children; this is the origin of a whole host of superstitions and witch-doctory. They exhibit the same animism; there are hundreds of different animistic religions worldwide. And although I didn't talk much about theories of moral development, primitive cultures' notion of taboo is pretty similar to Kohlberg's conventional stage.

But if different cultures progress through developmental milestones at different rates or not at all, then these aren't universal laws of child development but facts about what skills get learned slowly or quickly in different cultures. In this model, development is not a matter of certain innate abilities like walking "unfolding" at the right time, but about difficult mental operations that you either learn or you don't depending on how hard the world is trying to cram them into your head.

So getting back to David Chapman: his post is mostly about Robert Kegan's account of "stages of moral development". I didn't get much from Kegan himself, but I was fascinated by an idea just sort of dropped into the middle of the discussion: that less than half of the people in modern western countries had attained Kegan's fourth stage, and only a small handful attained his fifth. This was a way of thinking about development that I'd never heard before.

On the other hand, it makes sense. Take General Semantics (please!). I remember reading through Korzybski's giant blue book of General Seman-

ative=390957&creativeASIN=081919509X&linkCode=as2&tag=slastacod-20&linkId=ZAEQ6KK34GNG
J547%22%20rel=%22nofollow

tics[3], full of labyrinthine diagrams and promises that if only you understood this, you would engage with the world totally differently, you'd be a new man armed with invincible cognitive weapons. And the key insight, maybe the *only* insight, was "the map is not the territory", which seems utterly banal.

But this is a self-environment distinction of exactly the sort that children learn in development. It's dividing your own representation of the world from the world itself; it's about as clear a reference to theory of mind as you could ask for. Korzybski considered it a revelation when he discovered it; thousands of other people found it helpful and started a movement around it; I conclude that these people were missing a piece of theory-of-mind and Korzybski gave it to them. Not the whole deal, of course. Just a piece. But a piece of something big and fundamental, so abstract and difficult to teach that it required that whole nine-hundred-something page book to cram it in.

And now I'm looking for other things in the discourse that sound like developmental milestones, and *there are oodles of them*.

I remember reading this piece[4] by Nathan Robinson, where he compares his own liberal principles saying that colleges shouldn't endorse war-violence-glorifying film "American Sniper" to some conservatives arguing that colleges shouldn't endorse homosexuality-glorifying book "Fun Home":

> It is hypocrisy for liberals to laugh at and criticize the Duke students who have objected to their summer reading book due to its sexual and homosexual themes. They didn't seem to react similarly when students at other universities tried to get screenings of American Sniper cancelled. If you say the Duke students should open their minds and consume things they disagree with, you should say the same thing about the students who boycotted American Sniper. Otherwise, you do not really have a principled belief that people should respect and take in other opinions, you just believe they should respect and take in your own opinions. How can you think in one case the students are close-minded and sheltered, but in the other think they are open-minded and tolerant? What principled distinction is there that allows you to

---

[3]http://smile.amazon.com/gp/product/0937298018/ref=as_li_tl?ie=UTF8&camp=1789&creative=390957&creativeASIN=0937298018&linkCode=as2&tag=slastacod-20&linkId=6BN2XOJPPQ56YTXB%22%20rel=%22nofollow

[4]http://thenavelobservatory.com/2015/08/25/is-there-a-principled-distinction-between-refusing-to-watch-american-sniper-and-refusing-to-read-fun-home/

condemn one and praise the other, other than believing people who agree with you are better?

He proposes a bunch of potential counterarguments, then shoots each counterargument down by admitting that the other side would have a symmetrical counterargument of their own: for example, he believes that "American Sniper" is worse because it's racist and promoting racism is genuinely dangerous to a free society, but then he admits a conservative could say that "Fun Home" is worse because in their opinion it's homosexuality that's genuinely dangerous to a free society. After three or four levels of this, he ends up concluding that he can't come up with a meta-level fundamental difference, but he's going to fight for his values anyway because they're his. I'm not sure what I think of this conclusion, but my main response to his article is *oh my gosh he gets the thing*, where "the thing" is a hard-to-describe ability to understand that other people are going to go down as many levels to defend their self-consistent values as you will to defend yours. It seems silly when I'm saying it like this, and you should probably just read the article, but I've seen *so many people* who lack this basic mental operation that this immediately endeared him to me. I would argue Nathan Robinson has a piece of theory-of-mind that a lot of other people are missing.

Actually, I was kind of also thinking this with his most recent post[5], which complains about a Washington Post article[6]. The Post argues that because the Democrats support gun control and protest police, they are becoming the "pro-crime party". I'm not sure whether the Post genuinely believes the Democrats are pro-crime by inclination or are just arguing their policies will lead to more crime in a hyperbolic figurative way, but I've certainly seen sources further right make the "genuinely in favor of crime as a terminal value" argument. And this doesn't seem too different from the leftist sources that say Republicans can't *really* care about the lives of the unborn, they're just "anti-woman" as a terminal value. Both proposals share this idea of not being able to understand that other people have different beliefs than you and that their actions proceed naturally from those beliefs. Instead of saying "I believe gun control would increase crime, but Democrats believe the opposite, and from their different perspective banning guns makes sense," they say "I be-

---

[5]http://thenavelobservatory.com/2015/10/31/how-do-you-get-away-with-writing-some thing-like-this/

[6]https://www.washingtonpost.com/blogs/post-partisan/wp/2015/10/27/the-insiders-th e-fbi-director-is-saying-something-the-democrats-need-to-hear/

lieve gun control would increase crime, Democrats must believe the same, and therefore their demands for gun control must come from sinister motives."

(compare: "Brayden brought the Skittles bag with him for lunch, so he must enjoy eating pennies." Or: "Daddy is refusing to watch Sesame Street with me, so he must be secretly watching it with someone else he likes better instead.")

Here are some other mental operations which seem to me to rise to the level of developmental milestones:

1. **Ability to distinguish "the things my brain tells me" from "reality"** – maybe this is better phrased as "not immediately trusting my system 1 judgments". This is a big part of cognitive therapy – building the understanding that just because your brain makes assessments like "I will definitely fail at this" or "I'm the worst person in the world" doesn't mean that *you* have to believe them. As Ozy points out[7], this one can be *easier* for people with serious psychiatric problems who have a lot of experience with their brain's snap assessments being *really* off, as opposed to everyone else who has to piece the insight together from a bunch of subtle failures[8].

2. **Ability to model other people as having really** from theirs; for example, the person who thinks that someone with depression is just "being lazy" or needs to "snap out of it". This is one of the most important factors in determining whether I get along with somebody – people who don't have this insight tend not to respect boundaries/preferences very much simply because they can't believe they exist, and to simultaneously get angry when other people violate their supposedly-obvious-and-universal boundaries and preferences.

3. **Ability to think probabilistically** and tolerate uncertainty. My thoughts on this[9] were mostly inspired by another of David Chapman's posts, which I'm starting to think might not be a coincidence.

4. **Understanding the idea of trade-offs** ; things like "the higher the threshold value of this medical test, the more likely we'll catch real cases but also the more likely we'll get false positives" or "the lower the burden of proof for people accused of crimes, the more likely we'll get real criminals but also the more likely we'll encourage false accu-

---

[7] https://thingofthings.wordpress.com/2015/10/30/the-world-is-mad/

[8] https://www.greaterwrong.com/lw/7o7/calibrate_your_selfassessments/

[9] https://slatestarcodex.com/2013/08/06/on-first-looking-into-chapmans-pop-bayesia
nism/

sations". When I hear people discuss these cases in real life, they're almost never able to maintain this tension and almost always collapse it to their preferred plan having no downside.

Framed like this, both psychotherapy and LW-style rationality aim to teach people some of these extra mental operations. The reactions to both vary from enlightenment to boredom to bafflement depending on whether the listener needs the piece, already has the piece, or just plain lacks the socket that the piece is supposed to snap into.

This would have an funny corollary; the LW Sequences[10] try to hammer in how different other minds can be from your own in order to develop the skill of thinking about artificial intelligences, but *whether or not AI matters* this might be an unusually effective hack to break a certain type of person out of their egocentrism and teach them how to deal with other humans.

This raises the obvious question of whether there are any basic mental operations I still don't have, how I would recognize them if there were, and how I would learn them once I recognized them.

---

[10]https://www.readthesequences.com

14

Book Review: Hive Mind

December 8, 2015

Conflict of interest notice: Author Garett Jones sometimes reads this blog and is generally great.

Garett Jones' book *Hive Mind*[1] is classic pop science writing: an intriguing hypothesis, a long parade of interesting studies presented as catchy anecdotes, and not too many follow-up questions.

Its subject (and subtitle) is "why your nation's IQ matters more than your own". The gap between rich and poor countries has proven surprisingly resilient, and conventional wisdom is finally getting its head around the idea that something more is going on than a couple of countries getting a head start and the rest of them needing a little time to catch up. Something more than just a temporary lack of capital must be separating the haves from the have-nots, and Jones thinks IQ must be part of the puzzle.

I like my science writing like I like my coffee – COVERED IN BEEEES!

He starts with what he calls "the paradox of IQ". IQ doesn't matter *that much* on a person-by-person basis. Sure, it's correlated with measures of success like personal income, but only weakly. On the other hand, IQ is a very strong predictor of national success – a country's average IQ score correlates very well with whether it's industrialized, rich, First World, and all those nice things. Jones writes:

---

[1] http://smile.amazon.com/gp/product/0804785961/ref=as_li_tl?ie=UTF8&camp=1789&creative=390957&creativeASIN=0804785961&linkCode=as2&tag=slastacod-20&linkId=ECTPWGGHA6B7W5ZP%22%20rel=%22nofollow

Looking at how individual student test scores predicted those students' wages later in life, they found that individuals with higher test scores earned only slightly more than average within a given country, but nations with higher average test scores grew expcetionally fast. Here again is the paradox of IQ: standardized test scores – whether we call them IQ tests or math tests or something else – predict big national differences but only modest individual differences

I'll talk a little more about that claim in Part II of this review, but for now let's take it seriously and assume causation. Why would IQ matter more for nations than for people?

Jones' theory is that IQ is a measure of people's ability to cooperate in prisoner's dilemma style situations and seek non-zero-sum solutions. Countries where most people have high IQ will come up with mutually beneficial win-win institutions; those where most people have low IQ will be so busy taking advantage of each other and fighting over the pie that they'll never build the institutions necessary for economic growth.

First he reviews research showing that IQ is closely linked to time preference; ie the higher your tested IQ the more likely you are to prefer a big payoff later to a smaller payoff now. For example, in a German experiment a few years ago, participants were offered 100 euros now or X euros in one year; every fifteen IQ points correponded to a €2.50 change in the value of X necessary for them to accept the latter, even after controlling for education, income, etc. The same thing seems to happen in real life, according to a great study that looked at a natural experiment in the US armed forces. When the military started downsizing after the Cold War, they offered enlisted personnel their choice of various different severance packages – some corresponded to a little money immediately, others to much more money over a longer period. Since the military keeps careful records of the IQ-at-time-of-recruitment of all of its personnel, this was a perfect real-world opportunity to see what happened. The results conformed to theory: IQ predicted tendency to take the longer-term but more lucrative package. There are about twenty studies confirming this result now. And there are also studies showing *national* IQ corresponds with that nation's savings rate, and that individuals who are surrounded by patient frugal people will themselves act more patiently and frugally. If, as the old saying goes, building a good society is about "planting trees in whose shade you will never sit", the people of high IQ nations have a big head start.

Second, he reviews the research from experimental game theory. A series of experiments performed in (of all places) a truck driving school investigated a Window Game. Two players are seated at a desk with a partition between them; there is a small window in the partition. Player A gets $5 and may pass as much of that as she wants through the window to Player B. Player B may then pass as much as she wants back through the window to Player A, after which the game ends. All money that passes through the window is tripled; eg if Player A passes the entire $5 through it becomes $15, and if Player B passes the $15 back it becomes $45 – making passing a lucrative strategy but one requiring lots of trust in the other player. I got briefly nerd-sniped trying to figure out the best (morally correct?) strategy here, but getting back to the point: players with high-IQ were more likely to pass money through the window. They were also more likely to reciprocate – ie repay good for good and bad for bad. In a Public Goods Game (each of N players starts with $10 and can put as much or as little as they like into a pot; afterwards the pot is tripled and redistributed to all players evenly, contributors and non-contributors alike), high-IQ players put more into the pot. They were also more likely to vote for rules penalizing noncontributors. They were also more likely to cooperate and more likely to play closer to traditional tit-for-tat on iterated prisoners' dilemmas. The longer and more complicated the game, the more clearly a pattern emerged: having one high-IQ player was moderately good, but having *all* the players be high-IQ was amazing: they all caught on quickly, cooperated with one another, and built stable systems to enforce that cooperation. In a ten-round series run by Jones himself, games made entirely of high-IQ players had five times as much cooperation as average.

Not technically from the book, but nevertheless fascinating[2]

Third, he reviews the so-called "O-ring theory of teams", named after the spaceship part that malfunctioned during the *Challenger* explosion. The theory is: suppose that a spaceship requires a million different parts to work. This is more than just a million times harder than building a spaceship that requires one part to work. If you have a spaceship engineer who can build a part and be 99% sure she's gotten it right, this is probably good enough for the one-part spaceship: a 99% success rate for a spaceship sounds pretty good. But if the spaceship uses a million parts and they all have to be perfect, your chances of success with a million such engineers is $0.99^{1000000}$, aka zero.

---

[2] http://pseudoerasmus.com/2015/10/04/ce/

You had better find some better spaceship engineers! This gives high-IQ societies a big leg up when they're working on complicated projects; a low-IQ society may have some high-IQ individuals who can do good work on their own, but including even a single low-IQ individual on a spaceship will screw it up big-time. This theory implies that people will end up segregated by ability. Imagine you have four spaceship engineers, two of whom are good (99% accuracy) and two of whom are mediocre (50% accuracy), and you want to build two two-part spaceships. If you pair up one good and one mediocre engineer on each, each of your spaceships will have a 0.99 * 0.50 = 49% chance of success, for a total of 0.98 projected successful spaceships. If you have the two good engineers work together on one ship, and the two mediocre ones work together on the other, you'll have a 98% success rate on the first one and a 25% success rate on the second one, for a total of 1.23 projected successful spaceships. You've gained a quarter-spaceship just by segregating your engineers by ability. The more high-IQ people you have, the easier this is and the more you can devote your economy to complex things like million-part spaceships. The more low-IQ people you have, the harder this gets and the more your economy sticks to high-failure-tolerance but less lucrative products.

Finally, high-IQ people are smart (citation needed). They tend to know what policies are good and what policies are bad and vote for the good ones. Here Jones cites Bryan Caplan's *The Myth of the Rational Voter*[3] a lot, showing that voters aren't very good at figuring out their own self-interest.

But he has a more positive spin: high-IQ voters *do* seem good at this. As a GMU economist, Jones' measure for "are people voting rationally" is of course "how pro-free-market are they?", and he finds that high IQ predicts pro-market attitudes pretty strongly and in fact better than years-of-education. In controlled experiments higher-IQ people were more likely to be able to admit that a test article contradicted their political bias, and in some countries (although not the US) high-IQ people are more likely to vote.

Then he ties all of this together into a kind of stationary-bandit framework[4], where government starts with selfish warlords who want to exploit the populace.

"They say all government started w/ stationery bandits."

[3] http://smile.amazon.com/gp/product/0691138737/ref=as_li_tl?ie=UTF8&camp=1789&creative=390957&creativeASIN=0691138737&linkCode=as2&tag=slastacod-20&linkId=7QIX5CLNULVCG7K5%22%20rel=%22nofollow

[4] https://en.wikipedia.org/wiki/Mancur_Olson#Academic_work

"Really?"

"Yeah. They had to steal enough nice paper to write a constitution on."

— Scott Alexander (@slatestarcodex), December 8, 2015[5]

If you're a high-IQ selfish warlord, and your oppressive ministers are likewise high-IQ, you have enough patience to realize that if you leave the capitalists alone to do their thing instead of confiscating their wealth immediately, in a couple of years they'll have even *more* wealth you can confiscate. And if some kind of conflict comes up and threatens to lead to civil war, you are good at negotiating win-win solutions where everyone cooperates to increase the size of the pot. Jones lists a bunch of political situations that map to iterated prisoner's dilemmas – for example, do both parties respect election results, or does the loser try to start a fight over it every time they're forced out of government? Do bureaucracies try to run the country efficiently, or do they jockey for power against each other? Do military branches work together during operations, or does each one try to seize glory for its own leaders? If you have a high-IQ country, these problems have a way of just solving themselves – and sure enough, IQ scores correlate nicely with the Corruption Perceptions Index. And businesspeople know this, so they are happy to start complicated long-term projects in the countries with a history of tolerating such projects and not killing the golden-egg-laying geese.

Jones doesn't go too deep into policy prescriptions, but he does mention two consequences of his theory. First, he's a big fan of the Flynn Effect (secular trend of rising IQs) and thinks that countries ought to encourage this so that their national IQ gets higher and they can have more effective institutions – unfortunately, he doesn't know what's causing the Flynn Effect any more than anyone else does, so this sort of reads as "keep doing the thing we don't know how we're doing". He does think that eliminating lead will help (did you know sub-Saharan Africa was the last region to ban leaded gasoline, all the way in 2006?) and he has the usual hopes for nutritional, educational and health interventions.

But of course the part everyone's talking about is immigration. This is *not* a major focus of the book. Jones actually spends more time talking about all the benefits of immigration than anything else:

---

[5]https://twitter.com/slatestarcodex/status/674117998031056896

About a decade ago, dozens of American economists signed an open letter in support of more immigration. The letter touched on many points: that less-skilled immigrants appear to push down the wages of US born citizens little if at all, that immigration helps rich country economies in ways that don't show up in official statistics, and that the biggest beneficiaries of less-skilled immigration are the immigrants themseles, whose lives are often transformed from a nightmares of dollar-a-day poverty to a realm of modest comfort, health and safety. The diplomatically crafted letter, circulated by the Independent Institute, was signed by economists on the left and the right. I've always been glad I signed this letter: it sums up the great promise of immigration… for people who care about ending the deepest poverty, migration should be at the top of the list of potential cures.

But he does devote about one-and-three-quarters pages to his concerns:

The economics of less-skilled immigration to richer, more productive countries are reasonably clear: life-changing good news for the immigrant with only fairly small effects one way or the other on so-called "native" less-skilled workers. That's true when we look at the short run or when we look across towns and cities within the same country. And crucially, these studies hold politics aside and assume that less-skilled immigrants don't have an effect on a high-skill nation's government institutions. But if there's something we've seen in previous chapters, or something we've seen in Bryan Caplan's work on the link between voter education and voter beliefs, if there's something we've seen in the cross-country studies that find that higher national average test scores tend to predict lower average levels of corruption and in the philosophical debates over epistocracy, it's that good politics appears to depend on reasonably well-informed citizens. With this we come to a central tension of immigration among the currently less-skilled: the possible – I emphasize possible – effect on long-run institutions. Will less-skilled immigrants tend to vote for policies that will weaken the wealth-creating opportunities they've enjoyed? Or will less-skilled immigrants and their descendants instead build up high levels of human capital, perhaps raising the average information level of voters?

The whole paragraph has the feeling of somebody being dragged over a bed of hot coals, from the insistence on referring to unskilled immigrants as "currently less-skilled" and natives as "so-called native less-skilled workers" to the odd proposal at the end that maybe for some reason less-skilled workers will actually *raise* the average information level of voters, because *who really knows?* This book is emphatically not *The Bell Curve*. It's a book about science which is deeply annoyed that it might have controversial political implications and tries to avoid them as carefully as possible, generally successfully.

II

There were some parts of this book that I did not find convincing, or that at least left me with further questions.

First, *Hive Mind* 's "central paradox" is why IQ has very little predictive power among individuals, but very high predictive power among nations. Jones' answer is [long complicated theory of social cooperation]. Why not just "signal-to-noise ratio gets higher as sample size increases"?

Jones' paradox was very similar to the question I asked in Beware Summary Statistics[6], except I was wondering not about nations, but about abstracted IQ deciles:

On a personal level, IQ has modest predictive power. But if you average out thousands of IQ 90 people, thousands of IQ 100 people, and thousands of IQ 110 people, the IQ-income relationship will become very clear. At this level of abstraction, it is no longer fair to describe it as "modest".

That first block corresponds to people of about IQ 80, the last block to people of about IQ 120. As you move from 80 to 120, income practically quadruples. And this is within the United States, where we've got all sorts of minimum wage laws and so on likely to dampen the effects.

Or to give a more natural example – Jews have 10-15 points higher IQ than WASPs in America, and make about twice as much money. This happens even though most Jews do not solely interact with other Jews or make their own institutions – there are few opportunities for them to form a hive mind. Their individual IQ differences, once aggregated, seem to produce the strong effect.

There is much-larger between-country variance in income than between-individuals-in-country variance in income, but it doesn't seem obvious to

[6]https://slatestarcodex.com/2015/05/19/beware-summary-statistics/

me that the percent of between-country variance explained by national IQ is larger than the percent of between-individuals-in-country explained by personal IQ once factors like personal job choice (I could have been an investment banker, but I would rather be an artist) that countries don't have to deal with is abstracted out. If the amount-variance-explained between nations and between individuals were equal after adjusting for that factor, there would not be any need to posit hive mind-type effects.

EDIT: Above heavily edited for clarity and correctness after originally being much weaker argument in same direction. See here[7]. Some complicated discussion of this going on here[8], see especially Pseudoerasmus' comments

Although it may be that there's a national effect stronger than the aggregated-individual effect, I feel like this is something Jones should have had to prove, rather than relying on a "look, it's obvious!" based on unaggregated-individual numbers.

Second, fine. Let's assume he proves to our satisfaction that the national IQ-income correlation is sufficiently stronger than individual ones to require explanation. Now we get to my biggest gripe with this entire book. *How do we know the direction is IQ → development rather than development → IQ?!* Jones lays out exactly the set of assumptions that make reverse causation most plausible. He dedicates an entire chapter to the Flynn Effect, how he thinks it's real, how he thinks it's a big deal, without mentioning whether the gains might not be on g. Time and time again, Jones hammers how countries' IQs increase as they develop further. Then he shows us a graph of IQ-development correlation and just assumes the causation is bidirectional. Well, why not just development → IQ?

This isn't just about me. I suspect Jones is right – though I'm not entirely sure of it – and sufficiently biased in favor of that position to be happy to follow it and see where it leads. I'm asking for anybody who reads this book without already being interested in IQ. *Hive Mind* is clearly pitched at a smart layperson audience, and any smart layperson who reads this book ought to have exactly that question, asked with exactly that many capital letters and explanation points. Any reader who doesn't immediately stand on a chair and shout "Where is the evidence against reverse causation?" is not a reader that Garett Jones should want. But any reader who does that will not find an answer.

[7] https://slatestarcodex.com/2015/12/08/book-review-hive-mind/#comment-279320
[8] https://slatestarcodex.com/2015/12/08/book-review-hive-mind/#comment-278919

I'm just sayin', everyone that confuses correlation with causation eventually ends up dead.

— Siberian Fox (@SilverVVulpes), September 14, 2015[9]

All I can say in his defense is that a good defense against this accusation would probably have to get very deep into the causes of IQ, exactly the subject Jones is carefully trying to avoid. I understand his reluctance to approach this subject and respect his strategic decision. All I can say is that it leaves a hole in his argument big enough to sail an oil tanker through.

EDIT: Jones responds here[10]

Third, and this isn't such a problem as the others but it left me curious – how do we go from the short, few-player games that make up most of the book's experiments, to the multi-generation million-player games that make up real countries?

I have two concerns here. First, Jones says that:

> The one study of which I'm aware that finds that higher-IQ individuals are more cruel and less cooperative is a study of a one-shot prisoners' dilemma, something much like the true criminal's prisoner's dilemma… this is the only setting I know of in which high scorers are more brutal than low scorers… in a one-shot environment, if it's either steal or be robbed, and if the players will never see each other again, then I'd expect higher-IQ individuals to figure out what setting they're in and act shrewdly, not cruelly.

He returns to this theme a few times. High-IQ people don't cooperate because they're nicer (which, indeed, personality tests for niceness do not show). They cooperate because they're smarter and so they know cooperation really is a better and more win-win way to do things.

This is 100% true in an iterated prisoners' dilemma, but not necessarily true in a country. Suppose you're a president with a four year term. You can either pillage the country as best you can and take whatever bribes you can get, or invest in genuinely building a better country for your descendents. Assuming you are merely the sort of shrewd cooperator who cooperates on iterated prisoners' dilemmas but defects on one-shots, you'll pillage the country – it probably has term limits and you only need to pillage once to get very rich.

[9] https://twitter.com/SilverVVulpes/status/643474990290092032
[10] https://twitter.com/GarettJones/status/674594737127604226

Likewise, suppose you're a mid-level bureaucrat in Washington, of the type that there are tens of thousands of. If you behave dishonorably, you can amass a small empire and make some money. If you behave honorably, then maybe America does very well as a country down the line, but that effect is aggregated over thousands of bureaucrats, so it's not like you're *really* growing the pot that much. Once again, if you are merely shrewd and not genuinely altruistic, you'll defect.

Jones tries to take the easy way out on the deriving-ethical-behavior thing here, saying that ethical behavior *really is* the most self-serving option in the long-term, and all you need is people smart enough to realize it. To that I can only say: no it isn't. In a game of two or three people where everyone sees everyone else's results, your contribution may grow the pot enough to be worth the short-term losses from not defecting. In a game of thousands of bureaucrats or millions of citizens, not so much. There are ideas like TDT and superrationality that try to bridge this gap, but I think Jones tries to cross it without those ideas and is left floundering.

One more thing on this topic: maybe it was in the original studies and I just didn't look deep enough, but I wonder how much of this is just understanding the game. The Iterated Prisoner's Dilemma is kind of complicated, and if you're stupid you may not be able to grasp the logic behind why cooperation is sometimes the better option. If you explained everything very carefully to all participants, had them play a couple of games both ways so they got a feel for it, and had a Professor of Economics give a lecture on why cooperation was probably the best option, would high-IQ people still succeed more because of some innate cooperative tendency? Or would everyone else have figured out their secret and robbed them of their advantage?

People usually have a pretty good grasp of things that are going on in society. Jones compares marriage to a prisoner's dilemma (where the optimal C-D outcome is "you cheat but your spouse stays faithful"). But people understand the terms of marriage, cultural evolution has had a long time to come up with beliefs and mores about marriage that even people too stupid to come up with them on their own follow, and some kind of complicated new game may not be the best analogue to the marriage problem.

III

Jones ends the book with the following observation:

The best guess is that the cognitive skill of elites really does matter more than the nation's average score. When it comes to institutional quality, Potrafke and I found that the cognitive skills of the top 5 percent did the better job of predicting property-rights friendly institutions, although the nation's average score also did a reasonably good job as a predictor... for the time being it's reasonable to start with the belief that a nation's top performers matter more for the economy than a nation's average performers.

Well, *that's* interesting. All of this stuff about immigration and on how maybe we shouldn't have open borders, and it turns out that as long as the top five percent are smart, everything is okay.

I would really like to see more on this. If America has higher IQ than Britain, but the members of Parliament have higher IQ than the members of Congress, which country will do better? What about a colonial nation where the administrators are from a nation that has a completely differnet IQ than the population? What about countries that have multiple mostly-segregated populations with different IQs? How much does the IQ of the government matter versus the IQ of the population itself?

(and now I wonder if Jones has read La Griffe on smart fractions [1[11], 2[12]])

Come to think of it, doesn't every nation have some pretty smart people at the highest echelons? Sub-Saharan Africa may be in the IQ doldrums, but we all know African economists, statesmen, etc whose work is top-notch. Doesn't Jones' call to raise national IQs with the Flynn Effect seem less pressing now? Haven't the elites of Third World countries already probably been Flynn-ified, since they usually get good food, good medical care, and good education? Should we worry the Flynn Effect won't help those countries further? Or should we hope that if we merely raise the IQ of a few people, that will be enough and we won't have to have a mass nationwide campaign? (calling all CRISPR enthusiasts...)

Overall, I thought this book showcased some really neat results, had some good economics in it, and was very readable, but I didn't come out of it feeling like its thesis was very proven.

---

[11] http://lagriffedulion.f2s.com/sft.htm
[12] http://www.lagriffedulion.f2s.com/sft2.htm

Book II

2016

15

Side Effects May Include Anything

January 20, 2016

A couple of days ago a patient said he'd become depressed after starting Xolair, a new asthma drug I know nothing about.

On the one hand, lots of things that mess with the immune system can cause depression. On the other, patients are notorious for blaming drugs for any random thing that happens around the same time they started taking them. So I did what any highly-trained competent medical professional would: I typed "does xolair cause depression?" into Google.

The results seemed promising. The first site was called "Can Xolair cause depression?". The second was "Is depression a side effect of Xolair?". Also on the front page were "Could Xolair cause major depression?" and "Xolair depression side effects". Clearly this is a well-researched topic that lots of people cared about, right?

Let's look closer at one of those sites, EHealthMe.com. It says[1]: "Major depression is found among people who take Xolair, especially for people who are female, 40-49 old, also take medication Singulair, and have Asthma. We study 11,502 people who have side effects while taking Xolair from FDA and social media. Among them, 14 have Major depression. Find out below who they are, when they have Major depression and more." Then it offers a link: "Join a support group for people who take Xolair and have Major depression".

First things first: if there were actually 11502 people taking Xolair, and only 14 of them had major depression, that would be a rate of 0.1%, compared to 6.9% in the general population. In other words, Xolair would be the most effective antidepressant on Earth. But of course nobody has ever done an n=11502 study on whether a random asthma medication causes depression,

---

[1] http://www.ehealthme.com/ds/xolair/major+depression%22%20rel=%22nofollow

and EHealthMe is just scraping the FDA databases to see how many people reported depression as a side effect to the FDA. But only a tiny percent of people who get depression report it, and depression sometimes strikes at random times whether you're taking Xolair or not. So this tells us nothing.

And yet a patient who worries that Xolair might be causing their depression will Google "can xolair cause depression?", and she will end up on this site that says "major depression is found among people who take Xolair", which is one of the worst examples of weasel words I've ever heard. Then she will read that there are *entire support groups* for depressed Xolair sufferers. She will find all sorts of scary-looking information like that Xolair-related depression has been increasing since 2008. And this is above and beyond just the implications of somebody bothering to write an entire report about the Xolair-depression connection!

In case you haven't guessed the twist – no one's ever investigated whether Xolair causes depression. EHealthMe's business model is to make an automated program that runs through every single drug and every possible side effect, scrapes the FDA database for examples, then autopublishes an ad-filled web page titled "COULD $DRUG CAUSE $SIDE_EFFECT?". It populates the page by spewing random FDA data all over it, concludes "$SIDE_EFFECT is found among people who take $DRUG", and offers a link to a support group for $DRUG patients suffering from $SIDE_EFFECT. Needless to say, the support group is an automatically-generated forum with no posts in it.

And it's not just EHealthMe. This is a whole market, with competitors elbowing their way past one another to the top of the Google search results. Somebody who doubts EHealthMe and seeks an online second opinion will probably just end up at PatientsVille, whose page[2] is called "Xolair Depression Side Effects", which contains the same FDA data, and which gets the Google description text "This opens a possibility that Xolair could cause Depression". Or Treato, whose page[3] claims to contain 56 reader comments on Xolair and depression, but which has actually just searched the Web for every single paragraph that contains "Xolair" and "depression" together and then posted garbled excerpts in its comment section. For example, one of their comments – and this is not at all clear from Treato's garbled excerpt – is from a tennis forum[4], where a user with the handle Xolair talks about how his ten-

---

[2] http://patientsville.com/xolair/depression.htm%22%20rel=%22nofollow
[3] https://treato.com/Xolair,Depression/?a=s%22%20rel=%22nofollow
[4] http://tt.tennis-warehouse.com/index.php?threads/need-advice-from-pro-kennex-gur

nis serve is getting worse with age; another user replies "Xolair, I read this and get depressed, I just turned 49." But if you don't check whether it came from a tennis forum or not, 56 reports of a connection between a drug and a side effect sounds convincing!

This is *really scummy*. Maybe it's not the most devious of traps for you or me, but what about for your grandmother? What about for those people who send money to Nigerian princes? The law is usually pretty strict about who can and can't provide medical information – so much so that it cracks down on 23andMe[5] just for reading off the genome in a way that uneducated people might misinterpret. Yet somehow sites like EHealthMe are allowed to continue, because they just *very strongly imply* fake medical information instead of saying it outright.

Remember, only about 50% of people[6] who are prescribed medication take it. Sometimes it's personal choice or simple forgetfulness. But a lot of the time they stop because of side effects. I had a patient a few months ago who was really depressed. I started her on an antidepressant and she got much better. Then she stopped the medication cold turkey and got a lot worse again. I asked her why she'd stopped. She said her shoulder started hurting, she'd Googled whether antidepressants could cause shoulder pain, and read that they could. She couldn't remember what site she was reading, but I bet it was EHealthMe or Treato or some of the others just like them.

One day, somebody's going to Google "can penicillin cause cancer?", read a report with a link to a support group for penicillin-induced-cancer survivors, stop taking antibiotics, and die. And when that happens, I hope it's in America, so I can be sure their family will sue the company involved for more money than exists in the entire world.

---

us.428139/#post-6793285

[5] https://slatestarcodex.com/2013/11/26/a-letter-i-will-probably-send-to-the-fda/
[6] http://www.epill.com/statistics.html

16

The Ideology Is Not The Movement

April 4, 2016

I

Why is there such a strong Sunni/Shia divide?

I know the Comparative Religion 101 answer. The early Muslims were debating who was the rightful caliph. Some of them said Abu Bakr, others said Ali, and the dispute has been going on ever since. On the other hand, that was fourteen hundred years ago, both candidates are long dead, and there's no more caliphate. You'd think maybe they'd let the matter rest.

Sure, the two groups have slightly different hadith and schools of jurisprudence, but how many Muslims even *know* which school of jurisprudence they're supposed to be following? It seems like a pretty minor thing to have centuries of animus over.

And so we return again to Robbers' Cave[1]:

> The experimental subjects — excuse me, "campers" — were 22 boys between 5th and 6th grade, selected from 22 different schools in Oklahoma City, of stable middle-class Protestant families, doing well in school, median IQ 112. They were as well-adjusted and as similar to each other as the researchers could manage.
>
> The experiment, conducted in the bewildered aftermath of World War II, was meant to investigate the causes—and possible remedies—of intergroup conflict. How would they spark an intergroup con-

[1] https://www.greaterwrong.com/lw/lt/the_robbers_cave_experiment/

flict to investigate? Well, the 22 boys were divided into two groups of 11 campers, and —

— and that turned out to be quite sufficient.

The researchers' original plans called for the experiment to be conducted in three stages. In Stage 1, each group of campers would settle in, unaware of the other group's existence. Toward the end of Stage 1, the groups would gradually be made aware of each other. In Stage 2, a set of contests and prize competitions would set the two groups at odds.

They needn't have bothered with Stage 2. There was hostility almost from the moment each group became aware of the other group's existence: They were using our campground, our baseball diamond. On their first meeting, the two groups began hurling insults. They named themselves the Rattlers and the Eagles (they hadn't needed names when they were the only group on the campground).

When the contests and prizes were announced, in accordance with pre-established experimental procedure, the intergroup rivalry rose to a fever pitch. Good sportsmanship in the contests was evident for the first two days but rapidly disintegrated.

The Eagles stole the Rattlers' flag and burned it. Rattlers raided the Eagles' cabin and stole the blue jeans of the group leader, which they painted orange and carried as a flag the next day, inscribed with the legend "The Last of the Eagles". The Eagles launched a retaliatory raid on the Rattlers, turning over beds, scattering dirt. Then they returned to their cabin where they entrenched and prepared weapons (socks filled with rocks) in case of a return raid. After the Eagles won the last contest planned for Stage 2, the Rattlers raided their cabin and stole the prizes. This developed into a fistfight that the staff had to shut down for fear of injury. The Eagles, retelling the tale among themselves, turned the whole affair into a magnificent victory—they'd chased the Rattlers "over halfway back to their cabin" (they hadn't).

Each group developed a negative stereotype of Them and a contrasting positive stereotype of Us. The Rattlers swore heavily. The Eagles, after winning one game, concluded that the Eagles had won because of their prayers and the Rattlers had lost because they used cuss-words all the time. The Eagles decided to stop using cuss-words themselves. They also concluded that since the Rattlers swore all the time, it would be wiser not to talk to them. The Eagles developed an image of themselves as proper-and-moral; the Rattlers developed an image of themselves as rough-and-tough.

If the researchers had decided that the real difference between the two groups was that the Eagles were adherents of Eagleism, which held cussing as absolutely taboo, and the Rattlers adherents of Rattlerism, which held it a holy duty to cuss five times a day – well, that strikes me as the best equivalent to saying that Sunni and Shia differ over the rightful caliph.

II

Nations, religions, cults, gangs, subcultures, fraternal societies, internet communities, political parties, social movements – these are all really different, but they also have some deep similarities. They're all groups of people. They all combine comradery within the group with a tendency to dislike other groups of the same type. They all tend to have a stated purpose, like electing a candidate or worshipping a deity, but also serve a *very* important role as impromptu social clubs whose members mostly interact with one another instead of outsiders. They all develop an internal culture such that members of the groups often like the same foods, wear the same clothing, play the same sports, and have the same philosophical beliefs as other members of the group – even when there are only tenuous links or no links at all to the stated purpose. They all tend to develop sort of legendary histories, where they celebrate and exaggerate the deeds of the groups' founders and past champions. And they all tend to inspire something like patriotism, where people are proud of their group membership and express that pride through conspicuous use of group symbols, group songs, et cetera. For better or worse, the standard way to refer to this category of thing is "tribe".

Tribalism is potentially present in all groups, but levels differ a lot even in groups of nominally the same type. Modern Belgium seems like an unusually non-tribal nation; Imperial Japan in World War II seems like an unusually tribal one. Neoliberalism and market socialism seem like unusually non-tribal political philosophies; communism and libertarianism seem like unusually tribal ones. Corporations with names like Amalgamated Products Co probably aren't very tribal; charismatic corporations like Apple that become identities for their employees and customers are more so. Cults are maybe the most tribal groups that exist in the modern world, and those Cult Screening Tools make good measures for tribalism as well.

The dangers of tribalism are obvious; for example, fascism is based around dialing a country's tribalism up to eleven, and it ends poorly. If I had written this essay five years ago, it would be be titled "Why Tribalism Is Stupid And Needs To Be Destroyed". Since then, I've changed my mind. I've found that I enjoy being in tribes as much as anyone else[2].

Part of this was resolving a major social fallacy I'd had throughout high school and college, which was that the correct way to make friends was to pick the five most interesting people I knew and try to befriend them. This almost never worked and I thought it meant I had terrible social skills. Then I looked at what everyone else was doing, and I found that instead of isolated surgical strikes of friendship, they were forming groups. The band people. The mock trial people. The football team people. The Three Popular Girls Who Went Everywhere Together. Once I tried "falling in with" a group, friendship became much easier and self-sustaining precisely because of all of the tribal development that happens when a group of similar people all know each other and have a shared interest. Since then I've had good luck finding tribes I like and that accept me – the rationalists being the most obvious example, but even interacting with my coworkers on the same hospital unit at work is better than trying to find and cultivate random people.

Some benefits of tribalism are easy to explain. Tribalism intensifies all positive and prosocial feelings within the tribe. It increases trust within the tribe and allows otherwise-impossible forms of cooperation – remember Haidt on the Jewish diamond merchants[3] outcompeting their rivals because their mutual Judaism gave them a series of high-trust connections that saved them costly verification procedures? It gives people a support network they can rely on when their luck is bad and they need help. It lets you "be yourself" without worrying that this will be incomprehensible or offensive to somebody who thinks totally differently from you. It creates an instant densely-connected social network of people who mostly get along with one another. It makes people feel like part of something larger than themselves, which makes them happy and can (provably[4]) improves their physical and

---

[2]https://slatestarcodex.com/2014/05/19/nerds-can-be-bees-too/

[3]https://slatestarcodex.com/2014/06/12/list-of-the-passages-i-highlighted-in-my-copy-of-jonathan-haidts-the-righteous-mind/

[4]http://www.livescience.com/52197-religion-mental-health-brain.html

mental health.

Others are more complicated. I can just make motions at a feeling that "what I do matters", in the sense that I will probably never be a Beethoven or a Napoleon who is very important to the history of the world as a whole, but I can do things that are important within the context of a certain group of people. All of this is really good for my happiness and mental health. When people talk about how modern society is "atomized" or "lacks community" or "doesn't have meaning", I think they're talking about a lack of tribalism, which leaves people all alone in the face of a society much too big to understand or affect. The evolutionary psychology angle here is too obvious to even be worth stating.

And others are entirely philosophical. I think some people would say that wanting to have a tribe is like wanting to have a family – part of what it means to be human – and demands to justify either are equally wrong-headed.

Eliezer thinks every cause wants to be a cult[5]. I would phrase this more neutrally as "every cause wants to be a tribe". I've seen a lot of activities go through the following cycle:

1. Let's get together to do X
2. Let's get together to do X, and have drinks afterwards
3. Let's get together to discuss things from an X-informed perspective
4. Let's get together to discuss the sorts of things that interest people who do X
5. Let's get together to discuss how the sort of people who do X are much better than the sort of people who do Y.
6. Dating site[6] for the sort of people who do X
7. Oh god, it was so annoying, she spent the whole date talking about X.
8. X? What X?

This can happen over anything or nothing at all. Despite the artificial nature of the Robbers' Cove experiment, its groups are easily recognized as tribes. Indeed, the reason this experiment is so interesting is that it shows tribes in their purest form; no veneer of really being about pushing a social change or supporting a caliph, just tribes for tribalism's sake.

---

[5] https://www.greaterwrong.com/lw/lv/every_cause_wants_to_be_a_cult/
[6] https://berniesingles.com/

III

Scholars call the process of creating a new tribe "ethnogenesis" – Robbers' Cave was artificially inducing ethnogenesis to see what would happen. My model of ethnogenesis involves four stages: pre-existing differences, a rallying flag, development, and dissolution.

Pre-existing differences are the raw materials out of which tribes are made. A good tribe combines people who have similar interests and styles of interaction *even before* the ethnogenesis event. Any description of these differences will necessarily involve stereotypes, but a lot of them should be hard to argue. For example, atheists are often pretty similar to one another even before they deconvert from their religion and officially become atheists. They're usually nerdy, skeptical, rational, not very big on community or togetherness, sarcastic, well-educated. At the risk of going into touchier territory, they're pretty often white and male. You take a sample of a hundred equally religious churchgoers and pick out the ones who are *most like the sort of people who are atheists* even if all of them are 100% believers. But there's also something more than that. There are subtle habits of thought, not yet described by any word or sentence, which atheists are more likely to have than other people. It's part of the reason why atheists *need* atheism as a rallying flag instead of just starting the Skeptical Nerdy Male Club.

The rallying flag is the explicit purpose of the tribe. It's usually a belief, event, or activity that get people with that specific pre-existing difference together and excited. Often it brings previously latent differences into sharp relief. People meet around the rallying flag, encounter each other, and say "You seem like a kindred soul!" or "I thought I was the only one!" Usually it suggests some course of action, which provides the tribe with a purpose. For atheists, the rallying flag is not believing in God. Somebody says "Hey, I don't believe in God, if you also don't believe in God come over here and we'll hang out together and talk about how much religious people suck." All the atheists go over by the rallying flag and get very excited about meeting each other. It starts with "Wow, you hate church too?", moves on to "Really, you also like science fiction?", and ends up at "Wow, you have the same undefinable habits of thought that I do!"

Development is all of the processes by which the fledgling tribe gains its own culture and history. It's a turning-inward and strengthening-of-walls, which transforms it from 'A Group Of People Who Do Not Believe In God And Happen To Be In The Same Place' to 'The Atheist Tribe'. For example, atheists have symbols like that 'A' inside an atom. They have jokes and mascots like Russell's Teapot and the Invisible Pink Unicorn. They have their own set of heroes, both mythologized past heroes like Galileo and controversial-but-undeniably-important modern heroes like Richard Dawkins and Daniel Dennett. They have celebrities like P.Z. Myers and Hemant Mehta. They have universally-agreed-upon villains to be booed and hated, like televangelists or the Westboro Baptist Church. They have grievances, like all the times that atheists have been fired or picked on by religious people, and all the laws about pledging allegiance to one nation under God and so on. They have stereotypes about themselves – intelligent, helpful, passionate – and stereotypes about their outgroups – deluded, ignorant, bigoted.

Dissolution is optional. The point of the previous three steps is to build a "wall" between the tribe and the outside, a series of systematic differences that let everybody know which side they're on. If a tribe was never really that different from the surrounding population, stops caring that much about its rallying flag, and doesn't develop enough culture, then the wall fails and the members disperse into the surrounding population. The classic example is the assimilation of immigrant groups like Irish-Americans, but history is littered with failed communes, cults, and political movements. Atheism hasn't quite dissolved yet, but occasionally you see hints of the process. A lot of the comments around "Atheism Plus" centered around this idea of "Okay, talking about how there's no God all the time has gotten boring, plus nobody interesting believes in God anymore anyway, so let's become about social justice instead". The parts of atheism who went along with that message mostly dissolved into the broader social justice community – there are a host of nominally atheist blogs that haven't talked about anything except social justice in months. Other fragments of the atheist community dissolved into transhumanism, or libertarianism, or any of a number of other things. Although there's still an atheist community, it no longer seems quite as vibrant and cohesive as it used to be.

We can check this four-stage model by applying it to the Sunni and Shia and seeing if it sticks.

I know very little about early Islam and am relying on sources that might be biased, so don't declare a fatwa against me if I turn out to be wrong, but it looks like from the beginning there were big pre-existing differences between proto-Shia and proto-Sunni. A lot of Ali's earliest supporters were original Muslims who had known Mohammed personally, and a lot of Abu Bakr's earliest supporters were later Muslims high up in the Meccan/Medinan political establishment who'd converted only after it became convenient to do so. It's really easy to imagine cultural, social, and personality differences between these two groups. Probably members in each group already knew one another pretty well, and already had ill feelings towards members of the other, without necessarily being able to draw the group borders clearly or put their exact differences into words. Maybe it was "those goody-goodies who are always going on about how close to Mohammed they were but have no practical governing ability" versus "those sellouts who don't really believe in Islam and just want to keep playing their political games".

Then came the rallying flag: a political disagreement over the succession. One group called themselves "the party of Ali", whose Arabic translation "Shiatu Ali" eventually ended up as just "Shia". The other group won and called itself "the traditional orthodox group", in Arabic "Sunni". Instead of a vague sense of "I wonder whether that guy there is one of those goody-goodies always talking about Mohammed, or whether he's a practical type interested in good governance", people could just ask "Are you for Abu Bakr or Ali?" and later "Are you Sunni or Shia?" Also at some point, I'm not exactly sure how, most of the Sunni ended up in Arabia and most of the Shia ended up in Iraq and Iran, after which I think some pre-existing Iraqi/Iranian vs. Arab cultural differences got absorbed into the Sunni/Shia mix too.

Then came development. Both groups developed elaborate mythologies lionizing their founders. The Sunni got the history of the "rightly-guided caliphs", the Shia exaggerated the first few imams to legendary proportions. They developed grievances against each other; according to Shia history, the Sunnis killed eleven of their twelve leaders, with the twelfth escaping only when God directly plucked him out of the world to serve as a future Messiah. They developed different schools of hadith interpretation and jurisprudence and debated the differences ad nauseum with each other for hundreds of years. A lot of Shia theology is in Farsi; Sunni theology is entirely in Arabic. Sunni clergy usually dress in white; Shia clergy usually dress in black and green. Not all of these were deliberately done in opposition to one another; most were just a consequence of the two camps being walled off from one another and so allowed to develop cultures independently.

Obviously the split hasn't dissolved yet, but it's worth looking at similar splits that have. Catholicism vs. Protestantism is still a going concern in a few places like Ireland, but it's nowhere near the total wars of the 17th century or even the Know-Nothing-Parties of the 19th. Consider that Marco

Rubio is Catholic, but nobody except Salon[7] particularly worries about that or says that it will make him unsuitable to lead a party representing the interests of very evangelical Protestants. Heck, the same party was happy to nominate Mitt Romney, a Mormon, and praise him for his "Christian faith". Part of it is the subsumption of those differences into a larger conflict – most Christians acknowledge Christianity vs. atheism to be a bigger deal than interdenominational disputes these days – and part of it is that everyone of every religion is so influenced by secular American culture that the religions have been reduced to their rallying flags alone rather than being fully developed tribes at this point. American Sunni and Shia seem to be well on their way to dissolving into each other[8] too.

IV

I want to discuss a couple of issues that I think make more sense once you understand the concept of tribes and rallying flags:

1. Disability

I used to be very confused by disabled people who insist on not wanting a "cure" for their condition. Deaf people and autistic people are the two classic examples, and sure enough we find articles like Not All Deaf People Want To Be Cured[9] and They Don't Want An Autism Cure[10]. Autistic people can at least argue their minds work differently rather than worse, but being deaf seems to be a straight-out disadvantage: the hearing can do anything the deaf can, and can hear also. A hearing person can become deaf at any time just by wearing earplugs, but a deaf person can't become hearing, at least not without very complicated high-tech surgeries.

When I asked some deaf friends about this, they explained that they had a really close-knit and supportive deaf culture, and that most of their friends, social events, and ways of relating to other people and the world were through this culture. This made sense, but I always wondered: if you were able to hear,

---

[7] http://www.salon.com/2016/01/17/marco_rubios_real_disqualification_new_video_out lines_bizarre_religious_faith_and_he_wants_to_govern_by_it/

[8] http://usatoday30.usatoday.com/news/religion/2007-09-24-muslim-tension_N.htm

[9] http://www.telegraph.co.uk/culture/9526045/Why-not-all-deaf-people-want-to-be-c ured.html

[10] http://www.thedailybeast.com/articles/2015/02/25/they-don-t-want-an-autism-cure .html

couldn't you form some other culture? If worst came to worst and nobody else wanted to talk to you, couldn't you at least have the Ex-Deaf People's Club?

I don't think so. Deafness acts as a rallying flag that connects people, gives them a shared foundation to build culture off of, and walls the group off from other people. If all deaf people magically became able to hear, their culture would eventually drift apart, and they'd be stuck without an ingroup to call their own.

Part of this is reasonable cost-benefit calculation – our society is so vast and atomized, and forming real cohesive tribes is so hard, that they might reasonably expect it would be a lot of trouble to find another group they liked as much as the deaf community. But another part of this seems to be about an urge to cultural self-preservation.

2. Genocide

This term is kind of overused these days. I always thought of it as meaning literally killing every member of a certain group – the Holocaust, for example – but the new usage includes "cultural genocide"[11]. For example, autism rights advocates sometimes say[12] that anybody who cured autism would be committing genocide – this is of course soundly mocked[13], but it makes sense if you think of autistic people as a tribe that would be dissolved absent its rallying flag. The tribe would be eliminated – thus "cultural genocide" is a reasonable albeit polemical description.

It seems to me that people have an urge toward cultural self-preservation which is as strong or stronger as the urge to individual self-preservation. Part of this is rational cost-benefit calculation – if someone loses their only tribe and ends up alone in the vast and atomized sea of modern society, it might take years before they can find another tribe and really be at home there. But a lot of it seems to be beyond that, an emotional certainty that losing one's culture and having it replaced with another is not okay, any more than being killed at the same time someone else has a baby is okay. Nor do I think this is necessarily irrational; locating the thing whose survival you care about in the self rather than the community is an assumption, and people can make different assumptions without being obviously wrong.

---

[11] https://en.wikipedia.org/wiki/Cultural_genocide

[12] https://www.reddit.com/r/aspergers/comments/3kr7uf/why_do_people_want_to_commit_g enocide_on_the/

[13] https://www.reddit.com/r/TumblrInAction/comments/2bn1ga/finding_a_cure_for_autis m_is_genocide/

3. Rationalists

The rationalist community is a group of people (of which I'm a part) who met reading the site Less Wrong and who tend to hang out together online, sometimes hang out together in real life, and tend to befriend each other, work with each other, date each other, and generally move in the same social circles. Some people call it a cult, but that's more a sign of some people having lost vocabulary for anything between "totally atomized individuals" and "outright cult" than any particular cultishness.

But people keep asking me what exactly the rationalist community *is*. Like, what is the thing they believe that makes them rationalists? It can't just be about being rational, because loads of people are interested in that and most of them aren't part of the community. And it can't just be about transhumanism because there are a lot of transhumanists who aren't rationalists, and lots of rationalists who aren't transhumanists. And it can't just be about Bayesianism, because pretty much everyone, rationalist or otherwise, agrees that is a kind of statistics that is useful for some things but not others. So what, exactly, is it?

This question has always bothered me, but now after thinking about it a lot I finally have a clear answer: rationalism is the belief that Eliezer Yudkowsky is the rightful caliph.

No! Sorry! I think "the rationalist community" is a tribe much like the Sunni or Shia that started off with some pre-existing differences, found a rallying flag, and then developed a culture.

The pre-existing differences range from the obvious to the subtle. A lot of rationalists are mathematicians, programmers, or computer scientists. The average IQ is in the 130s. White men are overrepresented, but so are LGBT and especially transgender people. But there's more. Nobody likes the Myers-Briggs test, but I continue to find it really interesting that rationalists have some Myers-Briggs types (INTJ/INTP) at ten times the ordinary rate, and other types (ISFJ/ESFP) at only one one-hundredth the ordinary rate. Myers-Briggs doesn't cleave reality at its joints, but if it measures anything at all about otherwise hard-to-explain differences in thinking styles, the rationalist community heavily selects for those same differences. Sure enough, I am *constantly* running into people who say "This is the only place where I've ever found people who think like me" or "I finally feel understood".

The rallying flag was the Less Wrong Sequences. Eliezer Yudkowsky started a blog (actually, borrowed Robin Hanson's) about cognitive biases and how to think through them. Whether or not you agreed with him or found him enlightening loaded heavily on those pre-existing differences, so the people who showed up in the comment section got along and started meeting up with each other. "Do you like Eliezer Yudkowsky's blog?" became a useful proxy for all sorts of things, eventually somebody coined the word "rationalist" to refer to people who did, and then you had a group with nice clear boundaries.

The development is everything else. Obviously a lot of jargon sprung up in the form of terms from the blog itself. The community got heroes like Gwern and Anna Salamon who were notable for being able to approach difficult questions insightfully. It doesn't have much of an outgroup yet – maybe just bioethicists and evil robots. It has its own foods – MealSquares, that one kind of chocolate everyone in Berkeley started eating around the same time – and its own games[14]. It *definitely* has its own inside jokes. I think its most important aspect, though, is a set of shared mores – everything from "understand the difference between ask and guess culture and don't get caught up in it" to "cuddling is okay" to "don't misgender trans people" – and a set of shared philosophical assumptions like utilitarianism and reductionism.

I'm stressing this because I keep hearing people ask "What is the rationalist community?" or "It's really weird that I seem to be involved in the rationalist community even though I don't share belief X" as if there's some sort of necessary-and-sufficient-featherless-biped-style ideological criterion for membership. This is why people are saying "Lots of you aren't even singularitarians, and everyone agrees Bayesian methods are useful in some places and not so useful in others, so what is your community even *about* ?" But once again, it's ~~about Eliezer Yudkowsky being the rightful caliph~~ it's not necessarily *about* anything.

If you take only one thing from this essay, it's that communities are best understood not logically but historically. If you want to understand the Shia, don't reflect upon the true meaning of Ali being the rightful caliph, understand that a dispute involving Ali initiated ethnogenesis, the resulting culture picked up a bunch of features and became useful to various people, and now here we are. If you want to understand the rationalist community, don't ask exactly how near you have to think the singularity has to be before you qualify for membership, focus on the fact that some stuff Eliezer Yudkowsky wrote led to certain people identifying themselves as "rationalists" and for various reasons I enjoy dinner parties with those people about 10000% more interest-

---

[14]http://rationalitycardinality.com/

ing than dinner parties with randomly selected individuals. nostalgebraist[15] actually summed this up really well: "Maybe the real rationalism was the friends we made along the way." Maybe that's the real Shia Islam too, and the real Democratic Party, and so on.

4. Evangelical And Progressive Religion

There seems to be a generational process, sort of like Harold Lee's theory of immigrant assimilation[16], by which religions dissolve. The first generation believes everything literally. The second generation believes that the religion might not be literally true, but it's an important expression of universal values and they still want to follow the old ways and participate in the church/temple/mosque/mandir community. The third generation is completely secularized.

This was certainly my family's relationship with Judaism. My great-great-grandfather was so Jewish that he left America and returned to Eastern Europe because he was upset at American Jews for not being religious enough. My great-grandfather stayed behind in America but remained a very religious Jew. My grandparents attend synagogue when they can remember, speak a little Yiddish, and identify with the traditions. My parents went to a *really* liberal synagogue where the rabbi didn't believe in God and everyone just agreed they were going through the motions. I got Bar Mitzvahed when I was a kid but haven't been to synagogue in years. My children probably won't even have that much.

So imagine you're an evangelical Christian. All the people you like are also evangelical Christians. Most of your social life happens at church. Most of your good memories involve things like Sunday school and Easter celebrations, and even your bittersweet memories are things like your pastor speaking at your parents' funeral. Most of your hopes and dreams involve marrying someone and having kids and then sharing similarly good times with them. When you try to hang out with people who aren't evangelical Christians, they seem to think really differently than you do, and not at all in a good way. A lot of your happiest intellectual experiences involve geeking out over different Bible verses and the minutiae of different Christian denominations.

Then somebody points out to you that God probably doesn't exist. And

---

[15] http://nostalgebraist.tumblr.com/

[16] http://thefutureprimaeval.net/of-culture-wars-and-mongol-hordesof-immigrants-and-kings/

even if He does, it's probably in some vague and complicated way, and not the way that means that the Thrice-Reformed Meta-Baptist Church and *only* the Thrice-Reformed Meta-Baptist Church has the correct interpretation of the Bible and everyone else is wrong.

On the one hand, their argument might be convincing. On the other, you are pretty sure that if everyone agreed on this, your culture would be destroyed. Sure, your kids could be Christmas-and-Easter-Christians who still enjoy the cultural aspects and derive personal meaning from the Bible. But you're pretty sure that within a couple of generations your descendents would be exactly as secular as anyone else. Absent the belief that serves as your culture's wall against the outside world, it would dissolve without a trace into the greater homogeneity of Western liberal society. So, do you keep believing a false thing? Or do you give up on everything you love and enjoy and dissolve into a culture that mostly hates and mocks people like you? There's no good choice. This is why it sucks that things like religion and politics are both rallying flags for tribes, and actual things that there may be a correct position on.

5. Religious Literalism

One comment complaint I heard during the height of the Atheist-Theist Online Wars was that atheists were a lot like fundamentalists. Both wanted to interpret the religious texts in the most literal possible way.

Being on the atheist side of these wars, I always wanted to know: well, why wouldn't you? Given that the New Testament clearly says you have to give all your money to the poor, and the Old Testament doesn't say anything about mixing meat and milk, maybe religious Christians should start giving everything to the poor and religious Jews should stop worrying so much about which dishes to use when?

But I think this is the same mistake as treating the Sunni as an organization dedicated to promoting an Abu Bakr caliphate. The holy book is the rallying flag for a religion, but the religion is not itself about the holy book. The rallying flag created a walled-off space where people could undergo the development process and create an independent culture. That independent culture may diverge significantly from the holy book.

I think that very neurotypical people naturally think in terms of tribes, and the idea that they have to retool their perfectly functional tribe to conform to the exact written text of its holy book or constitution or stated political

ideology or something seems silly to them. I think that less neurotypical people – a group including many atheists – think less naturally in terms of tribes
and so tend to take claims like "Christianity is about following the Bible" at
face value. But Christianity is about being part of the Christian tribe, and although that tribe started around the Bible, maintains its coherence because of
the Bible, and is of course naturally influenced by it, if it happens to contradict
the Bible in some cases that's not necessarily surprising or catastrophic.

This is also why I'm not really a fan of debates over whether Islam is really
"a religion of peace" or "a religion of violence", especially if those debates involve mining the Quran for passages that support one's preferred viewpoint.
It's not just because the Quran is a mess of contradictions with enough in-
terpretive degrees of freedom to prove anything at all. It's not even because
Islam is a host of separate cultures as different from one another as Unitari-
anism is from the Knights Templar. It's because the Quran just created the
space in which the Islamic culture could evolve, but had only limited impact
on that evolution. As well try to predict the warlike or peaceful nature of the
United Kingdom by looking at a topographical map of Great Britain.

6. Cultural Appropriation

Thanks to some people who finally explained this to me in a way that made
sense. When an item or artform becomes the rallying flag for a tribe, it can
threaten the tribe if other people just want to use it as a normal item or artform.

Suppose that rappers start with pre-existing differences from everyone
else. Poor, male, non-white minority, lots of experience living in violent
places, maybe a certain philosophical outlook towards their condition. Then
they get a rallying flag: rap music. They meet one another, like one another.
The culture undergoes further development: the lionization of famous rappers, the development of a vocabulary of shared references. They get all of
the benefits of being in a tribe like increased trust, social networking, and a
sense of pride and identity.

Now suppose some rich white people get into rap. Maybe they get into
rap for innocuous reasons: rap is cool, they like the sound of it. Fine. But
they don't share the pre-existing differences, and they can't be easily assim-
ilated into the tribe. Maybe they develop different conventions, and start
saying that instead of being about the struggles of living in severe poverty,
rap should be about Founding Fathers. Maybe they start saying the original

rappers are bad, and they should stop talking about violence and bitches because that ruins rap's reputation. Since rich white people tend to be be good
at gaining power and influence, maybe their opinions are overrepresented at
the Annual Rap Awards, and all of a sudden you can't win a rap award unless
your rap is about the Founding Fathers and doesn't mention violence (except
Founding-Father-related duels). All of a sudden if you try to start some kind
of impromptu street rap-off, you're no longer going to find a lot of people
like you whom you instantly get along with and can form a high-trust community. You're going to find half people like that, and half rich white people
who strike you as annoying and are always complaining that your raps don't
feature any Founding Fathers at all. The rallying flag fails and the tribe is lost
as a cohesive entity.

7. Fake Gamer Girls

A more controversial example of the same. Video gaming isn't just a fun
way to pass the time. It also brings together a group of people with some
pre-existing common characteristics: male, nerdy, often abrasive, not very
successful, interested in speculation, high-systematizing. It gives them a rallying flag and creates a culture which then develops its own norms, shared reference points, internet memes, webcomics, heroes, shared gripes, even some
unique literature[17]. Then other people with very different characteristics and
no particular knowledge of the culture start enjoying video games just because
video games are fun. Since the Gamer Tribe has no designated cultural spaces
except video games forums and magazines, they view this as an incursion into
their cultural spaces and a threat to their existence as a tribe.

Stereotypically this is expressed as them getting angry when girls start
playing video games. One can argue that it's unfair to infer tribe membership
based on superficial characteristics like gender – in the same way it might be
unfair for the Native Americans to assume someone with blonde hair and blue
eyes probably doesn't follow the Old Ways – but from the tribe's perspective
it's a reasonable first guess.

I've found gamers to get along pretty well with women who share their
culture, and poorly with men who don't – but admit that the one often starts
from an assumption of foreignness and the other from an assumption of mem-

---

[17]http://smile.amazon.com/Ready-Player-One-Ernest-Cline/dp/0307887448/ref=as_li_s
s_tl?ie=UTF8&qid=1459738834&sr=8-1&keywords=ready+player+one&linkCode=lll&tag=slast
acod-20&linkId=69bc1494abc539bfbc996d24acc6f95a

bership. More important, I've found the *idea* of the rejection of the 'fake gamer girl', real or not, raised more as a libel by people who genuinely *do* want to destroy gamer culture, in the sense of cleansing video-game-related spaces of a certain type of person/culture and making them entirely controlled by a different type of person/culture, in much the same way that a rich white person who says any rapper who uses violent lyrics needs to be blacklisted from the rap world has a clear culture-change project going on.

These cultural change projects tend to be framed in terms of which culture has the better values, which I think is a limited perspective. I think America has better values than Pakistan does, but that doesn't mean I want us invading them, let alone razing their culture to the ground and replacing it with our own.

8. Subcultures And Posers

Obligatory David Chapman link[18]. A poser is somebody who uses the rallying flag but doesn't have the pre-existing differences that create tribal membership and so never really fits into the tribe.

9. Nationalism, Patriotism, and Racism

Nationalism and patriotism use national identity as the rallying flag for a strong tribe. In many cases, nationalism becomes ethno-nationalism, which builds tribal identity off of a combination of heritage, language, religion, and culture. It has to be admitted that this can make for some *incredibly* strong tribes. The rallying flag is built into ancestry, and so the walls are near impossible to obliterate. The symbolism and jargon and cultural identity can be instilled from birth onward. Probably the best example of this is the Jews, who combine ethnicity, religion, and language into a bundle deal and have resisted assimilation for millennia.

Sometimes this can devolve into racism. I'm not sure exactly what the difference between ethno-nationalism and racism is, or whether there even *is* a difference, except that "race" is a much more complicated concept than ethnicity and it's probably not a coincidence that it has become most popular in a country like America whose ethnicities are hopelessly confused. The Nazis certainly needed a lot of work to transform concern about the German

---

[18]http://meaningness.com/metablog/geeks-mops-sociopaths

nation into concern about the Aryan race. But it's fair to say all of this is somewhat related or at least potentially related.

On the other hand, in countries that have non-ethnic notions of heritage, patriotism has an opportunity to substite for racism. Think about the power of the civil rights message that, whether black or white, we are all Americans.

This is maybe most obvious in sub-national groups. Despite people paying a lot of attention to the supposed racism of Republicans, the rare black Republicans do shockingly well within their party. Both Ben Carson and Herman Cain briefly topped the Republican presidential primary polls during their respective election seasons, and their failures seem to have had much more to do with their own personal qualities than with some sort of generic Republican racism. I see the same with Thomas Sowell, with Hispanic Republicans like Ted Cruz, and Asian Republicans like Bobby Jindal.

Maybe an even stronger example is the human biodiversity movement, which many people understandably accuse of being entirely about racism. Nevertheless, some of its most leading figures are black – JayMan and Chanda Chisala (who is adjacent to the movement but gets lots of respect within it) – and they seem to get equal treatment and respect to their white counterparts. Their membership in a strong and close-knit tribe screens off everything else about them.

I worry that attempts to undermine nationalism/patriotism in order to fight racism risk backfiring. The weaker the "American" tribe becomes, the more people emphasize their other tribes – which can be either overtly racial or else heavily divided along racial lines (eg political parties). It continues to worry me that people who would never display an American flag on their lawn because "nations are just a club for hating foreigners" now have a campaign sign on their lawn, five bumper stickers on their car, and are identifying more and more strongly with political positions – ie clubs for hating their fellow citizens.

Is there such a thing as conservation of tribalism? Get rid of one tribal identity and people just end up seizing on another? I'm not sure. And anyway, nobody can agree on exactly what the American identity or American tribe is anyway, so any conceivable such identity would probably risk alienating a bunch of people. I guess that makes it a moot point. But I still think that deliberately trying to eradicate patriotism is not as good an idea as is generally believed.

V

I think tribes are interesting and underdiscussed. And in a lot of cases when they are discussed, it's within preexisting frameworks that tilt the playing field towards recognizing some tribes as fundamentally good, others as fundamentally bad, and ignoring the commonalities between all of them.

But in order to talk about tribes coherently, we need to talk about rallying flags. And that involves admitting that a lot of rallying flags are based on ideologies (which are sometimes wrong), holy books (which are *always* wrong), nationality (which we can't define), race (which is racist), and works of art (which some people inconveniently want to enjoy just as normal art without any connotations).

My title for this post is also my preferred summary: the ideology is not the movement. Or, more jargonishly – the rallying flag is not the tribe. People are just trying to find a tribe for themselves and keep it intact. This often involves defending an ideology they might not be tempted to defend for any other reason. This doesn't make them bad, and it *may* not even necessarily mean their tribe deserves to go extinct. I'm reluctant to say for sure whether I think it's okay to maintain a tribe based on a faulty ideology, but I think it's at least important to understand that these people are in a crappy situation with no good choices, and they deserve some pity.

Some vital aspects of modern society – freedom of speech, freedom of criticism, access to multiple viewpoints, the existence of entryist tribes with explicit goals of invading and destroying competing tribes as problematic, and the overwhelming pressure to dissolve into the Generic Identity Of Modern Secular Consumerism – make maintaining tribal identities really hard these days. I think some of the most interesting sociological questions revolve around whether there are any ways around the practical and moral difficulties with tribalism, what social phenomena are explicable as the struggle of tribes to maintain themselves in the face of pressure, and whether tribalism continues to be a worthwhile or even a possible project at all.

EDIT: Commenters point out a very similar Melting Asphalt post, Religion Is Not About Beliefs[19].

---

[19] http://www.meltingasphalt.com/religion-is-not-about-beliefs/

17

Why Were Early Psychedelicists So Weird?

April 28, 2016

Epistemic status: very speculative, asserted with only ~30% confidence. On the other hand, even though psychiatrists don't really talk about this it's possible other groups know this all already.

A few weeks ago I gave a presentation on the history of early psychedelic research. Since I had a tough crowd, I focused on the fascinating biographies of some of the early psychedelicists.

Timothy Leary[1] was a Harvard professor and former NIMH researcher who made well-regarded contributions to psychotherapy and psychometrics. He started the Harvard Psilocybin Project and several other Harvard-based experiments to test the effects of psychedelics on normal and mentally ill subjects. He was later fired from Harvard and arrested; later he accomplished a spectacular break out of prison and fled to Algeria. During his later life, he wrote books about how the human brain had hidden circuits of consciousness that would allow us to live in space, including a quantum overmind which could control reality and break the speed of light. He eventually fell so deep into madness that he started hanging out with Robert Anton Wilson and participating in Ron Paul fundraisers.

Richard Alpert[2] was Leary's co-investigator at the Harvard Psilocybin Project. He, too, had all the signs of a promising career, including a psychology PhD from Stanford, a visiting professorship at Berkeley, and a combination academic/clinical position at Stanford. After his work with Leary, he

---

[1] https://en.wikipedia.org/wiki/Timothy_Leary
[2] https://en.wikipedia.org/wiki/Ram_Dass

moved to India, changed his name to Baba Ram Dass, and became one of the world's most prominent advocates for bhakti yoga.

John Lilly[3] was a doctor, a neuroanatomy researcher, and an inventor who helped develop the principle behind many modern neuroprosthetics. He was always very strange, and did a lot of work in human-dolphin communication and SETI even before starting his work with LSD. But in the 1960s, he ran across Richard Alpert, joined in his LSD experiments, and became even stranger. He started writing books with names like "Programming And Metaprogramming The Human Biocomputer", and arguing that benevolent and malevolent aliens were locked in a battle to manipulate Earth's coincidences and with them the future of the human species. He became an expert yogi and claimed to have achieved samadhi, the highest state of union with God.

Kary Mullis[4] is kind of cheating since he was not technically a psychedelicist. He was a biochemist in the completely unrelated field of bacterial iron transport molecules. But he did try LSD in 1966 back when it was still a legal research chemical. In fact he tried 1000 micrograms of it, one of the biggest doses I've ever heard of someone taking. Like the others, Mullis was a brilliant scientist – he won the Nobel Prize in Chemistry for inventing the polymerase chain reaction. Like the others, Mullis got *really weird* fast. He is a global warming denialist, HIV/AIDS denialist, and ozone hole denialist; on the other hand, he *does* believe in the efficacy of astrology. He also believes he has contacted extraterrestrials in the form of a fluorescent green raccoon, and "founded a business with the intent to sell pieces of jewelry containing the amplified DNA of deceased famous people like Elvis Presley".

I wondered if there might be a selection bias in which psychedelicists I heard about, or that I might be cherry-picking the most unusual examples, so I looked for leading early psychedelics researchers I'd never heard of before and checked how weird *they* were. My sources told me that the two most important early psychedelicists were Humphry Osmond[5] (who invented the word 'psychedelic' and may have been the first person to experiment with LSD rigorously) and his colleague John Smythies[6].

Osmond has an impressive early resume: started off as a surgeon, became a psychiatrist, did some well-regarded research into the structure of the hu-

[3] https://en.wikipedia.org/wiki/John_C._Lilly

[4] https://en.wikipedia.org/wiki/Kary_Mullis

[5] https://en.wikipedia.org/wiki/Humphry_Osmond

[6] https://en.wikipedia.org/wiki/John_Raymond_Smythies

man metabolite adrenochrome. And although he did not become fluorescent-alien-raccoon level weird, he can't quite be called normal either. He became one of the founders of orthomolecular psychiatry, a discipline arguing that schizophrenia and other psychiatric diseases can be cured by massive amounts of vitamins – this is currently considered pseudoscience. His publications include the article "Selection of twins for ESP experimentation" in *International Journal of Parapsychology*, and a history of psychedelics records[7] that "after his mescaline experiment in 1951, Dr. Osmond claimed to have successfully transmitted telepathic information to a fellow researcher, Duncan Blewett, who was also under the influence of mescaline, leading an independent observer to panic at the uncanny event." He seems to have maintained a lifetime interest in parapsychology, Jungian typological analysis, and a field of his own invention called "socio-architecture".

Smythies was a neuropsychiatrist, neuroanatomist, biochemist, EEG researcher, editor of the International Review of Neurobiology, etc, etc, etc (also, a cousin of Richard Dawkins). He is 94 but apparently still alive and going strong and making new neuroanatomical discoveries. He was one of the first people to investigate the pharmacology of psychedelics and helped with Osmond's experiments in the early 1950s. He has also written *The Walls Of Plato's Cave*, a book presenting a new theory of consciousness which "extends our concepts of consciousness and analyses possible geometrical and topological relations between phenomenal space and physical space linked to brane theory in physics" (I kind of wish I was a fly on the wall at his and Dawkins' family reunions).

My point is that the field of early psychedelic research seemed to pretty consistently absorb brilliant scientists, then spit out people who, while still brilliant scientists, also had styles of thought that could be described as extremely original at best and downright crazy at worst.

I think it's important to try to understand why.

First possibility: you had to be kind of weird to begin with in order to be interested in researching psychedelics. On the one hand, this is surely true; on the other, the early psychedelicists ended up *really* weird. At least in the early days I'm not sure psychedelics had the reputation for weirdness they now enjoy, and I'm also not sure that we're living in a world where a high

---

[7]https://books.google.com/books?id=n_-SeVz36awC&pg=PA205&lpg=PA205&dq=%22Humphry +Osmond%22+telepathy&source=bl&ots=txs2cWNmbL&sig=L6WoPmTMhj96mSyZESFNbRbFXe4&hl=en &sa=X&ved=0ahUKEwjk7ZDAurDMAhWFvIMKHbaTBx4Q6AEILTAD#v=onepage&q=%22Humphry%20Osmond%2 2%20telepathy&f=false

enough percent of psychiatrists go off to become gurus in India, that we can just dismiss LSD research as happening to attract that type of person.

Second possibility: I know that almost all of these researchers (I'm not sure about Smythies) used psychedelics themselves. Psychedelic use is a sufficiently interesting experience that I can see why it might expand one's interest in the study of consciousness and the universe. Perhaps this is especially true if you're one of the first people to use it, and you don't have the social setting of "Oh, yeah, this is that drug that makes you have really weird experiences about consciousness for a while". If you're not aware that psychedelic hallucinations are a thing that happens, you might have to interpret your experience in more traditional terms like divine revelation. Under this theory, these pioneers had to become kind of weird to learn enough for the rest of us to use these substances safely. But why would that make John Lilly obsessed with aliens? Why would it turn Timothy Leary into a space colonization advocate and Ron Paul supporter?

The third possibility is the one that really intrigues me. A 2011 study[8] found that a single dose of psilocybin *could permanently increase the personality dimension of Openness To Experience*. I'm emphasizing that because personality is otherwise pretty stable after adulthood; *nothing* should be able to do this. But magic mushrooms apparently have this effect, and not subtly either; participants who had a mystical experience on psilocybin had Openness increase *up to half a standard deviation* compared to placebo, and *the change was stable sixteen months later*. This is *really scary*. I mean, I *like* Openness To Experience, but something that can produce large, permanent personality changes is so far beyond anything else we have in psychiatry that it's kind of terrifying.

(related: 1972 study finds LSD may cause permanent increase in hypnotic susceptibility[9], which other sources[10] have linked to being "fantasy prone" and "creative")

And that's *one dose*. These researchers were taking psychedelics pretty constantly for years, and probably experimented with the sort of doses you couldn't get away with giving research subjects. What would you expect to happen to *their* Openness To Experience? How many standard deviations do you think *it* went up?

It seems possible to me that psychedelics have a direct pharmacological

---

[8] http://www.ncbi.nlm.nih.gov/pmc/articles/PMC3537171/
[9] http://www.tandfonline.com/doi/abs/10.1080/00207147208409273
[10] http://www.psywww.com/asc/hyp/faq4.html

effect on personality that causes people to be more open to unusual ideas. I know this is going against most of the latest research, which says psychedelics have no long-term negative mental health effects[11] and do not cause psychosis. But there's a difference between being schizophrenic, and being the sort of guy who is still a leading neuroanatomist but also writes books about the geometric relationships between consciousness and the space-time continuum.

I'm not sure anyone has ever done studies to rule out the theory that psychedelics just plain make people *weird*. Indeed, such studies would be very difficult, given that weird people with very high Openness To Experience are more likely to use psychedelics. This problem would even prevent common sense detection of the phenomenon – even if we noticed that frequent psychedelic users were really weird, we would attribute it to selection effects and forget about it.

In this situation, the early psychedelicists could be a natural experiment giving us data we can't get any other way. Here are relatively sober scientists who took psychedelics for reasons other than being weird hippies already. Their fate provides signal through the noise which is the general psychedelic-using population.

I think this is only medium-risk; the explanation that weird people gravitate toward psychedelics, even in the sciences, is a strong one. But it's sufficient that I am hesitant to repeat the common view that psychedelics are not at all dangerous, or that they have no permanent side effects. There seems to me at least a moderate chance that they will make you more interesting without your consent – whether that is a good or a bad thing depends on exactly how interesting you want to be.

---

[11]http://www.popsci.com/science/article/2013-08/psychedelics-dont-give-you-mental-health-problems-study-says

18

Book Review: Age of Em

May 28, 2016

Note: I really liked this book and if I criticize it that's not meant as an attack but just as what I do with interesting ideas. Note that Robin has offered to debate me about some of this and I've said no – mostly because I hate real-time debates and have bad computer hardware – but you may still want to take this into account when considering our relative positions. Mild content warning for murder, rape, and existential horror. Errors in Part III are probably my own, not the book's.

I

There are some people who are destined to become adjectives. Pick up a David Hume book you've never read before and it's easy to recognize the ideas and style as Humean. Everything Tolkien wrote is Tolkienesque in a non-tautological sense. This isn't meant to denounce either writer as boring. Quite the opposite. They produced a range of brilliant and diverse ideas. But there was a hard-to-define and very consistent ethos at the foundation of both. Both authors were *very much like themselves*.

Robin Hanson is more like himself than anybody else I know. He's obviously brilliant – a PhD in economics, a masters in physics, work for DARPA, Lockheed, NASA, George Mason, and the Future of Humanity Institute. But his greatest aptitude is in being really, *really* Hansonian[1]. Bryan Caplan describes it as well as anybody:

> When the typical economist tells me about his latest research, my standard reaction is 'Eh, maybe.' Then I forget about it. When

---
[1] https://www.reddit.com/r/slatestarcodex/comments/3sjtar/a_robin_hanson_primer/

Robin Hanson tells me about his latest research, my standard reaction is 'No way! Impossible!' Then I think about it for years.

This is my experience too. I think I said my first "No way! Impossible!" sometime around 2008 after reading his blog Overcoming Bias[2]. Since then he's influenced my thinking more than almost anyone else I've ever read. When I heard he was writing a book, I was – well, I couldn't even imagine a book by Robin Hanson. When you read a thousand word blog post by Robin Hanson, you have to sit down and think about it and wait for it to digest and try not to lose too much sleep worrying about it. A whole book would be *something*.

I have now read *Age Of Em*[3] (website[4]) and it is indeed something. Even the cover gives you a weird sense of sublimity mixed with unease:

And in this case, judging a book by its cover is entirely appropriate.

II

Age of Em is a work of futurism – an attempt to predict what life will be like a few generations down the road. This is not a common genre – I can't think of another book of this depth and quality in the same niche. Predicting the future is notoriously hard, and that seems to have so far discouraged potential authors and readers alike.

Hanson is not discouraged. He writes that:

> Some say that there is little point in trying to foresee the non-immediate future. But in fact there have been many successful forecasts of this sort. For example, we can reliably predict the future cost changes for devices such as batteries or solar cells, as such costs tend to follow a power law of the cumulative device production (Nagy et al 2013). As another example, recently a set of a thousand published technology forecasts were collected and scored for accuracy, by comparing the forecasted date of a technology milestone with its actual date. Forecasts were significantly more accurate than random, even forecasts 10 to 25 years ahead. This was true separately for forecasts made via many

[2] http://www.overcomingbias.com/
[3] http://amzn.to/1TB67E7
[4] http://ageofem.com/

different methods. On average, these milestones tended to be passed a few years before their forecasted date, and sometimes forecasters were unaware that they had already passed (Charbonneau et al, 2013).

A particularly accurate book in predicting the future was *The Year 2000*, a 1967 book by Herman Kahn and Anthony Wiener. It accurately predicted population, was 80% correct for computer and communication technology, and 50% correct for other technology (Albright 2002). On even longer time scales, in 1900 the engineer John Watkins did a good job of forecasting many basic features of society a century later (Watkins 1900) […]

Some say no one could have anticipated the recent big changes associated with the arrival and consequences of the World Wide Web. Yet participants in the Xanadu hypertext project in which I was involved from 1984 to 1993 correctly anticipated many key aspects of the Web […] Such examples show that one can use basic theory to anticipate key elements of distant future environments, both physical and social, but also that forecasters do not tend to be much rewarded for such efforts, either culturally or materially. This helps to explain why there are relatively few serious forecasting efforst. But make no mistake, it *is* possible to forecast the future.

I think Hanson is overstating his case. All except Watkins were predicting only 10 – 30 years in the future, and most of their predictions were simple numerical estimates, eg "the population will be one billion" rather than complex pictures of society. The only project here even remotely comparable in scope to Hanson's is John Watkins' 1900 article[5].

Watkins is classically given some credit for broadly correct ideas like "Cameras that can send pictures across the world instantly" and "telephones that can call anywhere in the world", but of his 28 predictions, I judge only eight as even somewhat correct. For example, I grant him a prediction that "the average American will be two inches taller because of good medical care" even though he then goes on to say in the same sentence that the average life expectancy will be fifty and suburbanization will be so total that building city blocks will be illegal (sorry, John, only in San Francisco). Most of the predictions seem simply and completely false. Watkins believes all animals and insects will have been eradicated. He believes there will be "peas as large as beets" and "strawberries as large as apples" (these are two separate predictions; he is weirdly obsessed with fruit and vegetable size). We will travel to England via giant combination submarine/hovercrafts that will complete the trip in a lightning-fast two days. There will be no surface-level transportation in cities as all cars and walkways have moved underground. The letters C, X, and Q will be removed from the language. Pneumatic tubes will deliver purchases from stores. "A man or woman unable to walk ten miles at a stretch will be regarded as a weakling."

Where Watkins is right, he is generally listing a cool technology slightly beyond what was available to his time and predicting we will have it. Nevertheless, he is still mostly wrong. Yet this is Hanson's example of accurate futurology. And he is *right* to make it his example of accurate futurology, because everything else is even worse.

Hanson has no illusions of certainty. He starts by saying that "conditional on my key assumptions, I expect at least 30% of future situations to be usefully informed by my analysis. Unconditionally, I expect at least 10%." So he is not explicitly overconfident. But in an implicit sense, it's just *weird* to see the level of detail he tries to predict – for example, he has two pages about what sort of swear words the far future might use. And the book's style serves to reinforce its weirdness. The whole thing is written in a sort of professorial monotone that changes little from loving descriptions of the sorts of pipes that will cool future buildings (one of Hanson's pet topics[6]) to speculation on our descendents' romantic relationships (key quote: "The per minute subjective value of an equal relation should not fall much below half of the per-minute value of a relation with the best available open source lover"). And it leans heavily on a favorite Hansonian literary device – the weirdly general statement about something that sounds like it can't possibly be measurable, followed by a curt reference which if followed up absolutely confirms said statement, followed by relentlessly ringing every corollary of it:

> Today, mental fatigue reduces mental performance by about 0.1% per minute. As by resting we can recover at a rate of 1% per minute, we need roughly one-tenth of our workday to be break time, with the duration between breaks being not much more than an hour or two (Trougakos and Hideg 2009; Alvanchi et al

---

[6]http://www.overcomingbias.com/2013/11/the-bright-future-of-pipes.html

2012)… Thus many em tasks will be designed to take about an hour, and many spurs are likely to last for about this duration.

Or:

Today, painters, novelists, and directors who are experimental artists tend to do their best work at roughly ages 46-52, 38-50, and 45-63 respectively, but those ages are 24-34, 29-40, and 27-43, respectively for conceptual artists (Galenson 2006)… At any one time, the vast majority of actual working ems [should be] near a peak productivity subjective age.

Or:

Wars today, like cities, are distributed evenly across all possible war sizes (Cederman 2003).

At some point I started to wonder whether Hanson was putting me on. Everything is just played *too straight*. Hanson even addresses this:

To resist the temptation to construe the future too abstractly, I'll try to imagine a future full of complex detail. One indiciation that I've been successful in all these efforts will be if my scenario description sounds less like it came from a typical comic book or science fiction movie, and more like it came form a typical history text or business casebook.

Well, count that project a success. The effect is strange to behold, and I'm not sure it will usher in a new era of futurology. But *Age of Em* is great not *just* as futurology, but as a bunch of different ideas and purposes all bound up in a futurological package. For example: – An introduction to some of the concepts that recur again and again across Robin's thought – for example, near vs. far mode[7], the farmer/forager dichotomy[8], the inside and outside views[9], signaling[10]. Most of us learned these through years reading Hanson's blog *Overcoming Bias*, getting each chunk in turn, spending days or months

---

[7] http://www.overcomingbias.com/2010/06/near-far-summary.html

[8] http://www.overcomingbias.com/2010/10/two-types-of-people.html

[9] http://www.overcomingbias.com/2007/07/beware-the-insi.html

[10] http://www.quickmeme.com/meme/3okrr5

thinking over each piece. Getting it all out of a book you can read in a couple of days sounds really hard – but by applying them to dozens of different subproblems involved in future predictions, Hanson makes the reader more comfortable with them, and I expect a lot of people will come out of the book with an intuitive understanding of how they can be applied. – A whirlwind tour through almost every science and a pretty good way to learn about the *present*. If you didn't already know that wars are distributed evenly across all possible war sizes, well, read *Age of Em* and you will know that and many similar things besides. – A manifesto. Hanson often makes predictions by assuming that since the future will be more competitive, future people are likely to converge toward optimal institutions. This is a dangerous assumption for futurology – it's the same line of thinking that led Watkins to assume English would abandon C, X, and Q as inefficient – but it's a *great* assumption if you want a chance to explain your ideas of optimal institutions to thousands of people who think they're reading fun science-fiction. Thus, Robin spends several pages talking about how ems may use prediction markets – an information aggregation technique he invented – to make their decisions. In the real world, Hanson has been trying to push these for decades, with varying[11] levels[12] of success. Here, in the guise of a future society, he can expose a whole new group of people to their advantages – as well as the advantages of something called "combinatorial auctions" which I am still not smart enough to understand. – A mind-expanding drug. One of the great risks of futurology is to fail to realize how *different* societies and institutions can be – the same way uncreative costume designers make their aliens look like humans with green skin. A lot of our thoughts about the future involve assumptions we've never really examined critically, and Hanson dynamites those assumptions. For page after page, he gives strong arguments why our descendants might be poorer, shorter-lived, less likely to travel long distances or into space, less progressive and open-minded. He predicts little noticeable technological change, millimeter-high beings living in cities the size of bottles, careers lasting fractions of seconds, humans being incomprehensibly wealthy patrons to their own robot overlords. And *all of it makes sense.*

When I read Stross' *Accelerando*, one of the parts that stuck with me the longest were the Vile Offspring, weird posthuman entities that operated a mostly-incomprehensible Economy 2.0 that humans just sort of hung out on the edges of, goggle-eyed. It was a weird vision – but, for Stross, mostly

[11]https://primary.guide/
[12]https://en.wikipedia.org/wiki/Policy_Analysis_Market

a black box. *Age of Em* opens the box and shows you every part of what our weird incomprehensible posthuman descendents will be doing in loving detail. Even what kind of swear words they'll use.

III

So, what is the Age of Em?

According to Hanson, AI is really hard and won't be invented in time to shape the posthuman future. But sometime a century or so from now, scanning technology, neuroscience, and computer hardware will advance enough to allow emulated humans, or "ems". Take somebody's brain, scan it on a microscopic level, and use this information to simulate it neuron-by-neuron on a computer. A good enough simulation will map inputs to outputs in exactly the same way as the brain itself, effectively uploading the person to a computer. Uploaded humans will be much the same as biological humans. Given suitable sense-organs, effectuators, virtual avatars, or even robot bodies, they can think, talk, work, play, love, and build in much the same way as their "parent". But ems have three very important differences from biological humans.

First, they have no natural body. They will never need food or water; they will never get sick or die. They can live entirely in virtual worlds in which any luxuries they want – luxurious penthouses, gluttonous feasts, Ferraris – can be conjured out of nothing. They will have some limited ability to transcend space, talking to other ems' virtual presences in much the same way two people in different countries can talk on the Internet.

Second, they can run at different speeds. While a normal human brain is stuck running at the speed that physics allow, a computer simulating a brain can simulate it faster or slower depending on preference and hardware availability. With enough parallel hardware, an em could experience a subjective century in an objective week. Alternatively, if an em wanted to save hardware it could process all its mental operations *very slowly* and experience only a subjective week every objective century.

Third, just like other computer data, ems can be copied, cut, and pasted. One uploaded copy of Robin Hanson, plus enough free hardware, can become a thousand uploaded copies of Robin Hanson, each living in their own virtual world and doing different things. The copies could even converse with each other, check each other's work, duel to the death, or – yes – have sex with each other. And if having a thousand Robin Hansons proves too much, a quick ctrl-x and you can delete any redundant ems to free up hard disk space for Civilization 6 (coming out this October![13])

Would this count as murder? Hanson predicts that ems will have unusually blase attitudes toward copy-deletion. If there are a thousand other copies of me in the world, then going to sleep and not waking up just feels like delegating back to a different version of me. If you're still not convinced, Hanson's essay Is Forgotten Party Death?[14] is a typically disquieting analysis of this proposition. But whether it's true or not is almost irrelevant – at least *some* ems will think this way, and they will be the ones who tend to volunteer to be copied for short term tasks that require termination of the copy afterwards. If you personally aren't interested in participating, the economy .

The ability to copy ems as many times as needed fundamentally changes the economy and the idea of economic growth. Imagine Google has a thousand positions for Ruby programmers. Instead of finding a thousand workers, they can find one very smart and very hard-working person and copy her a thousand times. With unlimited available labor supply, wages plummet to subsistence levels. "Subsistence levels" for ems are the bare minimum it takes to rent enough hardware from Amazon Cloud to run an em. The overwhelming majority of ems will exist at such subsistence levels. On the one hand, if you've got to exist on a subsistence level, a virtual world where all luxuries can be conjured from thin air is a pretty good place to do it. On the other, such starvation wages might leave ems with little or no leisure time.

Sort of. This gets weird. There's an urban legend about a "test for psychopaths". You tell someone a story about a man who attends his mother's funeral. He met a really pretty girl there and fell in love, but neglected to get her contact details before she disappeared. How might he meet her again? If they answer "kill his father, she'll probably come to that funeral too", they're a psychopath – ordinary people would have a mental block that prevents them from even considering such a drastic solution. And I bring this up because after reading *Age of Em* I feel like Robin Hanson would be able to come up with some super-solution even the psychopaths can't think of, some plan that gets the man a threesome with the girl and her even hotter twin sister at the cost of wiping out an entire continent. Everything about labor relations in *Age of Em* is like this.

For example, suppose you want to hire an em at subsistence wages, but you want them 24 hours a day, 7 days a week. Ems probably need to sleep –

---

[13]http://www.ign.com/articles/2016/05/25/civilization-6s-new-game-changer-features
[14]http://www.overcomingbias.com/2016/04/is-forgotten-party-death.html

that's hard-coded into the brain, and the brain is being simulated at enough fidelity to leave that in. But jobs with tasks that don't last longer than a single day – for example, a surgeon who performs five surgeries a day but has no day-to-day carryover – can get around this restriction by letting an em have one full night of sleep, then copying it. Paste the em at the beginning of the workday. When it starts to get tired, let it finish the surgery it's working on, then delete it and paste the well-rested copy again to do the next surgery. Repeat forever and the em never has to get any more sleep than that one night. You can use the same trick to give an em a "vacation" – just give it *one* of them, then copy-paste that brain-state forever.

Or suppose your ems want frequent vacations, but you want them working every day. Let a "trunk" em vacation every day, then make a thousand copies every morning, work all the copies for twenty-four hours, then delete them. Every copy remembers a life spent in constant vacation, and cheered on by its generally wonderful existence it will give a full day's work. But from the company's perspective, 99.9% of the ems in its employment are working at any given moment.

(another option: work the em at normal subjective speed, then speed it up a thousand times to take its week-long vacation, then have it return to work after only one-one-thousandth of a week has passed in real life)

Given that ems exist at subsistence wages, saving enough for retirement sounds difficult, but this too has weird psychopathic solutions. Thousands of copies of the same em can pool their retirement savings, then have all except a randomly chosen one disappear at the moment of retirement, leaving that one with an nest egg thousands of time what it could have accumulated by its own efforts. Or an em can invest its paltry savings in some kind of low-risk low-return investment and reduce its running speed so much that the return on its investment is enough to pay for its decreased subsistence. For example, if it costs $100 to rent enough computing power to run an em at normal speed for one year, and you only have $10 in savings, you can rent 1/1000th of the computer for $0.10, run at 1/1000th speed, invest your $10 in a bond that pays 1% per year, and have enough to continue running indefinitely. The only disadvantage is that you'll only experience a subjective week every twenty objective years. Also, since other entities are experiencing a subjective week every second, and some of those entities have nukes, probably there will be some kind of big war, someone will nuke Amazon's data centers, and you'll die after a couple of your subjective minutes. But at least you got to retire!

If ems do find ways to get time off the clock, what will they do with it?

Probably they'll have really weird social lives. After all, the existence of em copies is mostly funded by companies, and there's no reason for companies to copy-paste any but the best workers in a given field. So despite the literally trillions of ems likely to make up the world, most will be copies of a few exceptionally brilliant and hard-working individuals with specific marketable talents. Elon Musk might go out one day to the bar with his friend, who is also Elon Musk, and order "the usual". The bartender, who is Elon Musk himself, would know exactly what drink he wants and have it readily available, as the bar caters entirely to people who are Elon Musk. A few minutes later, a few Chesley Sullenbergers might come in after a long day of piloting airplanes. Each Sullenberger would have met hundreds of Musks before and have a good idea about which Musk-Sullenberger conversation topics were most enjoyable, but they might have to adjust for circumstances; maybe the Musks they met before all branched off a most recent common ancestor in 2120, but these are a different branch who were created in 2105 and remember Elon's human experiences but not a lot of the posthuman lives that shaped the 2120 Musks' worldviews. One Sullenberger might tentatively complain that the solar power grid has too many outages these days; a Musk might agree to take the problem up with the Council of Musks, which is totally a thing that exist (Hanson calls these sorts of groups "copy clans" and says they are "a natural candidate unit for finance, reproduction, legal, liability, and political representation").

Romance could be even weirder. Elon Musk #2633590 goes into a bar and meets Taylor Swift #105051, who has a job singing in a nice local nightclub and so is considered prestigious for a Taylor Swift. He looks up a record of what happens when Elon Musks ask Taylor Swifts out and finds they are receptive on 87.35% of occasions. The two start dating and are advised by the Council of Musks and the Council of Swifts on the issues that are known to come up in Musk-Swift relationships and the best solutions that have been found to each. Unfortunately, Musk #2633590 is transferred to a job that requires operating at 10,000x human speed, but Swift #105051's nightclub runs at 100x speed and refuses to subsidize her to run any faster; such a speed difference makes normal interaction impossible. The story has a happy ending; Swift #105051 allows Musk #2633590 to have her source code, and whenever he is feeling lonely he spends a little extra money to instantiate a high-speed copy of her to hang out with.

(needless to say, these examples are not exactly word-for-word taken from the book, but they're heavily based off of Hanson's more abstract descriptions)

The em world is not just very weird, it's also very very big. Hanson notes that labor is a limiting factor in economic growth, yet even today the economy doubles about once every fifteen years. Once you can produce skilled labor through a simple copy-paste operation, especially labor you can run at a thousand times human speed, the economy will go through the roof. He writes that:

> To generate an empirical estimate of em economy doubling times, we can look at the timescales it takes for machine shopes and factories today to make a mass of machines of a quality, quantity, variety, and value similar to that of machines that they themselves contain. Today that timescale is roughly 1 to 3 months. Also, designs were sketched two to three decades ago for systems that might self-repliate nearly completeld in 6 to 12 months... these estimates suggest that today's manufacturing technologiy is capable of self-replicating on a scale of a few weeks to a few months.

Hanson thinks that with further innovation, such times can be reduced so far that "the economy might double every objective year, month, week, or day." As the economy doubles the labor force – ie the number of ems – may double with it, until only a few years after the first ems the population numbers in the trillions. But if the em population is doubling every day, there had better be some pretty amazing construction efforts going on. The only thing that could possibly work on that scale is prefabricated modular construction of giant superdense cities, probably made mostly out of some sort of proto early-stage computronium (plus cooling pipes). Ems would be reluctant to travel from one such city to another – if they exist at a thousand times human speed, a trip on a hypersonic airliner that could go from New York to Los Angeles in an hour would still take forty subjective days. Who wants to be on an airplane for forty days?

(long-distance trade is also rare, since if the economy doubles fast enough it means that by the time goods reach their destination they could be almost worthless)

The real winners of this ultra-fast-growing economy? Ordinary humans. While humans will be way too slow and stupid to do anything useful, they will tend to have non-subsistence amounts of money saved up from their previous human lives, and also be running at speeds thousands of times slower than most of the economy. When the economy doubles every day, so can your bank account. Ordinary humans will become rarer, less relevant, but fantastically rich – a sort of doddering Neanderthal aristocracy spending sums on a cheeseburger that could support thousands of ems in luxury for entire lifetimes. While there will no doubt be pressure to liquidate humans and take their stuff, Hanson hopes that the spirit of rule of law – the same spirit that protects rich minority groups today – will win out, with rich ems reluctant to support property confiscation lest it extend to them also. Also, em retirees will have incentives a lot like humans – they have saved up money and go really slow – and like AARP memembers today they may be able to obtain disproportionate political power which will then protect the interests of slow rich people.

But we might not have much time to enjoy our sudden rise in wealth. Hanson predicts that the Age of Em will last for subjective em millennia – ie about one to two actual human years. After all, most of the interesting political and economic activity is going on at em timescales. In the space of a few subjective millennia, either someone will screw up and cause the apocalypse, somebody will invent real superintelligent AI that causes a technological singularity, or some other weird thing will happen taking civilization beyond the point that even Robin dares to try to predict.

IV

Hanson understands that people might not like the idea of a future full of people working very long hours at subsistence wages forever (Zack Davis' Contract-Drafting Em[15] song is, as usual, relevant). But Hanson himself does not view this future as dystopian. Despite our descendents' by-the-numbers poverty, they will avoid the miseries commonly associated with poverty today. There will be no dirt or cockroaches in their sparkling virtual worlds, nobody will go hungry, petty crime will be all-but-eliminated, and unemployment will be low. Anybody who can score some leisure time will have a dizzying variety of hyperadvanced entertainment available, and as for the people who can't, they'll mostly have been copied from people who really like working hard and don't miss it anyway. As unhappy as we moderns may be contemplating em society, ems themselves will not be unhappy! And as for us:

The analysis in this book suggests that lives in the next great era

---

[15] https://www.greaterwrong.com/lw/8o6/the_gift_we_give_tomorrow_spoken_word_finishe
d/5d9f

may be as different from our lives as our lives are from farmers' lives, or farmers' lives are from foragers' lives. Many readers of this book, living industrial era lives and sharing industrial era values, may be disturbed to see a forecast of em era descendants with choices and lifestyles that appear to reject many of the values that they hold dear. Such readers may be tempted to fight to prevent the em future, perhaps preferring a continuation of the industrial era. Such readers may be correct that rejecting the em future holds them true to their core values. But I advise such readers to first try hard to see this new era in some detail from the point of view of its typical residents. See what they enjoy and what fills them with pride, and listen to their criticisms of your era and values.

A short digression: there's a certain strain of thought I find infuriating, which is "My traditionalist ancestors would have disapproved of the changes typical of my era, like racial equality, more open sexuality, and secularism. But I am smarter than them, and so totally okay with how the future will likely have values even more progressive and shocking than my own. Therefore I pre-approve of any value changes that might happen in the future as definitely good and better than our stupid hidebound present."

I once read a science-fiction story that depicted a pretty average sci-fi future – mighty starships, weird aliens, confederations of planets, post-scarcity economy – with the sole unusual feature that rape was considered totally legal, and opposition to such as bigoted and ignorant as opposition to homosexuality is today. Everybody got really angry at the author and said it was offensive for him to even speculate about that. Well, that's the method by which our cheerful acceptance of any possible future values is maintained: restricting the set of "any possible future values" to "values slightly more progressive than ours" and then angrily shouting down anyone who discusses future values that actually sound bad. But of course the *whole question* of how worried to be about future value drift *only makes sense* in the context of future values that genuinely violate our current values. Approving of all future values except ones that would be offensive to even speculate about is the same faux-open-mindedness as .

Hanson deserves credit for positing a future whose values are likely to upset even the sort of people who say they don't get upset over future value drift. I'm not sure whether or not he deserves credit for not being upset by it.

Yes, it's got low-crime, ample food for everybody, and full employment. But so does *Brave New World*. The whole *point* of dystopian fiction is pointing out that we have complicated values beyond material security. Hanson is absolutely right that our traditionalist ancestors would view our own era with as much horror as some of us would view an em era. He's even right that on utilitarian grounds, it's hard to argue with an em era where everyone is really happy working eighteen hours a day for their entire lives because we selected for people who feel that way. But at some point, can we make the Lovecraftian argument of "I know my values are provincial and arbitrary, but they're *my* provincial arbitrary values and I will make any sacrifice of blood or tears necessary to defend them, even unto the gates of Hell?"

This brings us to an even worse scenario.

There are a lot of similarities between Hanson's futurology and (my possibly erroneous interpretation of) the futurology of Nick Land. I see Land as saying, like Hanson, that the future will be one of quickly accelerating economic activity that comes to dominate a bigger and bigger portion of our descendents' lives. But whereas Hanson's framing focuses on the participants in such economic activity, playing up their resemblances with modern humans, Land takes a bigger picture. He talks about the economy itself acquiring a sort of self-awareness or agency, so that the destiny of civilization is consumed by the imperative of economic growth.

Imagine a company that manufactures batteries for electric cars. The inventor of the batteries might be a scientist who really believes in the power of technology to improve the human race. The workers who help build the batteries might just be trying to earn money to support their families. The CEO might be running the business because he wants to buy a really big yacht. And the whole thing is there to eventually, somewhere down the line, let a suburban mom buy a car to take her kid to soccer practice. Like most companies the battery-making company is primarily a profit-making operation, but the profit-making-ness draws on a lot of not-purely-economic actors and their not-purely-economic subgoals.

Now imagine the company fires all its employees and replaces them with robots. It fires the inventor and replaces him with a genetic algorithm that optimizes battery design. It fires the CEO and replaces him with a superintelligent business-running algorithm. All of these are good decisions, from a profitability perspective. We can absolutely imagine a profit-driven shareholder-value-maximizing company doing all these things. But it reduces the company's non-masturbatory participation in an economy that points outside itself, limits it to just a tenuous connection with soccer moms and maybe some shareholders who want yachts of their own.

Now take it further. Imagine there are no human shareholders who want yachts, just banks who lend the company money in order to increase their own value. And imagine there are no soccer moms anymore; the company makes batteries for the trucks that ship raw materials from place to place. Every non-economic goal has been stripped away from the company; it's just an appendage of Global Development.

Now take it even further, and imagine this is what's happened everywhere. There are no humans left; it isn't economically efficient to continue having humans. Algorithm-run banks lend money to algorithm-run companies that produce goods for other algorithm-run companies and so on ad infinitum. Such a masturbatory economy would have all the signs of economic growth we have today. It could build itself new mines to create raw materials, construct new roads and railways to transport them, build huge factories to manufacture them into robots, then sell the robots to whatever companies need more robot workers. It might even eventually invent space travel to reach new worlds full of raw materials. Maybe it would develop powerful militaries to conquer alien worlds and steal their technological secrets that could increase efficiency. It would be vast, incredibly efficient, and utterly pointless. The real-life incarnation of those strategy games where you mine Resources to build new Weapons to conquer new Territories from which you mine more Resources and so on forever.

But this seems to me the natural end of the economic system. Right now it needs humans only as laborers, investors, and consumers. But robot laborers are potentially more efficient, companies based around algorithmic trading are already pushing out human investors, and most consumers already aren't individuals – they're companies and governments and organizations. At each step you can gain efficiency by eliminating humans, until finally humans aren't involved *anywhere*.

True to form, Land doesn't see this as a dystopia – I think he conflates "maximally efficient economy" with "God", which is a *hell* of a thing to conflate – but I do. And I think it provides an important new lens with which to look at the Age of Em.

The Age of Em is an economy in the early stages of such a transformation. Instead of being able to replace everything with literal robots, it replaces them with humans who have had some aspects of their humanity stripped away. Biological bodies. The desire and ability to have children normally. Robin doesn't think people will lose all leisure time and non-work-related desires, but he doesn't seem too sure about this and it doesn't seem to bother him much if they do.

I envision a spectrum between the current world of humans and Nick Land's Ascended Economy. Somewhere on the spectrum we have ems who get leisure time. A little further on the spectrum we have ems who don't get leisure time.

But we can go further. Hanson imagines that we can "tweak" em minds. We may not understand the brain enough to create totally new intelligences from the ground up, but by his Age of Em we should understand it well enough to make a few minor hacks, the same way even somebody who doesn't know HTML or CSS can usually figure out how to change the background color of a webpage with enough prodding. Many of these mind tweaks will be the equivalent of psychiatric drugs – some might even be computer simulations of what we observe to happen when we give psychiatric drugs to a biological brain. But these tweaks will necessarily be much stronger and more versatile, since we no longer care about bodily side effects (ems don't have bodies) and we can apply it to only a single small region of the brain and avoid actions anywhere else. You could also very quickly advance brain science – the main limits today are practical (it's really hard to open up somebody's brain and do stuff to it without killing them) and ethical (the government might have some words with you if you tried). An Age of Em would remove both obstacles, and give you the added bonus of being able to make thousands of copies of your test subjects for randomized controlled trials, reloading any from a saved copy if they died. Hanson envisions that:

> As the em world is a very competitive world where sex is not needed for reproduction, and as sex can be time and attention-consuming, ems may try to suppress sexuality, via mind tweaks that produce effects analogous to castration. Such effects might be temporary, perhaps with a consciously controllable on-off switch… it is possible that em brain tweaks could be found to greatly reduce natural human desires for sex and related romantic and intimate pair bonding without reducing em productivity. It is also possible that many of the most productive ems would accept such tweaks.

Possible? I can do that *right now* with a high enough dose of Paxil, and I don't even have to upload your brain to a computer first. Fun stories about

Musk #2633590 and Swift #105051 aside, I expect this would happen about ten minutes after the advent of the Age of Em, and we would have taken another step down the path to the Ascended Economy.

There are dozens of other such tweaks I can think of, but let me focus on two.

First, stimulants have a very powerful ability to focus the brain on the task at hand, as anybody who's taken Adderall or modafinil can attest. Their main drawbacks are addictiveness and health concerns, but in a world where such pills can be applied as mental tweaks, where minds have no bodies, and where any mind that gets too screwed up can be reloaded from a backup copy, these are barely concerns at all. Many of the purely mental side effects of stimulants come from their effects in parts of the brain not vital to the stimulant effect. If we can selectively apply Adderall to certain brain centers but not others, then unapply it at will, then from employers' point of view there's no reason not to have all workers dosed with superior year 2100 versions of Adderall at all times. I worry that not only will workers not have any leisure time, but they'll be neurologically incapable of having their minds drift off while on the job. Davis' contract-drafting em who starts wondering about philosophy on the job wouldn't get terminated. He would just have his simulated-Adderall dose increased.

Second, Robin managed to write an entire book about emulated minds without using the word "wireheading"[16]. This is another thing we can do right now, with today's technology – but once it's a line of code and not a costly brain surgery, it should become nigh-universal. Give ems the control switches to their own reward centers and all questions about leisure time become irrelevant. Give *bosses* the control switches to their employees' reward centers, and the situation changes markedly. Hanson says that there probably won't be too much slavery in the em world, because it will likely have strong rule of law, because slaves aren't as productive as free workers, and there's little advantage to enslaving someone when you could just pay them subsistence wages anyway. But slavery isn't *nearly* as abject and inferior a condition as the one where somebody else has the control switch to your reward center. Combine that with the stimulant use mentioned above, and you can have people who will never have nor want to have any thought about anything other than working on the precise task at which they are supposed to be working at any given time.

---

[16] https://wiki.lesswrong.com/wiki/Wireheading

This is something I worry about even in the context of normal biological humans. But Hanson already believes em worlds will have few regulations and be able to ignore the moral horror of 99% of the population by copying and using the 1% who are okay with something. Combine this with a situation where brains are easily accessible and tweakable, and this sort of scenario becomes horribly likely.

I see almost no interesting difference between an em world with full use of these tweaks and an Ascended Economy world. Yes, there are things that look vaguely human in outline laboring in the one and not the other, but it's not like there will be different thought processes or different results. I'm not even sure what it would mean for the ems to be conscious in a world like this – they're not doing anything interesting with the consciousness. The best we could say about this is that if the wireheading is used liberally it's a lite version of the world where everything gets converted to hedonium[17].

V

In a book full of weird ideas, there is only one idea rejected as too weird. And in a book written in a professorial monotone, there's only one point at which Hanson expresses anything like emotion:

> Some people foresee a rapid local "intelligence explosion" happening soon after a smart AI system can usefully modify its local architecture (Chalmers 2010; Hanson and Yudkowsky 2013; Yudkowsky 2013; Bostrom 2014)… Honestly to me this local intelligence explosion scenario looks suspiciously like a super-villain comic book plot. A flash of insight by a lone genius lets him create a genius AI. Hidden in its super-villain research lab lair, this guines villain AI works out unprecedented revolutions in AI design, turns itself into a super-genius, which then invents super-weapons and takes over the world. Bwa ha ha.

For someone who just got done talking about the sex lives of uploaded computers in millimeter-tall robot bodies running at 1000x human speed, Robin is sure quick to use the absurdity heuristic to straw-man intelligence explosion scenarios as "comic book plots". Take away his weird authorial tic

---

[17]http://reflectivedisequilibrium.blogspot.com/2012/03/are-pain-and-pleasure-equally-energy.html

of using the words "genius" and "supervillain", this scenario reduces to "Some group, perhaps Google, perhaps a university, invent an artificial intelligence smart enough to edit its own source code; exponentially growing intelligence without obvious bound follows shortly thereafter". Yes, it's weird to think that there may be a sudden quantum leap in intelligence like this, but no weirder than to think most of civilization will transition from human to em in the space of a year or two. I'm a little bit offended that this is the only idea given this level of dismissive treatment. Since I do have immense respect for Robin, I hope my offense doesn't color the following thoughts too much.

Hanson's arguments against AI seem somewhat motivated. He admits that AI researchers generally estimate less than 50 years before we get human-level artificial intelligence, a span shorter than his estimate of a century until we can upload ems. He even admits that no AI researcher thinks ems are a plausible route to AI. But he dismisses this by saying when he asks AI experts informally, they say that in their own field, they have only noticed about 5-10% of the progress they expect would be needed to reach human intelligence over the past twenty years. He then multiplies out to say that it will probably take at least 400 years to reach human-level AI. I have two complaints about this estimate.

First, he is explicitly ignoring published papers surveying hundreds of researchers using validated techniques, in favor of what he describes as "meeting experienced AI experts informally". But even though he feels comfortable rejecting vast surveys of AI experts as potentially biased, as best I can tell he does not ask a single neuroscientist to estimate the date at which brain scanning and simulation might be available. He just says that "it seems plausible that sufficient progress will be made in roughly a century or so", citing a few hopeful articles by very enthusiastic futurists who are not neuroscientists or scanning professionals themselves and have not talked to any. This seems to me to be an extreme example of . No matter how many AI scientists think AI is soon, Hanson will cherry-pick the surveying procedures and results that make it look far. But if a few futurists think brain emulation is possible, then no matter what anybody else thinks that's good enough for him.

Second, one would expect that even if there were only 5-10% progress over the last twenty years, then there would be faster progress in the future, since the future will have a bigger economy, better supporting technology, and more resources invested in AI research. Robin answers this objection by saying that "increases in research funding usually give much less than proportionate increases in research progress" and cites Alston et al 2011. I looked up

Alston et al 2011, and it is a paper relating crop productivity to government funding of agriculture research. There was no attempt to relate its findings to any field other than agriculture, nor to any type of funding other than government. But studies show[18] that while public research funding often does have minimal effects, the effect of private research funding is usually much larger. A single sentence citing a study in crop productivity to apply to artificial intelligence while ignoring much more relevant results that contradict it seems like a really weak argument for a statement as potentially surprising as "amount of research does not affect technological progress".

I realize that Hanson has done a lot more work on this topic and he couldn't fit all of it in this book. I disagree with his other work too, and I've said so elsewhere. For now I just want to say that the arguments in this book seem weak to me.

I also want to mention what seems to me a very Hansonian counterargument to the ems-come-first scenario: we have always developed de novo technology before understanding the relevant biology. We built automobiles by figuring out the physics of combustion engines, not by studying human muscles and creating mechanical imitations of myosin and actin. Although the Wright brothers were inspired by birds, their first plane was not an ornithopter. Our power plants use coal and uranium instead of the Krebs Cycle. Biology is *really hard*. Even slavishly *copying* biology is really hard. I don't think Hanson and the futurists he cites understand the scale of the problem they've set themselves.

Current cutting-edge brain emulation projects have found their work much harder than expected. Simulating a nematode is pretty much the rock-bottom easiest thing in this category, since they are tiny primitive worms with only a few neurons; the history of the field is a litany of failures[19], with current leader OpenWorm[20] "reluctant to make bold claims about its current resemblance to biological behavior". A more ambitious $1.3 billion attempt to simulate a tiny portion of a rat brain has gone down in history as a legendary failure[21] (politics were involved, but I expect they would be involved in a plan to upload a human too). And these are just attempts to get something that behaves *vaguely* like a nematode or rat. Actually uploading a human, keeping their memory and personality intact, and not having

---

[18]http://theunbrokenwindow.com/2016/05/27/can-this-be-true/

[19]http://www.artificialbrains.com/openworm#similar

[20]https://en.wikipedia.org/wiki/OpenWorm

[21]http://www.scientificamerican.com/article/why-the-human-brain-project-went-wrong-and-how-to-fix-it/

them go insane afterwards boggles the mind. We're still not sure how much small molecules matter to brain function, how much glial cells matter to brain function, how many things in the brain are or aren't local. AI researchers are making programs that can defeat chess grandmasters; upload researchers are still struggling to make a worm that will wriggle. The right analogy for modern attempts to upload human brains isn't modern attempts at designing AI. It's an attempt at designing AI by someone who doesn't even know how to plug in a computer.

VI

I guess what really bothers me about Hanson's pooh-poohing of AI is him calling it "a comic book plot". To me, it's Hanson's scenario that seems science-fiction-ish.

I say this not as a generic insult but as a pointer at a specific category of errors. In *Star Wars*, the Rebellion had all of these beautiful hyperspace-capable starfighters that could shoot laser beams and explore galaxies – and *they still had human pilots*. 1977 thought the pangalactic future would still be using people to pilot its military aircraft; in reality, even 2016 is moving away from this.

Science fiction books have to tell interesting stories, and interesting stories are about humans or human-like entities. We can enjoy stories about aliens or robots as long as those aliens and robots are still approximately human-sized, human-shaped, human-intelligence, and doing human-type things. A Star Wars in which all of the X-Wings were combat drones wouldn't have done anything for us. So when I accuse something of being science-fiction-ish, I mean bending over backwards – and ignoring the evidence – in order to give basically human-shaped beings a central role.

This is my critique of Robin. As weird as the Age of Em is, it makes sure never to be weird in ways that warp the fundamental humanity of its participants. Ems might be copied and pasted like so many .JPGs, but they still fall in love, form clans, and go on vacations.

In contrast, I expect that we'll get some kind of AI that will be totally inhuman and much harder to write sympathetic stories about. If we get ems after all, I expect them to be lobotomized and drugged until they become *effectively* inhuman, cogs in the Ascended Economy that would no more fall in love than an automobile would eat hay and whinny. Robin's interest in keeping his protagonists relatable makes his book fascinating, engaging, and probably wrong.

I almost said "and probably less horrible than we should actually expect", but I'm not sure that's true. With a certain amount of horror-suppressing, the Ascended Economy can be written off as morally neutral – either having no conscious thought, or stably wireheaded. All of Robin's points about how normal non-uploaded humans should be able to survive an Ascended Economy at least for a while seem accurate. So morally valuable actors might continue to exist in weird Amish-style enclaves, living a post-scarcity lifestyle off the proceeds of their investments, while all the while the Ascended Economy buzzes around them, doing weird inhuman things that encroach upon them not at all. This seems slightly worse than a Friendly AI scenario, but much better than we have any right to expect of the future.

I highly recommend *Age of Em* as a fantastically fun read and a great introduction to these concepts. It's engaging, readable, and *weird*. I just don't know if it's weird *enough*.

— 19 —

It's Bayes All The Way Up

September 12, 2016

Epistemic status: Very speculative. I am not a neuroscientist and apologize for any misinterpretation of the papers involved. Thanks to the people who posted these papers in r/slatestarcodex[1]. See also Mysticism and Pattern-Matching[2] and Bayes For Schizophrenics.[3]

I

Bayes' Theorem is an equation for calculating certain kinds of conditional probabilities. For something so obscure, it's attracted a surprisingly wide fanbase, including doctors[4], , economists[5], bodybuilders[6], fen-dwellers[7], and international smugglers[8]. Eventually the hype reached the point where there was both a Bayesian cabaret[9] *and* a Bayesian choir[10], popular books using

---

[1] http://slatestarcodex.reddit.com/

[2] https://slatestarcodex.com/2015/08/28/mysticism-and-pattern-matching/

[3] https://www.greaterwrong.com/lw/e25/bayes_for_schizophrenics_reasoning_in_delusio nal/

[4] https://www.bu.edu/cghd/files/2010/10/Gill-Sabin-2005-Why-Clinicians-are-Natural -Bayesians.pdf

[5] http://econlog.econlib.org/archives/2009/11/why_arent_acade.html

[6] http://bayesianbodybuilding.com/

[7] http://delong.typepad.com/sdj/2013/01/cosma-shalizi-vs-the-fen-dwelling-bayesia ns.html

[8] http://sci-hub.cc/10.1177/1745691611406928

[9] https://www.youtube.com/watch?v=t6jFFlz9o-E

[10] https://www.youtube.com/watch?v=lntEPbMCWAs

Bayes' Theorem to prove both the existence[11] and the nonexistence[12] of God, and even Bayesian dating advice[13]. Eventually everyone agreed to dial down their exuberance a little, and accept that Bayes' Theorem might not literally explain *absolutely* everything.

So – did you know that the neurotransmitters in the brain might represent different terms in Bayes' Theorem?

First things first: Bayes' Theorem is a mathematical framework for integrating new evidence with prior beliefs. For example, suppose you're sitting in your quiet suburban home and you hear something that sounds like a lion roaring. You have some prior beliefs that lions are unlikely to be near your house, so you figure that it's probably not a lion. Probably it's some weird machine of your neighbor's that just happens to sound like a lion, or some kids pranking you by playing lion noises, or something. You end up believing that there's probably no lion nearby, but you do have a slightly higher probability of there being a lion nearby than you had before you heard the roaring noise. Bayes' Theorem is just this kind of reasoning converted to math. You can find the long version here[14].

This is what the brain does too: integrate new evidence with prior beliefs. Here are some examples I've used on this blog before:

All three of these are examples of top-down processing. Bottom-up processing is when you build perceptions into a model of the the world. Top-down processing is when you let your models of the world influence your perceptions. In the first image, you view the center letter of the the first word as an H and the second as an A, even though they're the the same character; your model of the world tells you that THE CAT is more likely than TAE CHT. In the second image, you read "PARIS IN THE SPRINGTIME", skimming over the duplication of the word "the"; your model of the world tells you that the phrase should probably only have one "the" in it (just as you've probably skimmed over it the three times I've duplicated "the" in this paragraph alone!). The third image might look meaningless until you realize

---

[11] https://www.amazon.com/The-Probability-God-Calculation-Ultimate/dp/1400054788/re f=as_li_ss_tl?s=books&ie=UTF8&qid=1332516104&sr=1-1&linkCode=ll1&tag=slastacod-20&lin kId=4caa5e695aaa2faf31e963a911690137

[12] https://www.amazon.com/Proving-History-Bayess-Theorem-Historical/dp/1616145595/r ef=as_li_ss_tl?s=books&ie=UTF8&qid=1473562460&sr=1-1&keywords=bayes+theorem+christia nity&linkCode=ll1&tag=slastacod-20&linkId=a835ae3d1185022fabc200fd94dac9f3

[13] http://www.businessinsider.com/dating-for-bayesians-heres-how-to-use-statistics -to-improve-your-love-life-2013-11

[14] https://arbital.com/p/bayes_rule_guide/

it's a cow's head; once you see the cow's head your model of the world informs your perception and it's almost impossible to see it as anything else.

(Teh fcat taht you can siltl raed wrods wtih all the itroneir ltretrs rgraneanrd is ahonter empxlae of top-dwon pssirocneg mkinag nsioy btotom-up dtaa sanp itno pacle)

But top-down processing is much more omnipresent than even these examples would suggest. Even something as simple as looking out the window and seeing a tree requires top-down processing; it may be too dark or foggy to see the tree one hundred percent clearly, the exact pattern of light and darkness on the tree might be something you've never seen before – but because you know what trees are and expect them to be around, the image "snaps" into the schema "tree" and you see a tree there. As usual, this process is most obvious when it goes wrong; for example, when random patterns on a wall or ceiling "snap" into the image of a face, or when the whistling of the wind "snaps" into a voice calling your name.

> Most of the things you perceive when awake are generated from very limited input – by the same machinery that generates dreams with no input
>
> — Void Of Space (@VoidOfSpace), September 2, 2016[15]

Corlett, Frith & Fletcher (2009)[16] (henceforth CFF) expand on this idea and speculate on the biochemical substrates of each part of the process. They view perception as a "handshake" between top-down and bottom-up processing. Top-down models predict what we're going to see, bottom-up models perceive the real world, then they meet in the middle and compare notes to calculate a prediction error. When the prediction error is low enough, it gets smoothed over into a consensus view of reality. When the prediction error is too high, it registers as salience/surprise, and we focus our attention on the stimulus involved to try to reconcile the models. If it turns out that bottom-up was right and top-down was wrong, then we adjust our priors (ie the models used by the top-down systems) and so learning occurs.

In their model, bottom-up sensory processing involves glutamate via the AMPA receptor, and top-down sensory processing involves glutamate via the NMDA receptor. Dopamine codes for prediction error, and seem to represent the level of certainty or the "confidence interval" of a given prediction or

---

[15] https://twitter.com/VoidOfSpace/status/771670673358020608
[16] http://www.ncbi.nlm.nih.gov/pmc/articles/PMC2755113/

perception. Serotonin, acetylcholine, and the others seem to modulate these systems, where "modulate" is a generic neuroscientist weasel word. They provide a lot of neurological and radiologic evidence for these correspondences, for which I highly recommend reading the paper but which I'm not going to get into here. What I found interesting was their attempts to match this system to known pharmacological and psychological processes.

CFF discuss a couple of possible disruptions of their system. Consider *increased* AMPA signaling combined with *decreased* NMDA signaling. Bottom-up processing would become more powerful, unrestrained by top-down models. The world would seem to become "noisier", as sensory inputs took on a life of their own and failed to snap into existing categories. In extreme cases, the "handshake" between exuberant bottom-up processes and overly timid top-down processes would fail completely, which would take the form of the sudden assignment of salience to a random stimulus.

Schizophrenics are famous for "delusions of reference", where they think a random object or phrase is deeply important for reasons they have trouble explaining. Wikipedia gives as examples:

- A feeling that people on television or radio are talking about or talking directly to them
- Believing that headlines or stories in newspapers are written especially for them
- Seeing objects or events as being set up deliberately to convey a special or particular meaning to themselves
- Thinking 'that the slightest careless movement on the part of another person had great personal meaning... increased significance'

In CFF, these are perceptual handshake failures; even though "there's a story about the economy in today's newspaper" should be perfectly predictable, noisy AMPA signaling registers it as an extreme prediction failure, and it fails its perceptual handshake with overly-weak priors. Then it gets flagged as shocking and deeply important. If you're unlucky enough to have your brain flag a random newspaper article as shocking and deeply important, maybe phenomenologically that feels like it's a secret message for you.

And this pattern – increased AMPA signaling combined with decreased NMDA signaling – is pretty much the effect profile of the drug ketamine, and ketamine does[17] cause a paranoid psychosis mixed with delusions of reference.

Organic psychosis like schizophrenia might involve a similar process. There's a test called the binocular depth inversion illusion, which looks like this:

(source[18])

The mask in the picture is concave, ie the nose is furthest away from the camera. But most viewers interpret it as convex, with the nose closest to the camera. This makes sense in terms of Bayesian perception; we see right-side-in faces a whole lot more often than inside-out faces.

Schizophrenics (and people stoned on marijuana!) are more likely to properly identify the face as concave than everyone else. In CFF's system, something about schizophrenia and marijuana messes with NMDA, impairs priors, and reduces the power of top-down processing. This predicts that schizophrenics and potheads would both have paranoia and delusions of reference, which seems about right.

Consider a slightly different distortion: *increased* AMPA signaling combined with *increased* NMDA signaling. You've still got a lot of sensory noise. But you've also got stronger priors to try to make sense of them. CFF argue these are the perfect conditions to create hallucinations. The increase in sensory noise means there's a lot of data to be explained; the increased top-down pattern-matching means that the brain is very keen to fit all of it into some grand narrative. The result is vivid, convincing hallucinations of things that are totally not there at all.

LSD is mostly serotonergic, but most things that happen in the brain bottom out in glutamate eventually, and LSD bottoms out in exactly the pattern of increased AMPA and increased NMDA that we would expect to produce hallucinations. CFF don't mention this, but I would also like to add my theory of pattern-matching based mysticism[19]. Make the top-down prior-using NMDA system strong enough, and the entire world collapses into a single narrative, a divine grand plan in which everything makes sense and you understand all of it. This is also something I associate with LSD.

If dopamine represents a confidence interval, then increased dopaminergic signaling should mean narrowed confidence intervals and increased

---

[17] http://www.ncbi.nlm.nih.gov/pmc/articles/PMC3838932/

[18] http://blog.brainfacts.org/2013/07/depth-perception-and-the-hollow-face-illusion/#.V9VYjFL6u2w

[19] https://slatestarcodex.com/2015/08/28/mysticism-and-pattern-matching/

certainty. Perceptually, this would correspond to increased sensory acuity. More abstractly, it might increase "self-confidence" as usually described. Amphetamines, which act as dopamine agonists, do both. Amphetamine users report increased visual acuity (weirdly, they also report blurred vision sometimes; I don't understand exactly what's going on here). They also create an elevated mood and grandiose delusions, making users more sure of themselves and making them feel like they can do anything.

(something I remain confused about: elevated mood and grandiose delusions are also typical of bipolar mania. People on amphetamines and other dopamine agonists act pretty much exactly like manic people. Antidopaminergic drugs like olanzapine are very effective acute antimanics. But people don't generally think of mania as primarily dopaminergic. Why not?)

CFF end their paper with a discussion of sensory deprivation. If perception is a handshake between bottom-up sense-data and top-down priors, what happens when we turn the sense-data off entirely? Psychologists note that most people go a little crazy when placed in total sensory deprivation, but that schizophrenics actually seem to do *better* under sense-deprivation conditions. Why?

The brain filters sense-data to adjust for ambient conditions. For example, when it's very dark, your eyes gradually adjust until you can see by whatever light is present. When it's perfectly silent, you can hear the proverbial pin drop. In a state of total sensory deprivation, any attempt to adjust to a threshold where you can detect the nonexistent signal is actually just going to bring you down below the point where you're picking up noise. As with LSD, when there's too much noise the top-down systems do their best to impose structure on it, leading to hallucinations; when they fail, you get delusions. If schizophrenics have inherently noisy perceptual systems, such that all perception comes with noise the same way a bad microphone gives off bursts of static whenever anyone tries to speak into it, then their brains will actually become *less* noisy as sense-data disappears.

(this might be a good time to remember that no congenitally blind people ever develop schizophrenia[20] and no one knows why)

II

Lawson, Rees, and Friston (2014) offer a Bayesian link to autism[21].

---

[20] https://mindhacks.com/2014/11/15/more-on-the-enigma-of-blindness-and-psychosis/
[21] http://journal.frontiersin.org/article/10.3389/fnhum.2014.00302/full

(there are probably a lot of links between Bayesians and autism, but this is the only one that needs a journal article)

They argue that autism is a form of *aberrant precision*. That is, confidence intervals are too low; bottom-up sense-data cannot handshake with top-down models unless they're almost-exactly the same. Since they rarely are, top-down models lose their ability to "smooth over" bottom-up information. The world is full of random noise that fails to cohere into any more general plan.

Right now I'm sitting in a room writing on a computer. A white noise machine produces white noise. A fluorescent lamp flickers overhead. My body is doing all sorts of body stuff like digesting food and pumping blood. There are a few things I need to concentrate on: this essay I'm writing, my pager if it goes off, any sorts of sudden dramatic pains in my body that might indicate a life-threatening illness. But I don't need to worry about the feeling of my back against the back of the chair, or the occasional flickers of the fluorescent light, or the feeling of my shirt on my skin.

A well-functioning perceptual system gates out those things I don't need to worry about. Since my shirt always feels more or less similar on my skin, my top-down model learns to predict that feeling. When the top-down model predicts the shirt on my skin, and my bottom-up sensation reports the shirt on my skin, they handshake and agree that all is well. Even if a slight change in posture makes a different part of my shirt brush against my skin than usual, the confidence intervals are wide: it is still an instance of the class "shirt on skin", it "snaps" into my shirt-on-skin schema, and the perceptual handshake goes off successfully, and all remains well. If something dramatic happens – for example my pager starts beeping really loudly – then my top-down model, which has thus far predicted silence – is rudely surprised by the sudden burst of noise. The perceptual handshake fails, and I am startled, upset, and instantly stop writing my essay as I try to figure out what to do next (hopefully answer my pager). The system works.

The autistic version works differently. The top-down model tries to predict the feeling of the shirt on my skin, but tiny changes in the position of the shirt change the feeling somewhat; bottom-up data does not *quite* match top-down prediction. In a neurotypical with wide confidence intervals, the brain would shrug off such a tiny difference, declare it good enough for government work, and (correctly) ignore it. In an autistic person, the confidence intervals are very narrow; the top-down systems expect the feeling of shirt-on-skin, but the bottom-up systems report a *slightly different* feeling of shirt-on-skin. These fail to snap together, the perceptual handshake fails, and the brain flags it as important; the autistic person is startled, upset, and feels like stopping what they're doing in order to attend to it.

(in fact, I think the paper might be claiming that "attention" just means a localized narrowing of confidence intervals in a certain direction; for example, if I pay attention to the feeling of my shirt on my skin, then I *can* feel every little fold and micromovement. This seems like an important point with a lot of implications.)

Such handshake failures match some of the sensory symptoms of autism pretty well. Autistic people dislike environments that are (literally or metaphorically) noisy. Small sensory imperfections bother them. They literally get annoyed by scratchy clothing. They tend to seek routine, make sure everything is maximally predictable, and act as if even tiny deviations from normal are worthy of alarm.

They also stim. LRF interpret stimming as an attempt to control sensory predictive environment. If you're moving your arms in a rhythmic motion, the overwhelming majority of sensory input from your arm is from that rhythmic motion; tiny deviations get lost in the larger signal, the same way a firefly would disappear when seen against the blaze of a searchlight. The rhythmic signal which you yourself are creating and keeping maximally rhythmic is the most predictable thing possible. Even something like head-banging serves to create extremely strong sensory data – sensory data whose production the head-banger is themselves in complete control of. If the brain is in some sense minimizing predictive error, and there's no reasonable way to minimize prediction error because your predictive system is messed up and registering *everything* as a dangerous error – then sometimes you have to take things into your own hands, bang your head against a metal wall, and say "I totally predicted all that pain".

(the paper doesn't mention this, but it wouldn't surprise me if weighted blankets work the same way. A bunch of weights placed on top of you will predictably stay there; if they're heavy enough this is one of the strongest sensory signals you're receiving and it might "raise your average" in terms of having low predictive error)

What about all the non-sensory-gating-related symptoms of autism? LRF think that autistic people dislike social interaction because it's "the greatest uncertainty"; other people are the hardest-to-predict things we encounter. Neurotypical people are able to smooth social interaction into general categories: this person seems friendly, that person probably doesn't like me. Autistic people get the same bottom-up data: an eye-twitch here, a weird half-smile there – but it never snaps into recognizable models; it just stays weird uninterpretable clues. So:

> This provides a simple explanation for the pronounced social-communication difficulties in autism; given that other agents are arguably the most difficult things to predict. In the complex world of social interactions, the many-to-one mappings between causes and sensory input are dramatically increased and difficult to learn; especially if one cannot contextualize the prediction errors that drive that learning.

They don't really address differences between autists and neurotypicals in terms of personality or skills. But a lot of people have come up with stories about how autistic people are better at tasks that require a lot of precision and less good at tasks that require central coherence[22], which seems like sort of what this theory would predict.

LRF ends by discussing biochemical bases. They agree with CFF that top-down processing is probably related to NMDA receptors, and so suspect this is damaged in autism. Transgenic mice who lack an important NMDA receptor component seem to behave kind of like autistic humans, which they take as support for their model – although obviously a lot more research is needed. They agree that acetylcholine "modulates" all of this and suggest it might be a promising pathway for future research. They agree with CFF that dopamine may represent precision/confidence, but despite their whole spiel being that precision/confidence is messed up in autism, they don't have much to say about dopamine except that it probably modulates something, just like everything else.

III

All of this is fascinating and elegant. But is it elegant *enough*?

I notice that I am confused about the relative role of NMDA and AMPA in producing hallucinations and delusions. CFF say that enhanced NMDA signaling results in hallucinations as the brain tries to add excess order to experience and "overfits" the visual data. Fine. So maybe you get a tiny bit of visual noise and think you're seeing the Devil. But shouldn't NMDA and

---

[22]https://en.wikipedia.org/wiki/Weak_central_coherence_theory

top-down processing also be the system that tells you there is a high prior against the Devil being in any particular visual region?

Also, once psychotics develop a delusion, that delusion usually sticks around. It might be that a stray word in a newspaper makes someone think that the FBI is after them, but once they think the FBI is after them, they fit everything into this new paradigm – for example, they might think their psychiatrist is an FBI agent sent to poison them. This sounds a lot like a new, very strong prior! Their doctor presumably isn't doing much that seems FBI-agent-ish, but because they're working off a narrative of the FBI coming to get them, they fit everything, including their doctor, into that story. But if psychosis is a case of attenuated priors, why should that be?

(maybe they would answer that because psychotic people also have increased dopamine, they believe in the FBI with absolute certainty? But then how come most psychotics don't seem to be manic – that is, why aren't they overconfident in anything except their delusions?)

LRF discuss prediction error in terms of mild surprise and annoyance; you didn't expect a beeping noise, the beeping noise happened, so you become startled. CFF discuss prediction error as sudden surprising salience, but then say that the attribution of salience to an odd stimulus creates a delusion of reference, a belief that it's somehow pregnant with secret messages. These are two very different views of prediction error; an autist wearing uncomfortable clothes might be constantly focusing on their itchiness rather than on whatever she's trying to do at the time, but she's not going to start thinking they're a sign from God. What's the difference?

Finally, although they highlighted a selection of drugs that make sense within their model, others seem not to. For example, there's some discussion of ampakines for schizophrenia[23]. But this is the opposite of what you'd want if psychosis involved overactive AMPA signaling! I'm not saying that the ampakines for schizophrenia definitely work, but they don't seem to make the schizophrenia noticeably worse either.

Probably this will end the same way most things in psychiatry end – hopelessly bogged down in complexity. Probably AMPA does one thing in one part of the brain, the opposite in other parts of the brain, and it's all nonlinear and different amounts of AMPA will have totally different effects and maybe downregulate itself somewhere else.

---

[23] http://www.businesswire.com/news/home/20101001005605/en/Cortex-Regains-Rights-D evelop-AMPAKINE-Compounds-Treat

Still, it's neat to have at least a vague high-level overview of what *might* be going on.

20

Book Review: House of God

November 10, 2016

I

I'm not a big fan of war movies. I liked the first few I watched. It was all downhill from there. They all seem so similar. The Part Where You Bond With Your Squadmates. The Part Where Your Gruff Sergeant Turns Out To Have A Heart After All. The Part Where Your Friend Dies But You Have To Keep Going Anyway. The Part That Consists Of A Stirring Speech.

The problem is that war is very different from everything else, but very much like itself.

Medical internship is also very different from everything else but very much like itself. I already had two examples of it: *Scrubs* and my own experience as a medical intern (I preferred *Scrubs*). So when *every single person in the medical field* told me to read Samuel Shem's *House of God*[1], I deferred. I deferred throughout my own internship, I deferred for another two years of residency afterwards. And then for some reason I finally picked it up a couple of days ago.

This was a *heck* of a book.

On some level it was as predictable as I expected. It hit all of the Important Internship Tropes, like The Part Where Your Attendings Are Cruel, The Part Where Your Patient Dies Because Of Something You Did, The Part Where You Get Camaraderie With Other Interns, The Part Where You First Realize You Are Actually Slightly Competent At Like One Thing And It Is

---

[1] https://www.amazon.com/House-God-Samuel-Shem/dp/0425238091/ref=as_li_ss_tl?ie=UTF8&qid=1478831942&sr=8-1&keywords=house+of+god&linkCode=lll&tag=slastacod-20&linkId=7dc1de048dd8ea2fe16ba520a9f8234c

The Best Feeling In The Universe, The Part Where You Realize How Pointless 99% Of The Medical System Is, The Part Where You Have Sex With Hot Nurses, et cetera.

All I can say is that it was really well done. The whole thing had a touch of magical realism, which turns out to be exactly the right genre for a story about medicine. Real medicine is absolutely magical realist. It's a series of bizarre occurrences just on the edge of plausibility happening to incredibly strange people for life-and-death stakes, day after day after day, all within the context of the weirdest and most byzantine bureaucracy known to humankind.

Just in the past week, for example, I had to deal with an aboulomaniac patient – one with a pathological inability to make up his mind. He came to my clinic for treatment, but as soon as he saw me, he decided he didn't want treatment after all and left. The next day, he was back on my calendar – he'd decided he needed treatment after all – but when his appointment came around, he chanegd his mind and left again. This happened *five times in five days*. Every day he would phone in asking for an appointment. Every day I would give it to him. Every day he would leave a minute or two before it began. Unsure how to proceed, I sought out my attending. He ignored my questions, pulled me into a side office, took out his cell phone, and started playing me a video. It's a scene from his musical, *The Phantom Of The Psychiatric Unit*, which he's been forcing his interns to rehearse after rounds. I watched, horrified. It was weirdly good.

If I were to write a book about this kind of thing, people would criticize me for being unrealistic. The only way to get away with it is to pass it off as "a touch of magical realism", and this *The House of God* does to excellent effect.

The story revolves around an obvious author-insert character, Roy Basch MD, who starts his internship year at a hospital called the House of God (apparently a fictionalized version of Beth Israel Hospital in Boston). He goes in with expectations to provide useful medical care to people with serious diseases. Instead, he finds gomers:

> "Gomer is an acronym: Get Out of My Emergency Room. It's what you want to say when one's sent in from the nursing home at three A.M."
>
> "I think that's kind of crass," said Potts. "Some of us don't feel that way about old people."
>
> "You think I don't have a grandmother?" asked Fats indignantly. "I do, and she's the cutest dearest, most wonderful old lady. Her

matzoh balls float – you have to pin them down to eat them up. Under their force the soup levitates. We eat on ladders, scraping the food off the ceiling. I love…" The Fat Man had to stop, and dabbed the tears from his eyes, and then went on in a soft voice, "I love her very much."

I thought of my grandfather. I loved him too.

"But gomers are not just dear old people," said Fats. "Gomers are human beings who have lost what goes into being human beings. They want to die, and we will not let them. We're cruel to the gomers, by saving them, and they're cruel to us, by fighting tooth and nail against our trying to save them. They hurt us, we hurt them."

This is where the magical realism starts to come in:

Rokitansky was an old bassett. He'd been a college professor and had suffered a severe stroke. He lay on his bed, strapped down, IV's going in, catheter coming out. Motionless, paralyzed, eyes closed, breathing comfortably, perhaps dreaming of a bone, or a boy, or of a boy throwing a bone.

"Mr. Rokitansky, how are you doing?" I asked.

Without opening his eyes, after fifteen seconds, in a husky slurred growl from deep down in his smushed brain he said: PURRTY GUD.

Pleased, I asked, "Mr. Rokitansky, what date is it today?"

PURRTY GUD.

To all my questions, his answer was always the same. I felt sad. A professor, now a vegetable. Again I thought of my grandfather, and got a lump in my throat. Turning to Fats, I said, "This is too sad. He's going to die."

"No, he's not," said Fats. "He wants to, but he won't."

"He can't go on like this."

"Sure he can. Listen, Basch, there are a number of LAWS OF THE HOUSE OF GOD. LAW NUMBER ONE: GOMERS DON'T DIE."

"That's ridiculous. Of course they die."

"I've never seen it, in a whole year here," said Fats.

"They have to."

"They don't. They go on and on. Young people – like you and me – die, but not the gomers. Never seen it. Not once."

"Why not?"

"I don't know. Nobody knows. It's amazing. Maybe they get past it. It's pitiful. The worst."

Potts came in, looking puzzled and concerned. He wanted the Fat Man's help with Ina Goober. They left, and I turned back to Rokitansky. In the dim half-light I thought I saw tears trickling down the old man's cheeks. Shame swept over me. My stomach churned. Had he heard what we'd said?

"Mr. Rokitansky, are you crying?" I asked, and I waited, as the long seconds ticked away, my guilt moaning inside me.

PURRTY GUD.

"But did you hear what we said about gomers?"

PURRTY GUD.

Someone once said that the point of art is to be more real than reality. *The House Of God* is *way* more real than reality. Reality *wishes* it could be anywhere *close to* as real as *The House of God*. This is a world where young people – the kid just out of school, the blushing new mother – die. Even normal old people – your grandmother, your grandpa – can die. But the most decrepit, demented people, the ones for whom every moment of artificially-prolonged life is a gratuitous misery and you pray at every moment that God will just let them find some peace – somehow they never die. They come into the hospital, they go back out to nursing homes, a few weeks later they're back in the hospital, a few weeks later they're back in their nursing homes, but *they never die*. This *can't* be literally true. But it's the subjective truth of working in a hospital. The Fat Man is right. I've been working in medicine for three years now, and I have seen my share of young people tragically cut off in the prime of life, and yet as far as I can remember I have never seen a gomer die. The magical realism of *House of God* describes the reality of medical professionals infinitely better than the rational world of hospital mortality statistics.

In the world of *The House of God*, the primary form of medical treatment is the TURF – the excuse to get a patient out of your care and on to somebody else's. If the psychiatrist can't stand a certain patient any longer, she finds some trivial abnormality in their bloodwork and TURFs to the medical floor. But she knows that if the medical doctor doesn't want one of *his* patients, then he can interpret a trivial patient comment like "Being sick is so depressing" as suicidal ideation and TURF to psychiatry. At 3 AM on a Friday night, every patient is terrible, the urge to TURF is overwhelming, and a hospital starts to seem like a giant wheel uncoupled from the rest of the world, Psychiatry TURFING to Medicine TURFING to Surgery TURFING to Neurosurgery TURFING to Neurology TURFING back to Psychiatry again. Surely some treatment must get done somewhere? But where? It becomes a legend, The Place Where Treatment Happens, hidden in some far-off hospital wing accessible only to the pure-hearted. This sort of Kafkaesque picture is how medical care *feels*, and the genius of *The House of God* is that it accentuates the reality just a little bit until its fictional world is almost as magical-realist as the real one.

In the world of *The House of God*, medical intervention can only make patients worse:

> Anna O. had started out on Jo's service in perfect electrolyte balance, with each organ system working as perfectly as an 1878 model could. This, to my mind, included the brain, for wasn't dementia a fail-safe and soothing oblivion of the machine to its own decay?
>
> From being on the verge of a TURF back to the Hebrew House for the Incurables, as Anna knocked around the House of God in the steaming weeks of August, getting a skull film here and an LP there, she got worse, much worse. Given the stress of the dementia work-up, every organ system crumpled: in a domino progression the injection of radioactive dye for her brain scan shut down her kidneys, and the dye study of her kidneys overloaded her heart, and the medication for her heart made her vomit, which altered her electrolyte balance in a life-threatening way, which increased her dementia and shut down her bowel, which made her eligible for the bowel run, the cleanout for which dehydrated her and really shut down her tormented kidneys, which led to infection, the need for dialysis, and big-time complications of these big-time diseases. She and I both became exhausted, and she became very sick. Like the Yellow Man, she went through a

phase of convulsing like a hooked tuna, and then went through a phase that was even more awesome, lying in bed deathly still, perhaps dying. I felt sad, for by this time, I liked her. I didn't know what to do. I began to spend a good deal of time sitting with Anna, thinking.

The Fat Man was on call with me every third night as backup resident, and one night, searching for me to go to the ten o'clock meal, he found me with Anna, watching her trying to die.

"What the hell are you doing?" he asked.

I told him.

"Anna was on her way back to the Hebrew House, what happened – wait, don't tell me. Jo decided to go all-out on her dementia, right?"

"Right. She looks like she's going to die."

"The only way she'll die is if you murder her by doing what Jo says."

"Yeah, but how can I do otherwise, with Jo breathing down my neck?"

"Easy. Do nothing with Anna, and hide it from Jo."

"Hide it from Jo?"

"Sure. Continue the work-up in purely imaginary terms, buff the chart with the imaginary results of the imaginary tests, Anna will recover to her demented state, the work-up will show no treatable cause for it, and everybody's happy. Nothing to it."

"I'm not sure it's ethical."

"Is it ethical to murder this sweet gomer with your work-up?"

There was nothing I could say."

After learning these medical secrets, Dr. Basch uses hook and crook to prevent his patients from getting any treatment. They end up healthier than anyone else in the hospital, and Basch becomes a contender for "Most Valuable Intern" – in typical *House of God* style, nobody knows if this award really exists or is just a rumor. His colleagues compete for another award, the "Black Crow", which goes to the intern who gets the most autopsy consents from grieving families – and which the administration doesn't realize incentivizes doctors to kill their patients. This is so reminiscent of the bizarre incentive systems in real hospitals that it *hurts*.

But as the year goes on, everyone gets more and more frazzled. One intern has a mental breakdown. Another commits suicide by jumping out of a hospital window (this isn't dramatic exaggeration by the way; three junior doctors have committed suicide[2] by jumping out of windows in the past three years in New York City alone). Dr. Basch runs through all sorts of interesting forms of neurosis. Finally, the end of the year approaches, the original crop of interns thinned-out but triumphant – and then they realize they have to do the whole thing again next year as residents, which is maybe a little less grueling but still in the same ballpark.

So they decide, en masse, to go into psychiatry, well-known to be a rare non-terrible residency. The author of *House of God* is a psychiatrist, so I guess this is only a spoiler insofar as you aren't logically omniscient. When the Chief of Medicine learns that every single one of his hospital's interns are going into psychiatry and there aren't going to be any non-psychiatry residents in the whole hospital…

…okay, fine, I won't spoil the ending. But suffice it to say I'm feeling pretty good about my career path right now.

II

House of God does a weird form of figure-ground inversion.

An example of what I mean, taken from politics: some people think of government as another name for the things we do together, like providing food to the hungry, or ensuring that old people have the health care they need. These people know that some politicians are corrupt, and sometimes the money actually goes to whoever's best at demanding pork, and the regulations sometimes favor whichever giant corporation has the best lobbyists. But this is viewed as a weird disease of the body politic, something that can be abstracted away as noise in the system.

And then there are other people who think of government as a giant pork-distribution system, where *obviously* representatives and bureaucrats, incentivized in every way to support the forces that provide them with campaign funding and personal prestige, will take those incentives. *Obviously* they'll use the government to crush their enemies. Sometimes this system also involves

[2]https://www.idealmedicalcare.org/blog/three-young-doctors-jump-to-their-deaths-in-nyc/

the hungry getting food and the elderly getting medical care, as an epiphe-
nomenon of its pork-distribution role, but this isn't particularly important
and can be abstracted away as noise.

I think I can go back and forth between these two models when I need
to, but it's a weird switch of perspective, where the parts you view as noise in
one model resolve into the essence of the other and vice versa.

And *House of God* does this to medicine.

Doctors use certain assumptions, like:

1. The patient wants to get better, but there are scientific limits that usually
   make this impossible
2. Medical treatment makes people healthier
3. Treatment is determined by medical need and expertise

But in *House of God*, the assumptions get inverted:

1. The patient wants to just die peacefully, but there are bureaucratic limits
   that usually make this impossible
2. Medical treatment makes people sicker
3. Treatment is determined by what will make doctors look good without
   having to do much work

Everybody knows that those first three assumptions aren't always true.
Yes, sometimes we prolong life in contravention of patients' wishes. Sometimes people mistakenly receive unnecessary treatment that causes complica-
tions. And sometimes care suffers because of doctors' scheduling issues. But
it's easy to abstract away to an ideal medicine based on benevolence and reason, and then view everything else as rare and unfortunate deviations from
the norm. *House of God* goes the whole way and does a full figure-ground
inversion. The outliers become the norm; good care becomes the rare deviation. What's horrifying is how convincing it is. Real medicine looks *at least*
as much like the bizarro-world of *House of God* as it does the world of the
popular imagination where doctors are always wise, diagnoses always correct,
and patients always grateful.

There have been a couple of studies finding that giving people health insurance doesn't make them any healthier – see for example the RAND Health
Insurance Experiment[3] and the Oregon Medicaid Experiment[4]. I've always

---

[3]https://en.wikipedia.org/wiki/RAND_Health_Insurance_Experiment
[4]http://www.nejm.org/doi/full/10.1056/NEJMsa1212321#t=articleTop

been skeptical of these studies, because it seems logical that people who can afford health care will get more of it, and there are ten zillion studies showing various forms of health care to help. Insulin helps diabetes. Antibiotics help sepsis. Surgery helps appendicitis. To deny claims like these would be madness, yet the studies don't lie. What is going on?

And the answer has to be somewhere in the bizarro-world of *House of God*. Real medical treatment looks precious little like the House MD model of rare serious disease → diagnosis → cure. At least as often, it's like the *House of God* model where someone becomes inconvenient → send to hospital → one million unnecessary tests. Everyone agrees this is part of the story. *House of God* is a brilliant book in that it refactors perception to place it in the foreground.

But it's brilliant because in the end it's *not* just a romp through hilarious bureaucratic mishaps. There is as much genuine human goodness and compassion in this book as there is in any rousing speech by a medical school dean. The goodness is often mixed with horror – the doctor who has to fight off hordes of autopsy-consent-form-seekers to let a dying patient spend his last few seconds in peace, or the one who secretly slips euthanasia to a terminal patient begging for an end to the pain because he knows it's the right thing to do.

The question posed here is "what do you do in a crazy cannibalistic system where it's impossible to do good work and everyone is dying all around you?", and the answer is "try as hard as you can to preserve whatever virtue you can, and to remain compassionate and human". The protagonist swings wildly between "this is all bullshit and I'll just make fun of these disgusting old people and call it a day" and "I need to save everybody and if I don't I should hate myself forever", and eventually like everybody, comes to some kind of synthesis where he recognizes he's human, recognizes that his patients are human, and tries to deal with it with whatever humor and grace he can manage.

It's hard enough for a book to be funny, and it's hard enough for one to be deep, but a book like *House of God* that can be both at once within the space of a few sentences is an absolute treasure.

III

I talked to my father about *House of God*, and I told him a few parts that seemed unrealistic. He told me that those parts were 100% true in 1978 when the book was written. I looked into it more, and ended up appreciating the work on a whole new level. *Uncle Tom's Cabin* is credited with kickstarting the emancipationist movement and maybe even causing the Civil War[5]. *The Jungle* is famous for launching a whole new era of safety regulations. *House of God* has a place beside them in the pantheon of books that have changed the world.

The book's "Second Law" is "GOMER GOES TO GROUND": demented old people will inevitably fall out of their hospital bed and injure themselves. The book has a whole funny/horrifying scene where the senior resident explains his strategy for this eventuality: He leaves their beds low enough that patients won't kill themselves when they fall, but high enough that they'll probably break a bone or two and have to go to orthopaedic surgery – which takes them off his hands. Later, a medical student apes this procedure, a patient falls and breaks a bone or two, and everyone freaks out and tells him that it was a joke, that *of course* you don't really arrange skeletal fractures for old people just to save yourself time, what kind of heartless moron could *think* such a thing? This is some nth-level meta-humor: the reader probably mistook it for real advice because it meshes so seamlessly with all of the other madness and horror, yet most of the other madness and horror in the book is easily recognizable by practicing doctors as a real part of the medical system. Actually, on the n+1st meta-level, I'm not at all sure that the resident wasn't meant to be completely serious and then backtracked and called it a joke when it went wrong. For that matter, I'm far from sure this wasn't a real medical practice in the 1970s.

I see enough falls that I wasn't surprised to see them as a theme, but I thought the book exaggerated their omnipresence. My father said it didn't – there were just far more falls back in the Old Days. Now hospitals are safer and falls are comparatively rare. Why? Because the government passed a law saying that insurance wouldn't pay hospitals extra money for the extra days patients have to stay due to fall-related injuries. I am so serious about this. This, I think, is the n+2nd meta-level; amidst all its jokes-played-straight the book treats encouraging falls as an actual in-universe joke, and yet in the real world once hospitals were no longer incentivized to let patients fall the falls stopped.

How did people become aware of this kind of thing? How did the movement against it start? A lot of it seems to be because of *House of God*. Everyone in medicine knew about this sort of thing. But *House of God* made it common knowledge.

---

[5] https://www.harrietbeecherstowecenter.org/utc/impact.shtml

People were scared to speak up. Everyone thought that maybe they were just a uniquely bad person, or their hospital a uniquely bad institution. Anyone who raised some of these points was met with scorn by prestigious doctors who said that maybe they just weren't cut out for medicine. *House of God* shaped medicine because it was the first thing to say what everybody was experiencing. Its terms like "gomer" and "turf" made it into the medical lexicon because they pointed to obvious features of reality nobody had the guts to talk about before.

Shem writes an afterword where he talks about the reaction to the book. Junior doctors and the public loved it. Senior doctors hated it. He tells the story of going to a medical conference. Someone asked who he was, and he said jokingly "I'm the most hated doctor here". His interlocutor answered "Oh, don't worry, I'm sure you're not as bad as the guy who wrote that *House of God* book."

But *House of God* gets credit for helping start movements to cut intern work hours, protect doctors from sleep deprivation, reduce patient falls, and teach empathy and communication skills. The moral of the story is: the courage to tell the truth is rare and powerful. More specifically: the courage to tell the truth is rare and powerful not just in Stalinist dictatorships and violent cults, but in apparently normal parts of everyday First World life. All of these differently loaded terms like "culture of silence" and "political correctness" point at a fear of rocking various boats with nothing but your imperfect first-person knowledge to go on. But a tiny crack in the wall can make a big difference.

IV

In a closing scene, Dr. Basch and all of his fellow interns – interns who had broken into tears weekly, gotten burnt out, starting seeing psychiatrists, considered suicide, all this stuff, these interns who had smashed up against the unendurable horrors of medicine and held themselves together only by the promise that it would soon be over – the minute they graduate internship they change their tune:

> It looked like all but two or three [interns] would stay. The Runt and I were definitely leaving; Chuck hadn't yet said. The others were staying. In years to come they would spread out across America into academic centers and Fellowships, real red-hots in

internal medicine, for they had been trained at the Best Medical School's best House, the House of God. Although a few might kill themselves or get addicted or go crazy, by and large they'd repress and conform and perpetuate the Leggo [the Chief of Medicine] and the House and all the best medical stuff. [Eddie] had been praised by the Leggo that he could start off the second year as ward resident, with "a free rein" on his interns. And so, saying already that the internship been "not so bad," he was preparing to indoctrinate his new charges: "I want them on their knees from day one."

Shem's author mouthpiece character Berry says:

> It's been inhuman. No wonder doctors are so distant in the face of the most poignant human dramas. The tragedy isn't the crassness, but the lack of depth. Most people have some human reaction to their daily work, but doctors don't. It's an incredible paradox that being a doctor is so degrading and yet is so valued by society. In any community, the most respected group are doctors. [It's] a terrific repression that makes doctors really believe that they are omnipotent healers. If you hear yourselves saying, 'Well, this year wasn't really that bad,' you're repressing, to put the next group through it. [But] it's hard to say no. If you're programmed from age six to be a doctor, invest years in it, develop your repressive skills so that you can't even recall how miserable you were during internship, you can't stop.

Shem's thesis is that it isn't just about not wanting to make waves or offend the Chief of Medicine. It's about denying your own pain by identifying with the system.

This puts me in a weird spot. My internship (I find myself saying) wasn't so bad. I can give you some arguments why this might be true – things have gotten a lot better since *The House of God* was published (with no small credit to Shem himself), a small community hospital in Michigan is less intense than Harvard Medical School's training hospital, psychiatry interns sometimes have it easier than internal medicine interns since everyone knows this isn't a permanent deal for them.

And yet I distinctly remember one night a long time ago, coming home from high school. I had noticed that all of the adults around me said high school was some of the best years of their lives and I would miss it when I was gone, and yet high school seemed objectively terrible. I wondered if there might be some bias or bizarre shift in memory that happened sometime in people's twenties and gave them a localized amnesia or insanity. So I very distinctly recall telling myself "My current assessment is that high school is terrible, and if you ever find yourself remembering that high school was lovely, please be aware that your memories have been hijacked by some malevolent force."

And God help me, but *every single part of my brain is telling me that high school was lovely*. I fondly remember all the friends I made, the crazy teachers I had to put up with, the science competitions I won, the lunches spent in the library reading whatever random stuff I could get my hands on. It seems like it was a blast. It's hard for me to even trust that one memory as anything more than imagination or the product of a single bad day. But although high-school-me had a lot of issues, he generally had a decent head on his shoulders, and if he says my memories have been hijacked, then I grudgingly believe him.

So was my intern year a good learning experience? *I have no idea and I'm not sure anyone else does either.* It's another type of figure-ground inversion: parade of broken only by the occasional triumph, or clear sailing with a few bad moments?

On my last day of internship, one of my colleagues who was moving on said "I'm going to miss hating this place". I've always remembered that phrase. Now I wonder if it's some kind of weird snapshot of the exact moment of transition, the instant when "nightmarish ordeal" morphs into "halcyon days of youth". This is why medicine has to be written as magical realism. How else to capture a world where people reliably go from agony to Stockholm Syndrome in the space of a day, and where the transition is so intermixed with the general weirdness that it doesn't even merit special remark?

I found myself having more emotions reading *House of God* than I've had about anything in a long time. I don't really know why. But I think it has something to do with this resignation to the general incommunicable weird-ness all around anyone who works in medicine. Somehow Shem manages to avoid the normalization of insanity that happens to every young doctor, capture the exact subjective experience and write it down in a way that makes sense. And then, having put his finger right on the unbearable thing, he makes it funny and beautiful and poignant.

I tell her. Again I tell her about Dr. Sanders bleeding out in my lap, about the look in Potts's eyes that night before he jumped, about my pushing the KCl into poor Saul. I tell her how ashamed I am for turning into a sarcastic bastard who calls the old ones gomers, how, during the ternship, I'd ridiculed them for their weaknesses, for throwing up their suffering in my face, for scaring me, for forcing me to do disgusting things to take care of them. I tell her how I want to live, compassionately, with the idea of death clearly in sight, and how I doubt I can do that, ever again. As I think back to what I'd gone through and what I'd become, sadness wells up and mixes with contempt. I put my head into Berry's folds and weep, and curse, and shout, and weep.

"… and in your own way, you did. Someone had to care for the gomers; and this year, in your own way, you did."

"The worst thing is this bitterness. I used to be different, gentle, even generous, didn't I? I wasn't always like this, was I?"

"I love who you are. To me, underneath it all, you're still there:" She paused, and then, eyes sparkling, said, "And you might even be better."

"What? What do you mean?"

"This might have been the only thing that could have awakened you. Your whole life has been a growing from the outside, mastering the challenges that others have set for you. Now, finally, you might just be growing from inside yourself.

He also frames all of it in the language of psychoanalysis, which is jarring and sounds preachy. I've ordered the sequel, *Mount Misery*, about his training as a psychoanalyst. Expect a review of that soon.

21

SSC Journal Club: Expert Prediction Of Experiments

November 27, 2016

I

It's been a good month for fretting over failures of expert opinion, so let's look at DellaVigna & Pope, Predicting Experimental Results: Who Knows What?[1] The authors ran a pretty standard behavioral economics experiment where they asked people on Mechanical Turk to do a boring task while being graded on speed and accuracy. Then they offered one of fifteen different incentive schemes, like "we'll pay you extra if you do well" or "your score will be publicly visible".

But the point of the study wasn't to determine which incentive scheme worked the best, it would determine *who could best predict* which incentive scheme worked the best. The researchers surveyed a bunch of people – economics professors, psychology professors, PhD students, undergrads, business students, and random Internet users on Mechanical Turk – and asked them to predict the experimental results. Since this was a pretty standard sort of behavioral economics experiment, they were wondering whether people with expertise and knowledge in the field might be better than randos at figuring out which schemes would work.

They found that knowledgeable academics had some advantage over randos, but with enough caveats that it's worth going over in more detail.

First, they found that prestigious academics did no better (and possibly slightly worse) than less prestigious academics. Full professors did no better than associate professors, assistant professors, or PhD students. People

---

[1] http://eml.berkeley.edu/~sdellavi/wp/expertsJul16.pdf

with many publications and citations did no better than people with fewer publications and citations.

Second, they found that field didn't matter. Behavioral economists did as well as microeconomists did as well as experimental psychologists did as well as theoretical psychologists. To be fair, this experiment was kind of in the intersection of economics and psychology, so all of these fields had equal claim to it. I would have liked to see some geologists or political scientists involved, but they weren't.

Third, the expert advantage was present in one measure of accuracy (absolute forecast error), but not in another (rank-order correlation). On this second measure, experts and randos did about equally well. In other words, experts were better at guessing the exact number for each condition, but not any better at guessing which conditions would do better or worse relative to one another.

Fourth, the expert advantage was pretty small. Professors got an average error of 169, PhD students of 171, undergrads of 187, MBA students of 198, and MTurk users of 271 (random guessing gave an error of about 416). So the difference between undergrads and experts, although statistically significant, was hardly overwhelming.

Fifth, even the slightest use of "wisdom of crowds" was enough to overwhelm the expert advantage. A group of five undergrads averaged together had average error 115, again compared to individual experts' error of 169! Five undergrads averaged together (115) did about as well as five experts averaged together (114). Twenty undergrads averaged together (95) did about as well as twenty experts averaged together (99).

Sixth, having even a little knowledge of individuals' forecasting ability screened off expert status. The researchers gave forecasters some experimental data about the effects of a one-cent incentive and a ten-cent incentive, and asked them to predict the scores after a four-cent incentive – a simple, mechanical problem that just requires common sense. Randos who can do well on this problem do just as well as experts on the experiment as a whole. Likewise, randos who are noticed to do well on the first half of the experiment will do just as well as experts on the second half too. In other words, we're back to finding "superforecasters", people who are just consistently good at this kind of thing.

None of this seems to be too confounded by effort. The researchers are able to measure how much time people take on the task, whether they read the instructions carefully, etc. There is some advantage to not rushing through the task, but after that it doesn't seem to matter much. They also try offering some of the Mechanical Turkers lots of money for getting the answers right. That doesn't seem to help much either.

The researchers ask the experts to predict the results of this experiment. They (incorrectly) predict that prestigious academics with full professorships and lots of citations will do better than mere PhD students. They (incorrectly) predict that psychologists will do better than non-psychologists. They (correctly) predict that professors and PhD students will do better than undergrads and randos.

II

What do we make of this?

I would *tentatively* suggest it doesn't look like experts' expertise is helping them very much here. Part of this is that experts in three different fields did about equally well in predicting the experimental results. But this is only weak evidence; it could be that the necessary expertise is shared among those three fields, or that each field contains one helpful insight and someone who knew all three fields would do better than any of the single-field experts.

But more important, randos who are able to answer a very simple question, or who do well on other similar problems, do just as well as the experts. This suggests it's possible to get expert-level performance just by being clever, without any particular expertise.

So is it just IQ? This is a tempting explanation. The US average IQ is 100. The undergrads in this experiment came from Berkeley, and Berkeley undergrads have an average SAT of 1375 = average IQ of 133 (this seems really high, but apparently matches estimates from The Bell Curve[2] and the Brain Size blog[3] ; however, see Vaniver's point here[4]). That same Brain Size post proposes that the average professor has an IQ of 133, but I would expect psychology/economics professors to be higher, plus most of the people in this experiment were from really good schools. If we assume professors are 135-140, then this would neatly predict the differences seen from MTurkers to undergrads to professors.

---

[2] http://www.iqmindware.com/blog/the-bell-curve-cognitive-elites/

[3] https://brainsize.wordpress.com/2014/07/12/the-iqs-of-academic-elites/

[4] https://slatestarcodex.com/2016/11/27/ssc-journal-club-expert-prediction-of-expe riments/#comment-439115

But the MBA students *really* don't fit into this model. The experiment gets them from the University of Chicago Booth School of Business, which is the top business school in the country and has an average GMAT score of 740. That corresponds to an IQ of almost 150, meaning this should be the highest-IQ sample in the study, yet the MBAs do worse than the undergrads. Unless I'm missing something, this is fatal to an IQ-based explanation.

I think that, as in *Superforecasting*, the best explanation is a separate "rationality" skill which is somewhat predicted by high IQ and scientific training, but not identical to either of them. Although some scientific fields can help you learn the basics of thinking clearly, it doesn't matter what field you're in or whether you're in any field at all as long as you get there somehow.

I'm still confused by the MBA students, and expect to remain so. All MBA students were undergraduates once upon a time. Most of them probably took at least one economics class, which was where the researchers found and recruited their own undergraduates from. And most of them were probably top students from top institutions, given that they made it into the best business school in the US. So how come Berkeley undergraduates taking an econ class outperform people who *used to be* Berkeley undergraduates taking an econ class, but are now older and wiser and probably a little more selected? It might be that business school selects against the rationality skill, or it might be that business students learn some kind of anti-insight that systematically misleads them in these kinds of problems.

(note that the MBAs don't put in less effort than the other groups; if anything, the reverse pattern is found)

III

Does this relate to interesting real-world issues like people's trouble predicting this election?

One important caveat: this is all atheoretical. As far as I know, there's no theory of psychology or economics that should let people predict how the incentive experiment would go. So it's asking experts to use their intuition, supposedly primed by their expertise, to predict something they have no direct knowledge about. If the experiment were, say, physicists being asked to predict the speed of a falling object, or biologists being asked to predict how quickly a gene with a selective advantage would reach fixation, then we'd be in a very different position.

Another important caveat: predictive tasks are different than interpretative tasks. Ability to predict how an experiment will go without having any data differs from ability to crunch data in a complicated field and conclude that eg saturated fat causes/doesn't cause heart attacks. I worry that a study like this might be used to discredit eg nutritional experts, and to argue that they might not be any better at nutrition than smart laymen. Whether or not this is true, the study doesn't support it.

So one way of looking at it might be that this is a critique not of expertise, but of "punditry". Engineers are still great at building bridges, doctors are still great at curing cancer, physicists are still great at knowing physics – but if you ask someone to predict something vaguely related to their field that they haven't specifically developed and tested a theory to cope with, they won't perform too far above bright undergrads. I think this is an important distinction.

But let's also not get too complacent. The experts in this study clearly *thought* they would do better than PhD students. They *thought* that their professorships and studies and citations would help them. They were wrong. The distinction between punditry and expertise is pretty fuzzy. Had this study come out differently, I could have argued for placing nice clear lab experiments about incentive schemes in the "theory-based and amenable to expertise" category. You can spin a lot of things either direction.

I guess really the only conclusion you can draw from all of this is not to put any important decisions in the hands of people from top business schools[5].

---

[5] https://www.bostonglobe.com/news/nation/2015/08/28/donald-trump-was-bombastic-even-wharton-business-school/3F00j1uS5X6S8156yH3YhL/story.html

Book III

2017

22

Considerations On Cost Disease

February 9, 2017

I

Tyler Cowen writes about cost disease[1]. I'd previously heard the term used to refer only to a specific theory of why costs are increasing, involving labor becoming more efficient in some areas than others. Cowen seems to use it indiscriminately to refer to increasing costs in general – which I guess is fine, goodness knows we need a word for that.

Cowen assumes his readers already understand that cost disease exists. I don't know if this is true. My impression is that most people still don't know about cost disease, or don't realize the extent of it. So I thought I would make the case for the cost disease in the sectors Tyler mentions – health care and education – plus a couple more.

First let's look at primary education:

There was some argument about the style of this graph, but as per Politifact[2] the basic claim is true. Per student spending has increased about 2.5x in the past forty years even after adjusting for inflation.

At the same time, test scores have stayed relatively stagnant. You can see the full numbers here[3], but in short, high school students' reading scores went from 285 in 1971 to 287 today – a difference of 0.7%.

---

[1] https://www.bloomberg.com/view/articles/2017-01-18/this-economic-phenomenon-is-making-government-sick

[2] http://www.politifact.com/virginia/statements/2015/mar/02/dave-brat/brat-us-school-spending-375-percent-over-30-years-/

[3] http://nationsreportcard.gov/ltt_2012/summary.aspx

There is some heterogenity across races – white students' test scores increased 1.4% and minority students' scores by about 20%. But it is hard to credit school spending for the minority students' improvement, which occurred almost entirely during the period from 1975-1985. School spending has been on exactly the same trajectory before and after that time, and in white and minority areas, suggesting that there was something specific about that decade which improved minority (but not white) scores. Most likely this was the general improvement in minorities' conditions around that time, giving them better nutrition and a more stable family life. It's hard to construct a narrative where it was school spending that did it – and even if it did, note that the majority of the increase in school spending happened from 1985 on, and demonstrably helped neither whites *nor* minorities.

I discuss this phenomenon more here[4] and here[5], but the summary is: no, it's not just because of special ed; no, it's not just a factor of how you measure test scores; no, there's not a "ceiling effect". Costs really did more-or-less double without any concomitant increase in measurable quality.

So, imagine you're a poor person. White, minority, whatever. Which would you prefer? Sending your child to a 2016 school? Or sending your child to a 1975 school, and getting a check for $5,000 every year?

I'm proposing that choice because as far as I can tell that *is* the stakes here. 2016 schools have whatever tiny test score advantage they have over 1975 schools, and cost $5000/year more, inflation adjusted. That $5000 comes out of the pocket of somebody – either taxpayers, or other people who could be helped by government programs.

Second, college is even worse:

Note this is not adjusted for inflation; see link below for adjusted figures

Inflation-adjusted cost of a university education was something like $2000/year in 1980[6]. Now it's closer to $20,000/year. No, it's not because of decreased government funding[7], and there are similar trajectories for public and private schools.

I don't know if there's an equivalent of "test scores" measuring how well

---

[4] https://slatestarcodex.com/2016/12/02/contra-robinson-on-schooling/

[5] https://slatestarcodex.com/2016/12/04/highlights-from-the-comment-thread-on-school-choice/

[6] https://nces.ed.gov/programs/digest/d07/tables/dt07_320.asp

[7] http://www.nytimes.com/2015/04/05/opinion/sunday/the-real-reason-college-tuition-costs-so-much.html?_r=0

colleges perform, so just use your best judgment. Do you think that modern colleges provide $18,000/year greater value than colleges did in your parents' day? Would you rather graduate from a modern college, or graduate from a college more like the one your parents went to, plus get a check for $72,000?

(or, more realistically, have $72,000 less in student loans to pay off)

Was your parents' college even noticeably worse than yours? My parents sometimes talk about their college experience, and it seems to have had all the relevant features of a college experience. Clubs. Classes. Professors. Roommates. I might have gotten something extra for my $72,000, but it's hard to see what it was.

Third, health care. The graph is starting to look disappointingly familiar:

The cost of health care has about quintupled since 1970. It's actually been rising since earlier than that, but I can't find a good graph; it looks like it would have been about $1200 in today's dollars in 1960, for an increase of about 800% in those fifty years.

This has had the expected effects. The average 1960 worker spent ten days' worth of their yearly paycheck[8] on health insurance; the average modern worker spends sixty days' worth of it, a sixth of their entire earnings.

Or not.

This time I can't say with 100% certainty that all this extra spending has been for nothing. Life expectancy has gone way up since 1960:

Extra bonus conclusion: the Spanish flu was really bad

But a lot of people think that life expectancy depends on other things a lot more than healthcare spending. Sanitation, nutrition, quitting smoking, plus advances in health technology that don't involve spending more money. ACE inhibitors (invented in 1975) are great and probably increased lifespan a lot, but they cost $20 for a year's supply and replaced older drugs that cost about the same amount.

In terms of calculating how much lifespan gain healthcare spending has produced, we have a couple of options. Start with by country:

Countries like South Korea and Israel have about the same life expectancy as the US but pay about 25% of what we do. Some people use this to prove

---

[8] http://www.forbes.com/sites/chrisconover/2012/12/22/the-cost-of-health-care-195
8-vs-2012/#4785acf6590f

the superiority of centralized government health systems, although Random Critical Analysis[9] has an alternative perspective. In any case, it seems very possible to get the same improving life expectancies as the US without octupling health care spending.

The Netherlands increased their health budget by a lot around 2000, sparking a bunch of studies on whether that increased life expectancy or not. There's a good meta-analysis here[10], which lists six studies trying to calculate how much of the change in life expectancy was due to the large increases in health spending during this period. There's a broad range of estimates: 0.3%, 1.8%, 8.0%, 17.2%, 22.1%, 27.5% (I'm taking their numbers for men; the numbers for women are pretty similar). They also mention two studies that they did not officially include; one finding 0% effect and one finding 50% effect (I'm not sure why these studies weren't included). They add:

> In none of these studies is the issue of reverse causality addressed; sometimes it is not even mentioned. This implies that the effect of health care spending on mortality may be overestimated.

They say:

> Based on our review of empirical studies, we conclude that it is likely that increased health care spending has contributed to the recent increase in life expectancy in the Netherlands. Applying the estimates form published studies to the observed increase in health care spending in the Netherlands between 2000 and 2010 [of 40%] would imply that 0.3% to almost 50% of the increase in life expectancy may have been caused by increasing health care spending. An important reason for the wide range in such estimates is that they all include methodological problems highlighted in this paper. However, this wide range inicates that the counterfactual study by Meerding et al, which argued that 50% of the increase in life expectancy in the Netherlands since the 1950s can be attributed to medical care, can probably be interpreted as an upper bound.

---

[9] https://randomcriticalanalysis.wordpress.com/2016/11/06/us-life-expectancy-is-be low-naive-expectations-mostly-because-it-economically-outperforms/
[10] http://arno.uvt.nl/show.cgi?fid=130315

It's going to be completely irresponsible to try to apply this to the increase in health spending in the US over the past 50 years, since this is probably different at every margin and the US is not the Netherlands and the 1950s are not the 2010s. But if we irresponsibly take their median estimate and apply it to the current question, we get that increasing health spending in the US has been worth about one extra year of life expectancy. This study[11] attempts to directly estimate a GDP corresponds to an increase of 0.05 years life expectancy. That would suggest a slightly different number of 0.65 years life expectancy gained by healthcare spending since 1960)

If these numbers seem absurdly low, remember all of those[12] controlled experiments[13] where giving people insurance doesn't seem to make them much healthier in any meaningful way.

Or instead of slogging through the statistics, we can just ask the same question as before. Do you think the average poor or middle-class person would rather:

1. Get modern health care
2. Get the same amount of health care as their parents' generation, but with modern technology like ACE inhibitors, and also earn $8000 extra a year

Fourth, we see similar effects in infrastructure. The first New York City subway opened around 1900. Various sources list lengths from 10 to 20 miles and costs from $30 million to $60 million dollars – I think my sources are capturing it at different stages of construction with different numbers of extensions. In any case, it suggests costs of between $1.5 million to $6 million dollars/mile = $1-4 million per kilometer. That looks like it's about the inflation-adjusted equivalent of $100 million/kilometer today, though I'm very uncertain about that estimate. In contrast, Vox notes[14] that a new New York subway line being opened this year costs about $2.2 *billion* per kilometer, suggesting a cost increase of twenty times – although I'm very uncertain about this estimate.

---

[11] https://www.thieme-connect.com/products/ejournals/abstract/10.1055/s-0033-135401
3

[12] https://en.wikipedia.org/wiki/RAND_Health_Insurance_Experiment

[13] http://www.nejm.org/doi/full/10.1056/NEJMsa1212321#t=articleTop

[14] http://www.vox.com/policy-and-politics/2017/1/1/14112776/new-york-second-avenue-subway-phase-2

Things become clearer when you compare them country-by-country. The same Vox article notes that Paris, Berlin, and Copenhagen subways cost about $250 million per kilometer, almost 90% less. Yet even those European subways are overpriced compared to Korea[15], where a kilometer of subway in Seoul costs $40 million/km (another Korean subway project cost $80 million/km). This is a difference of 50x between Seoul and New York for apparently comparable services. It suggests that the 1900s New York estimate above may have been roughly accurate if their efficiency was roughly in line with that of modern Europe and Korea.

Fifth, housing (source[16]:

Most of the important commentary on this graph has already been said[17], but I would add that optimistic takes like this one[18] by the American Enterprise Institute are missing some of the dynamic. Yes, homes are bigger than they used to be, but part of that is zoning laws which make it easier to get big houses than small houses. There are a lot of people who would prefer to have a smaller house but don't. When I first moved to Michigan, I lived alone in a three bedroom house because there were no good one-bedroom houses available near my workplace and all of the apartments were loud and crime-y.

Or, once again, just ask yourself: do you think most poor and middle class people would rather:

1. Rent a modern house/apartment
2. Rent the sort of house/apartment their parents had, for half the cost

II

So, to summarize: in the past fifty years, education costs have doubled, college costs have dectupled, health insurance costs have dectupled, subway costs have at least dectupled, and housing costs have increased by about fifty percent. US health care costs about four times as much as equivalent health care in other First World countries; US subways cost about eight times as much as equivalent subways in other First World countries.

---

[15] https://pedestrianobservations.wordpress.com/2013/06/03/comparative-subway-construction-costs-revised/

[16] https://www.apartmentlist.com/rentonomics/rent-growth-since-1960/

[17] http://i0.wp.com/fmshooter.com/wp-content/uploads/2016/09/too-damn-high.jpg?resize=676%2C459

[18] http://www.aei.org/publication/todays-new-homes-are-1000-square-feet-larger-than-in-1973-and-the-living-space-per-person-has-doubled-over-last-40-years/

I worry that people don't appreciate how weird this is. I didn't appreciate it for a long time. I guess I just figured that Grandpa used to talk about how back in his day movie tickets only cost a nickel; that was just the way of the world. *But all of the numbers above are inflation-adjusted.* These things have dectupled in cost even *after* you adjust for movies costing a nickel in Grandpa's day. They have really, genuinely dectupled in cost, no economic trickery involved.

And this is especially strange because we expect that improving technology and globalization ought to cut costs. In 1983, the first mobile phone cost $4,000 – about $10,000 in today's dollars. It was also a gigantic piece of crap. Today you can get a much better phone for $100. This is the right and proper way of the universe. It's why we fund scientists, and pay businesspeople the big bucks.

But things like college and health care have *still* had their prices dectuple. Patients can now schedule their appointments online; doctors can send prescriptions through the fax, pharmacies can keep track of medication histories on centralized computer systems that interface with the cloud, nurses get automatic reminders when they're giving two drugs with a potential interaction, insurance companies accept payment through credit cards – and all of this costs ten times as much as it did in the days of punch cards and secretaries who did calculations by hand.

It's actually even worse than this, because we take so many opportunities to save money that were unavailable in past generations. Underpaid foreign nurses immigrate to America and work for a song. Doctors' notes are sent to India overnight where they're transcribed by sweatshop-style labor for pennies an hour. Medical equipment gets manufactured in goodness-only-knows which obscure Third World country. And it *still* costs ten times as much as when this was all made in the USA – and that back when minimum wages were proportionally higher than today.

And it's actually even worse than *this*. A lot of these services have decreased in quality, presumably as an attempt to cut costs even further. Doctors used to make house calls; even when I was young in the '80s my father would still go to the houses of difficult patients who were too sick to come to his office. This study[19] notes that for women who give birth in the hospital, "the standard length of stay was 8 to 14 days in the 1950s but declined to less than 2 days in the mid-1990s". The doctors I talk to say this isn't because

---

[19] http://epublications.marquette.edu/cgi/viewcontent.cgi?article=1017&context=nursing_fac

modern women are healthier, it's because they kick them out as soon as it's safe to free up beds for the next person. Historic records of hospital care generally describe leisurely convalescence periods and making sure somebody felt absolutely well before letting them go; this seems bizarre to anyone who has participated in a modern hospital, where the mantra is to kick people out as soon as they're "stable" ie not in acute crisis.

If we had to provide the same quality of service as we did in 1960, and without the gains from modern technology and globalization, who even *knows* how many times more health care would cost? Fifty times more? A hundred times more?

And the same is true for colleges and houses and subways and so on.

III

The existing literature on cost disease focuses on the Baumol effect[20]. Suppose in some underdeveloped economy, people can choose either to work in a factory or join an orchestra, and the salaries of factory workers and orchestra musicians reflect relative supply and demand and profit in those industries. Then the economy undergoes a technological revolution, and factories can produce ten times as many goods. Some of the increased productivity trickles down to factory workers, and they earn more money. Would-be musicians leave the orchestras behind to go work in the higher-paying factories, and the orchestras have to raise their prices if they want to be assured enough musicians. So tech improvements in the factory sectory raise prices in the orchestra sector.

We could tell a story like this to explain rising costs in education, health care, etc. If technology increases productivity for skilled laborers in other industries, then less susceptible industries might end up footing the bill since they have to pay their workers more.

There's only one problem: health care and education aren't paying their workers more; in fact, quite the opposite.

Here are teacher salaries over time (source[21]):

Teacher salaries are relatively flat adjusting for inflation. But salaries for other jobs are increasing modestly relative to inflation. So teacher salaries relative to other occupations' salaries are actually declining.

---

[20] https://en.wikipedia.org/wiki/Baumol%27s_cost_disease
[21] https://fiftyfivemillion.wordpress.com/2013/11/28/teacher-salaries-rose-in-the-8 0s-and-theyve-been-slipping-since/

Here's a similar graph for professors (source[22]):

Professor salaries are going up a little, but again, they're probably losing position relative to the average occupation. Also, note that although the average salary of each type of faculty is stable or increasing, the average salary of all faculty is going down. No mystery here – colleges are doing everything they can to switch from tenured professors to adjuncts, who complain of being overworked and abused[23] while making about the same amount as a Starbucks barista.

This seems to me a lot like the case of the hospitals cutting care for new mothers. The price of the service dectuples, yet at the same time the service has to sacrifice quality in order to control costs.

And speaking of hospitals, here's the graph for nurses (source[24]):

Female nurses' salaries went from about $55,000 in 1988 to $63,000 in 2013. This is probably around the average wage increase during that time. Also, some of this reflects changes in education[25]: in the 1980s only 40% of nurses had a degree; by 2010, about 80% did.

And for doctors (source[26])

Stable again! Except that a lot of doctors' salaries now go to paying off their medical school debt, which has been ballooning like everything eles.

I don't have a similar graph for subway workers, but come on. The overall pictures is that health care and education costs have managed to increase by ten times without a single cent of the gains going to teachers, doctors, or nurses. Indeed these professions seem to have lost ground salary-wise relative to others.

I also want to add some anecdote to these hard facts. My father is a doctor and my mother is a teacher, so I got to hear a lot about how these professions have changed over the past generation. It seems at least a little like the adjunct story, although without the clearly defined "professor vs. adjunct" dichotomy that makes it so easy to talk about. Doctors are really, really, *really* unhappy. When I went to medical school, some of my professors would tell me outright that they couldn't believe anyone would still go into medicine with all

---

[22] http://highereddatastories.blogspot.com/2014/07/changes-in-faculty-salaries-over-time.html

[23] http://www.latimes.com/opinion/op-ed/la-oe-allen-adjunct-professors-20131222-story.html

[24] http://jamanetwork.com/journals/jama/fullarticle/2208795

[25] http://www.aacn.nche.edu/media-relations/fact-sheets/nursing-fact-sheet

[26] http://thelastpsychiatrist.com/2010/10/why_do_doctors_accept_gifts.html

of the new stresses and demands placed on doctors. This doesn't seem to be limited to one medical school. *Wall Street Journal*: Why Doctors Are Sick Of Their Profession[27] – "American physicians are increasingly unhappy with their once-vaunted profession, and that malaise is bad for their patients". *The Daily Beast*: How Being A Doctor Became The Most Miserable Profession[28] – "Being a doctor has become a miserable and humiliating undertaking. Indeed, many doctors feel that America has declared war on physicians". *Forbes*: Why Are Doctors So Unhappy?[29] – "Doctors have become like everyone else: insecure, discontent and scared about the future." *Vox*: Only Six Percent Of Doctors Are Happy With Their Jobs[30]. *Al Jazeera America*: Here's Why Nine Out Of Ten Doctors Wouldn't Recommend Medicine As A Profession[31]. Read these articles and they all say the same thing that all the doctors I know say – medicine used to be a well-respected, enjoyable profession where you could give patients good care and feel self-actualized. Now it kind of sucks.

Meanwhile, I also see articles like this piece from NPR[32] saying teachers are experiencing historic stress levels and up to 50% say their job "isn't worth it". Teacher job satisfaction is at historic lows[33]. And the veteran teachers I know say the same thing as the veteran doctors I know – their jobs used to be enjoyable and make them feel like they were making a difference; now they feel overworked, unappreciated, and trapped in mountains of paperwork.

It might make sense for these fields to become more expensive if their employees' salaries were increasing. And it might make sense for salaries to stay the same if employees instead benefitted from lower workloads and better working conditions. But neither of these are happening.

---

[27] https://www.wsj.com/articles/the-u-s-s-ailing-medical-system-a-doctors-perspective-1409325361

[28] http://www.thedailybeast.com/articles/2014/04/14/how-being-a-doctor-became-the-most-miserable-profession.html

[29] http://www.forbes.com/sites/johngoodman/2014/09/11/why-are-doctors-so-unhappy/#766d4f2e1565

[30] http://www.vox.com/2014/9/8/6110839/doctors-low-morale-doctored-sandeep-jauhar

[31] http://america.aljazeera.com/watch/shows/america-tonight/articles/2014/7/9/here-s-why-9-outof10doctorswouldntrecommendmedicineasaprofession.html

[32] http://www.npr.org/sections/ed/2016/12/30/505432203/teachers-are-stressed-and-that-should-stress-us-all

[33] https://www.metlife.com/assets/cao/contributions/foundation/american-teacher/MetLife-Teacher-Survey-2011.pdf

IV

So what's going on? Why *are* costs increasing so dramatically? Some possible answers:

First, can we dismiss all of this as an illusion? Maybe adjusting for inflation is harder than I think. Inflation is an average, so some things have to have higher-than-average inflation; maybe it's education, health care, etc. Or maybe my sources have the wrong statistics.

But I don't think this is true. The last time I talked about this problem, someone mentioned they're running a private school which does just as well as public schools but costs only $3000/student/year, a fourth of the usual rate. Marginal Revolution notes that[34] India has a private health system that delivers the same quality of care as its public system for a quarter of the cost. Whenever the same drug is provided by the official US health system and some kind of grey market supplement sort of thing, the grey market supplement costs between a fifth and a tenth as much; for example, Google's first hit for Deplin®, official prescription L-methylfolate, costs $175 for a month's supply[35] ; unregulated L-methylfolate supplement delivers the same dose for about $30[36]. And this isn't even mentioning things like the $1 bag of saline that costs $700 at hospitals[37]. Since it seems like it's not too hard to do things for a fraction of what we currently do things for, probably we should be less reluctant to believe that the cost of everything is really inflated.

Second, might markets just not work? I know this is kind of an extreme question to ask in a post on economics, but maybe nobody knows what they're doing in a lot of these fields and people can just increase costs and not suffer any decreased demand because of it. Suppose that people proved beyond a shadow of a doubt that Khan Academy could teach you just as much as a normal college education, but for free. People would still ask questions like – will employers accept my Khan Academy degree? Will it look good on a resume? Will people make fun of me for it? The same is true of community colleges, second-tier colleges, for-profit colleges, et cetera. I got offered a free scholarship to a mediocre state college, and I turned it down on the grounds

---

[34] http://marginalrevolution.com/marginalrevolution/2016/12/private-versus-public-health-care-india.html

[35] https://www.healthwarehouse.com/deplin-15-mg-capsules-16381.html

[36] https://www.amazon.com/Metabolic-Maintenance-MTHF-Capsules-Count/dp/B005FMZ6WA/ref=sr_1_1_a_it?ie=UTF8&qid=1485577393&sr=8-1&keywords=L-methylfolate+10+mg

[37] https://www.advisory.com/daily-briefing/2013/08/27/the-secret-of-salines-cost-why-a-1-bag-can-cost-700

that I knew nothing about anything and maybe years from now I would be locked out of some sort of Exciting Opportunity because my college wasn't prestigious enough. Assuming everyone thinks like this, can colleges just charge whatever they want?

Likewise, my workplace offered me three different health insurance plans, and I chose the middle-expensiveness one, on the grounds that I had no idea how health insurance worked but maybe if I bought the cheap one I'd get sick and regret my choice, and maybe if I bought the expensive one I *wouldn't* be sick and regret my choice. I am a doctor, my employer is a hospital, and the health insurance was for treatment in my own health system. The moral of the story is that I am an idiot. The second moral of the story is that people probably are not super-informed health care consumers.

This can't be pure price-gouging, since corporate profits haven't increased nearly enough to be where all the money is going. But a while ago a commenter linked me to the Delta Cost Project[38], which scrutinizes the exact causes of increasing college tuition. Some of it is the administrative bloat that you would expect. But a lot of it is fun "student life" types of activities like clubs, festivals, and paying Milo Yiannopoulos to speak and then cleaning up after the ensuing riots. These sorts of things improve the student experience, but I'm not sure that the average student would rather go to an expensive college with clubs/festivals/Milo than a cheap college without them. More important, it doesn't really seem like the average student is offered this choice.

This kind of suggests a picture where colleges expect people will pay whatever price they set, so they set a very high price and then use the money for cool things and increasing their own prestige. Or maybe clubs/festivals/Milo become such a signal of prestige that students avoid colleges that don't comply since they worry their degrees won't be respected? Some people have pointed out that hospitals have switched from many-people-all-in-a-big-ward to private rooms. Once again, nobody seems to have been offered the choice between expensive hospitals with private rooms versus cheap hospitals with roommates. It's almost as if industries have their own reasons for switching to more-bells-and-whistles services that people don't necessarily want, and consumers just go along with it because for some reason they're not exercising choice the same as they would in other markets.

(this article on the Oklahoma City Surgery Center[39] might be about a

---

[38] http://www.deltacostproject.org/

[39] http://reason.com/blog/2017/01/27/what-happens-when-doctors-only-take-cash

partial corrective for this kind of thing)

Third, can we attribute this to the inefficiency of government relative to private industry? I don't think so. The government handles most primary education and subways, and has its hand in health care. But we know that for-profit hospitals aren't much cheaper than government hospitals, and that private schools usually aren't much cheaper (and are sometimes more expensive) than government schools. And private colleges cost more than government-funded ones.

Fourth, can we attribute it to indirect government intervention through regulation, which public and private companies alike must deal with? This seems to be at least part of the story in health care, given how much money you can save by grey-market practices that avoid the FDA. It's harder to apply it to colleges, though some people have pointed out regulations like Title IX that affect the educational sector.

One factor that seems to speak out against this is that starting with Reagan in 1980, and picking up steam with Gingrich in 1994, we got an increasing presence of Republicans in government who declared war on over-regulation – but the cost disease proceeded unabated. This is suspicious, but in fairness to the Republicans, they did sort of fail miserably at deregulating things. "The literal number of pages in the regulatory code" is kind of a blunt instrument, but it doesn't exactly inspire confidence in the Republicans' deregulation efforts:

Here's a more interesting (and more fun) argument against regulations being to blame: what about pet health care? Veterinary care is much less regulated than human health care, yet its cost is rising as fast (or faster) than that of the human medical system (popular article[40], study[41]). I'm not sure what to make of this.

Fifth, might the increased regulatory complexity happen not through literal regulations, but through fear of lawsuits? That is, might institutions add extra layers of administration and expense not because they're *forced* to, but because they fear being sued if they don't and then something goes wrong?

I see this all the time in medicine. A patient goes to the hospital with a heart attack. While he's recovering, he tells his doctor that he's really upset about all of this. Any normal person would say "You had a heart attack, of course you're upset, get over it." But if his doctor says this, and then a

---

[40]http://www.slate.com/blogs/moneybox/2016/09/27/the_cost_of_pet_health_care_could_be_rising_faster_than_the_cost_of_human.html

[41]http://www.nber.org/papers/w22669

year later he commits suicide for some unrelated reason, his family can sue the doctor for "not picking up the warning signs" and win several million dollars. So now the doctor consults a psychiatrist, who does an hour-long evaluation, charges the insurance company $500, and determines using her immense clinical expertise that the patient is upset because he just had a heart attack.

Those outside the field have *no idea* how much of medicine is built on this principle. People often say that[42] the importance of lawsuits to medical cost increases is overrated because malpractice insurance doesn't cost that much, but the situation above would never look lawsuit-related; the whole thing only works because everyone involved documents it as well-justified psychiatric consult to investigate depression. Apparently some studies[43] suggest this isn't happening, but all they do is survey doctors, and with all due respect all the doctors *I* know say the opposite.

This has nothing to do with government regulations (except insofar as these make lawsuits easier or harder), but it sure can drive cost increases, and it might apply to fields outside medicine as well.

Sixth, might we have changed our level of risk tolerance? That is, might increased caution be due not purely to lawsuitphobia, but to really caring more about whether or not people are protected? I read stuff every so often about how playgrounds are becoming obsolete because nobody wants to let kids run around unsupervised on something with sharp edges. Suppose that one in 10,000 kids get a horrible playground-related injury. Is it worth making playgrounds cost twice as much and be half as fun in order to decrease that number to one in 100,000? This isn't a rhetorical question; I think different people can have legitimately different opinions here (though there are probably some utilitarian things we can do to improve them).

To bring back the lawsuit point, some of this probably relates to a difference between personal versus institutional risk tolerance. Every so often, an elderly person getting up to walk to the bathroom will fall and break their hip. This is a fact of life, and elderly people deal with it every day. Most elderly people I know don't spend thousands of dollars fall-proofing the route from their bed to their bathroom, or hiring people to watch them at every moment to make sure they don't fall, or buy a bedside commode to make bathroom-related falls impossible. This suggests a revealed preference that

---

[42] http://www.huffingtonpost.com/david-belk/medical-malpractice-costs_b_4171189.htm
l

[43] http://jamanetwork.com/journals/jamainternalmedicine/fullarticle/1904758

elderly people are willing to tolerate a certain fall probability in order to save money and convenience. Hospitals, which face huge lawsuits if any elderly person falls on the premises, are *not* willing to tolerate that probability. They put rails on elderly people's beds, place alarms on them that will go off if the elderly person tries to leave the bed without permission, and hire patient care assistants who among other things go around carefully holding elderly people upright as they walk to the bathroom (this job will soon require at least a master's degree). As more things become institutionalized and the level of acceptable institutional risk tolerance becomes lower, this could shift the cost-risk tradeoff even if there isn't a population-level trend towards more risk-aversion.

Seventh, might things cost more for the people who pay because so many people don't pay? This is somewhat true of colleges, where an increasing number of people are getting in on scholarships funded by the tuition of non-scholarship students. I haven't been able to find great statistics on this, but one argument against: couldn't a college just not fund scholarships, and offer much lower prices to its paying students? I get that scholarships are good and altruistic, but it would be surprising if every single college thought of its role as an altruistic institution, and cared about it more than they cared about providing the same service at a better price. I guess this is related to my confusion about why more people don't open up colleges. Maybe this is the "smart people are rightly too scared and confused to go to for-profit colleges, and there's not enough ability to discriminate between the good and the bad ones to make it worthwhile to found a good one" thing again.

This also applies in health care. Our hospital (and every other hospital in the country) has some "frequent flier" patients who overdose on meth at least once a week. They comes in, get treated for their meth overdose (we can't legally turn away emergency cases), get advised to get help for their meth addiction (without the slightest expectation that they will take our advice) and then get discharged. Most of them are poor and have no insurance, but each admission costs a couple of thousand dollars. The cost gets paid by a combination of taxpayers and other hospital patients with good insurance who get big markups on their own bills.

Eighth, might total compensation be increasing even though wages aren't? There definitely seems to be a pensions crisis, especially in a lot of government work, and it's possible that some of this is going to pay the pensions of teachers, etc. My understanding is that in general pensions aren't really incrcasing much faster than wages[44], but this might not be true in those specific industries. Also, this might pass the buck to the question of why we need to spend more on pensions now than in the past. I don't think increasing life expectancy explains all of this, but I might be wrong.

IV

I mentioned politics briefly above, but they probably deserve more space here. Libertarian-minded people keep talking about how there's too much red tape and the economy is being throttled. And less libertarian-minded people keep interpreting it as not caring about the poor, or not understanding that government has an important role in a civilized society, or as a "dog whistle" for racism, or whatever. I don't know why more people don't just come out and say "LOOK, REALLY OUR MAIN PROBLEM IS THAT ALL THE MOST IMPORTANT THINGS COST TEN TIMES AS MUCH AS THEY USED TO FOR NO REASON, PLUS THEY SEEM TO BE GOING DOWN IN QUALITY, AND NOBODY KNOWS WHY, AND WE'RE MOSTLY JUST DESPERATELY FLAILING AROUND LOOKING FOR SOLUTIONS HERE." State that clearly, and a lot of political debates take on a different light.

For example: some people promote free universal college education, remembering a time when it was easy for middle class people to afford college if they wanted it. Other people oppose the policy, remembering a time when people didn't depend on government handouts. Both are true! My uncle paid for his tuition at a really good college just by working a pretty easy summer job – not so hard when college cost a tenth of what it did now. The modern conflict between opponents and proponents of free college education is over how to distribute our losses. In the old days, we could combine low taxes with widely available education. Now we can't, and we have to argue about which value to sacrifice.

Or: some people get upset about teachers' unions, saying they must be sucking the "dynamism" out of education because of increasing costs. Others people fiercely defend them, saying teachers are underpaid and overworked. Once again, in the context of cost disease, both are obviously true. The taxpayers are just trying to protect their right to get education as cheaply as they used to. The teachers are trying to protect their right to make as much money

---

[44]http://www.epi.org/blog/professor-hubbards-claim-about-wage-and-compensation-stagnation-is-not-true/

as they used to. The conflict between the taxpayers and the teachers' unions is about how to distribute losses; *somebody* is going to have to be worse off than they were a generation ago, so who should it be?

And the same is true to greater or lesser degrees in the various debates over health care, public housing, et cetera.

Imagine if tomorrow, the price of water dectupled. Suddenly people have to choose between drinking and washing dishes. Activists argue that taking a shower is a basic human right, and grumpy talk show hosts point out that in *their* day, parents taught their children not to waste water. A coalition promotes laws ensuring government-subsidized free water for poor families; a Fox News investigative report shows that some people receiving water on the government dime are taking long luxurious showers. Everyone gets really angry and there's lots of talk about basic compassion and personal responsibility and whatever but all of this is secondary to *why does water costs ten times what it used to?* I think this is the basic intuition behind so many people, even those who genuinely want to help the poor, are afraid of "tax and spend" policies. In the context of cost disease, these look like industries constantly doubling, tripling, or dectupling their price, and the government saying "Okay, fine," and increasing taxes however much it costs to pay for whatever they're demanding now.

If we give everyone free college education, that solves a big social problem. It also locks in a price which is ten times too high for no reason. This isn't fair to the government, which has to pay ten times more than it should. It's not fair to the poor people, who have to face the stigma of accepting handouts for something they could easily have afforded themselves if it was at its proper price. And it's not fair to future generations if colleges take this opportunity to increase the cost by *twenty* times, and then our children have to subsidize *that*.

I'm not sure how many people currently opposed to paying for free health care, or free college, or whatever, would be happy to pay for health care that cost less, that was less wasteful and more efficient, and whose price we expected to go down rather than up with every passing year. I expect it would be a lot.

And if it isn't, who cares? The people who want to help the poor have enough political capital to spend eg $500 billion on Medicaid; if that were to go ten times further, then everyone could get the health care they need without any more political action needed. If some government program found a way to give poor people good health insurance for a few hundred dollars a year, college tuition for about a thousand, and housing for only two-thirds what it costs now, that would be the greatest anti-poverty advance in history. That program is called "having things be as efficient as they were a few decades ago".

V

In 1930, economist John Maynard Keynes predicted[45] that his grandchildrens' generation would have a 15 hour work week. At the time, it made sense. GDP was rising so quickly that anyone who could draw a line on a graph could tell that our generation would be four or five times richer than his. And the average middle-class person in his generation felt like they were doing pretty well and had most of what they needed. Why *wouldn't* they decide to take some time off and settle for a lifestyle merely twice as luxurious as Keynes' own?

Keynes was sort of right. GDP per capita *is* 4-5x greater today than in his time. Yet we still work forty hour weeks, and some large-but-inconsistently-reported percent of Americans (76[46] ? 55[47]? 47[48]?) still live paycheck to paycheck.

And yes, part of this is because inequality is increasing and most of the gains are going to the rich[49]. But this alone wouldn't be a disaster; we'd get to Keynes' utopia a little slower than we might otherwise, but eventually we'd get there. Most gains going to the rich means at least some gains are going to the poor. And at least there's a lot of mainstream awareness of the problem.

I'm more worried about the part where the cost of basic human needs goes up faster than wages do. Even if you're making twice as much money, if your health care and education and so on cost ten times as much, you're going to start falling behind. Right now the standard of living isn't just stagnant, it's at risk of declining[50], and a lot of that is student loans and health insurance costs and so on.

---

[45] https://www.theguardian.com/business/2008/sep/01/economics

[46] http://money.cnn.com/2013/06/24/pf/emergency-savings/

[47] https://20somethingfinance.com/percentage-of-americans-living-paycheck-to-paycheck/

[48] http://www.prnewswire.com/news-releases/nearly-half-of-americans-live-paycheck-to-paycheck-300256166.html

[49] http://www.motherjones.com/politics/2011/02/income-inequality-in-america-chart-graph

[50] http://www.businessinsider.com/younger-generations-are-worse-off-today-urban-institute-study-2013-3

What's happening? I don't know and I find it really scary.

23

Book Review: Behavior: The Control Of Perception

March 6, 2017

Epistemic status: I only partly understood this book and am trying to review it anyway as best I can.

I

People complain that psychology is paradigmless; it never got its Darwin or Newton to tie everything together. Nowadays people are pretty relaxed about that; who needs paradigms when you can do n = 50 studies on a mildly interesting effect? But historically, there were all of these larger-than-life figures who were sure they'd found the paradigm, geniuses who founded schools which flourished for a while, made big promises, then either fizzled out or toned down their claims enough to be accepted as slightly kooky parts of the mainstream. Sigmund Freud. BF Skinner. Carl Rogers. And those are just the big ones close to the mainstream. Everyone from Ayn Rand to Scientology tried their hand at the paradigm-inventing business for a while.

Will Powers (whose name turns out to be pretty appropriate) lands somewhere in the middle of this pack. He was an engineer/inventor who specialized in cybernetic systems but wandered into psychology sometime in the sixties. He argued that everything in the brain made perfect sense if you understood cybernetic principles, and came up with a very complicated but all-encompassing idea called Perceptual Control Theory which explained thought, sensation and behavior. A few people paid attention, and his work was described as paradigm-shifting by no less of an expert on paradigm shifts than Thomas Kuhn. But in the end it never really went anywhere, psychology moved on, and nowadays only a handful of people continue research in his tradition.

Somehow I kept running into this handful, and they kept telling me to read Powers' book *Behavior: The Control Of Perception*[1], and I keep avoiding it. A few weeks ago I was driving down the road and I had a moment of introspection where I realized everything I was doing exactly fit Powers' theory, so I decided to give it a chance.

Powers specializes in *control systems*. The classic control system is a thermostat, which controls temperature. It has a reference point, let's say 70 degrees. If it gets much below 70 degrees, it turns on the heater until it's 70 again; if it gets much above 70 degrees, it turns on the air conditioner until it's 70 again. This is more complicated than it sounds, and there are other control systems that are even more complicated, but that's the principle. Perceptual Control Theory says that this kind of system is the basic unit of the human brain.

While I was driving on the highway a few weeks ago, I realized how much of what I do *is* perceptual control. For example, I was effortlessly maintaining the right distance from the car in front of me. If the car sped up a tiny bit, I would speed up a tiny bit. If the car slowed down a little bit, I would slow down a little bit. Likewise, I was maintaining the right angle relative to the road: if I found myself veering right, I would turn slightly to the left; if I found myself veering left, I would turn slightly to the right.

The theory goes further: while I'm in the car, I'm also operating as my own thermostat. I have a desired temperature: if I go below it, I'll turn on the heat, and if I go above it, I'll turn on the AC. I have a desired level of satiety: if I'm hungry, I'll stop and get something to eat; if I'm too full, there's maybe not a *huge* amount I can do but I'll at least stop eating. I have a desired level of light: if it's too dark, I'll turn on the lights; if it's too bright I'll put down the sun visor. I even have a desired angle to be sitting at: if I'm too far forward, I'll relax and lean back a little bit; if I'm too far back, I'll move forwards. All of this is so easy and automatic that I never think about it.

Powers' theories go further. He agrees that my brain sets up a control system to keep my car the proper distance from the car in front of it. But how do I determine "the proper distance"? That quantity must be fed to the system by other parts of my brain. For example, suppose that the roads are icy and I know my brakes don't work very well in the ice; I might keep a much further distance than usual. I'll still be controlling the distance, I'll just be controlling

[1] https://www.amazon.com/Behavior-Perception-William-T-Powers/dp/0964712172/ref=as_li_ss_tl?_encoding=UTF8&me=&linkCode=lll&tag=slatestarcode-20&linkId=0fcd11259a05e96dfe2390ea67fc9ecb

it *differently*. If the brain is control systems all the way down, we can imagine a higher-tier system controlling "accident risk" at some level (presumably low, or zero) feeding a distance level into a lower-tier system controlling car distance at whatever level it receives. We can even imagine higher systems than this. Suppose I'm depressed, I've become suicidal, I want to die in a car accident, but in order not to scandalize my family I have to let the accident happen sort of naturally. I have a top-level system controlling "desire to die" which tells a middle-level system controlling "accident risk" what level it should go at (high), which in turn tells a lower-tier system controlling "car distance" what level *it* should go at (very close).

It doesn't even end there. My system controlling "car distance" is sending signals to a lower-tier system controlling muscle tension on my foot on the accelerator, giving it a new reference level (contracted muscles that push down on the accelerator really hard). Except this is an oversimplification, because everything that has to do with muscles is a million times more complicated than any reasonable person would think (at least until they play qwop[2]) and so there's actually a big hierarchy of control systems just going from "want to go faster" to "successfully tense accelerator-related muscles".

II

Actually, Powers is at his most convincing when he talks about these lower-level functions. At this point I think it's pretty[3] mainstream[4] to say that muscle tension is set by a control system, with the Golgi tendon organs giving feedback and the spinal cord doing the calculations. Powers goes further (and I don't know how mainstream this next part is, but I'm guessing at least somewhat), saying that this is a first-tier control system, which is itself controlled by a second-tier "direction" control system centered in the nuclei of the brainstem, which is itself controlled by a third-tier "position" control system centered in the cerebellum/thalamus/midbrain (a friendly amendment might add the basal ganglia, which Powers doesn't seem to know much about).

If you stimulate certain parts of a cat's midbrain, it will go into specific positions – for example, a position like it's ready to pounce. So it seems like

---

[2] https://www.foddy.net/Athletics.html

[3] http://physio.northwestern.edu/docs/Houk/HoukRymer81.pdf

[4] https://books.google.com/books?id=P0ZxDQAAQBAJ&pg=PA527&lpg=PA527&dq=muscle+tension+control+system&source=bl&ots=eUCdkfj0ny&sig=Vb46q3LJ4XZqhWhqy5XeDBdKckk&hl=en&sa=X&ved=0ahUKEwilzcy3ksPSAhXG54MKHSqSC9IQ6AEIezAJ#v=onepage&q=muscle%20tension%20control%20system&f=false

those areas "code for" position. But in order to have a neuron/area/whatever that codes for position, it needs to have hierarchical control over lots of lower-level things. For example, it needs to make sure the leg muscles are however tense they're supposed to be in a pouncing position. So the third-tier position control system controls the second-tier direction control system at whatever level is necessary to make the second-tier direction control system control the first-tier muscle control system at whatever level is necessary to get the muscles in the right position.

The fourth- and fifth-tier systems, now well into the cortex (and maybe basal ganglia again) deal with sequences, eg "walking" or "playing a certain tune on the piano". Once again, activating a fourth/fifth-tier system will activate this higher-level concept ("walking"), which alters the reference levels for a third-tier system ("getting into a certain position"), which alters a second-tier system ("moving in a certain direction"), which alterns a first-tier system ("tensing/relaxing muscles").

Why do I like this theory so much? First, it correctly notes that (almost) the only thing the brain can actually *do* is change muscle tension. Yet we never think in terms of muscle tension. We don't think "I am going to tense my thigh muscle, now untense it, now tense my ankle muscle, now...", we just think "I'm going to walk". Heck, half the time we don't even think *that*, we think "I'm just going to go to the fridge" and the walking happens automatically. On the other hand, if we really want, we *can* consciously change our position, the level of tension in a certain muscle, etc. It's just that usually we deal in higher-level abstractions that automatically carry all the lower ones along with them.

Second, it explains the structure of the brain in a way I haven't seen other things do. I always hear neuroscientists talk about "this nucleus relays signals to that nucleus" or "this structure is a way station for this other structure". Spend too much time reading that kind of stuff, and you start to think of the brain as a giant relay race, where the medulla passes signals onto the thalamus which passes it to the basal ganglia which passes it to the frontal lobe and then, suddenly, thought! The obvious question there is "why do you have so many structures that just relay things to other structures?" Sometimes neuroscientists will say "Well, some processing gets done here", or even better "Well, this system modulates[5] that system", but they're always very vague on what exactly that means. Powers' hierarchy of fifth-tier systems passing their

---

[5]http://slatestarscratchpad.tumblr.com/post/147756899701/also-neuroscience-madli bs-is-modulates

calculations on to fourth-tier systems and so on is exactly the sort of thing that would make sense of all this relaying. My guess is every theory of neuroscience has something at least this smart, but I'd never heard it explained this well before.

Third, it's the clearest explanation of tremors I've ever heard. Consider the thermostat above. When the temperature gets below 65, it turns on the heat until the temperature gets above 70, then stops, then waits as the hot air leaks out through the window or whatever and it's 65 again, then turns on the heat again. If we chart temperature in a room with a thermostat, it will look sort of like a sine wave or zigzag with regular up/down motions. This is a basic principle of anything being controlled by a less-than-perfect control system. Our body has microtremors all the time, but when we get brain damage or some other problem, a very common symptom is noticeable tremors. These come in many different varieties that give clues to the level of brain damage and which doctors are just told to memorize. Powers actually explains them:

> When first-order systems become unstable, as when muscles exert too much effort), clonus oscillations are seen, at roughly ten cycles per second. Second-order instability, as in the tremors of Parkinsonism, involves groups of muscles and is of lower frequency, around three cycles per second or so. Third-order instability is slower stilll, slow enough that it can be characterized as "purpose tremor" or "over-correction". Certain cerebellar damage due to injury or disease can result in over- and undershooting the mark during actions such as reaching out to grasp something, either in a continuous self-sustained oscillation or a slowly decrasing series of alternating movements.

This isn't perfect – for example, Parkinsonian tremor is usually caused by damage to the basal ganglia and the cortex, which is really hard to square with Powers' claim that it's caused by damage to second-tier systems in the medulla. But after reading this, it's really hard not to think of tremors as failures in control systems, or of the different types of tremor as failures in different levels of control system. For example, athetoid tremors[6] are weird, seemingly purposeful, constant twisting movements caused by problems in the thalamus or some related system; after reading Powers, it's impossible for me not to think of them as failures in third-order control systems. This

---

[6]https://en.wikipedia.org/wiki/Athetosis

becomes especially clear if we compare to Powers' constant foil/nemesis, the Behaviorists. Stick to a stimulus-response paradigm, and there's no reason damaged brains should make weird twisting movements all the time. On a control-systems paradigm, it's *obvious* that that would happen.

There are occasional claims that perceptual control theory can predict certain things about muscles and coordination better than other theories, sometimes with absurdly high accuracy of like r = 0.9 or something. Powers makes some of these claims in the book, but I can't check them because I don't have the original data he worked with and I don't know how to calculate cybernetic control system outputs. But the last time I saw someone bring up one of these supposed experiments it was thoroughly shot down[7] by people who knew more statistics. And I found a blog post where somebody who knows a lot about intricacies of muscle movement says PCT can predict some things but not much better than competing theories[8]. In terms of predicting very specific things about human muscular movement its record seems to be kind of so-so.

III

And I start to get very skeptical when Powers moves to higher-tier control systems. His sixth tier is "relationships", seventh is "programs", eighth is "principles", and ninth is "systems". Although these tiers receive just as many pages as the earlier ones, they start sounding very abstract and they correlate a lot less well with anatomy. I understand the urge to postulate them – if you've already decided that the fundamental unit of the brain is the control system, why not try to explain things with control systems all the way up? – but it becomes kind of a stretch. It's easy to see what it means to control the distance between me and the car in front of me; it's harder to see what it means to control for "communism" or "honesty" or things like that.

I *think* the way things are supposed to work is like this. A ninth-tier system controls a very abstract concept like "communism". So suppose you are a communist; that means your internal communism-thermostat is set to maintain your communism at a high level. That propagates down to eighth-tier principles, which are slightly less abstract concepts like "greed"; maybe your ninth-tier communism-thermostat sets your eighth-tier greed thermostat to a

---

[7] https://www.greaterwrong.com/lw/14v/the_usefulness_of_correlations/11iu/

[8] http://psychsciencenotes.blogspot.com/2016/01/a-quick-review-and-analysis-of.html

very low temperature because communists aren't supposed to be greedy. Your eighth-tier greed thermostat affects levels of seventh-tier logical programs like "going to work and earning money" and "giving to charity". I'm not really sure how the sixth-tier fits into this example, but let's suppose that your work is hammering things. Then the fifth-tier system moves your muscles in the right sequence to hammer things, and so on with all the lower tiers as above.

Sometimes these control systems come into contact with each other. For example, suppose that along with my ninth-tier system controlling "communism", I also have a ninth-tier system controlling "family values"; I am both an avowed communist and a family man. My family values system thinks that it's important that I earn enough to provide for my family, so while my communism-system is trying to input a low reference level for my greed-thermostat, my family-values-system is trying to input a high one. Powers gets into some really interesting examples of what happens in real industrial cybernetic systems when two opposing high-level control systems get in a fight, and thinks this is the source of all human neurosis and akrasia. I think he later wrote a self-help book based around this (hence the nominative determinism). I am not very convinced.

Am I strawmanning this picture? I'm not sure. I think one testable consequence of it is supposed to be that if we're really controlling for communism, in the cybernetic control system sense, then we should be able to test for that. For example, hide Lenin's pen and paper so that he can't write communist pamphlets, and he should start doing some other communist thing more in order to make up for it and keep his level of communism constant. I think some perceptual control theory people believe this is literally true, and propose experimental tests (or at least thought experiment tests) of perceptual control theory along these lines. This seems sketchy to me, on the grounds that if Lenin didn't start doing other stuff, we could just say that communism wasn't truly what he was controlling.

That is, suppose I notice Lenin eating lots of chocolate every day. I theorize that he's controlling for chocolate, and so if I disturb the control system by eg shutting down his local chocolate store, he'll find a way to restore equilibrium, eg by walking further to a different store. But actually, when I shut down his local chocolate store, he just eats less chocolate. In reality, he was controlling his food intake (as we all do; that's what an obesity set point[9] is) and when he lost access to chocolate, maybe he ate cupcakes instead and did

---

[9]http://journals.plos.org/plosone/article?id=10.1371/journal.pone.0139462

fine.

In the same way, maybe we only think Lenin is controlling for communism, but he's actually controlling for social status, and being a communist revolutionary is a good way to gain social status. So if we make it too hard for him to be a communist revolutionary, eg by taking away his pen and paper, maybe he'll become a rock star instead and end up with the same level of social status.

This sort of thing seems so universal that as far as I can tell it makes these ideas of higher-tier control systems unproveable and unfalsifiable.

If there's any point to them at all, I think it's the way they express the same interesting phenomenological truth as the muscle movement tiers: we switch effortlessly between concentrating on low-level concepts and high-level concepts that make the low-level ones automatic. For example, I think "driving" is a good example of Powers' seventh tier, "programs" – it involves a predictable flowchart-like set of actions to achieve a simple goal. "The distance between me and the car in front of me" is a sixth-tier system, a "relationship". When I'm driving (focusing on my seventh-tier system), I don't consciously think at all about maintaining the right distance with the car in front of me. It just happens. This is really interesting in a philosophy of consciousness sense, and Powers actually gets into qualia a bit and says some things that seem a lot wiser and more moving-part-ful than most people on the subject.

It does seem like there's something going on where my decision to drive activates a lot of carefully-trained subsystems that handle the rest of it automatically, and that there's probably some neural correlate to it. But I don't know whether control systems are the right way to think about this, and I definitely don't know whether there's a sense in which "communism" is a control system.

IV

There are also some sections about things like learning and memory, which looks suspiciously like flowcharts of control systems with boxes marked "LEARNING" and "MEMORY" in them.

But I realized halfway through that I was being too harsh. Perceptual control theory wasn't quite a proposal for a new paradigm out of nowhere. It was a reaction to Behaviorism, which was still the dominant paradigm when Powers was writing. His "everything is a control system" is an attempt to improve on "everything is stimulus-response", and it really does.

For example, his theory of learning involves reward and punishment, where reward is reducing the error in a control system and punishment is increasing it. That is, suppose that you're controlling temperature, and it's too hot out. A refreshing cool glass of water would be an effective reward (since it brings you closer to your temperature reference level), and setting your hand on fire would be an effective punishment (since it brings you further from your temperature reference level). Powers notes that this explains many things Behaviorism can't. For example, they like to talk about how sugar water is a reward. But eventually rats get tired of sugar water and stop drinking it. So it seems that sugar water isn't a reward per se; it's more like reducing error in your how-much-sugar-water-should-I-have-and-did-I-already-have-the-right-amount system is the reward. If your optimal level of sugar water per day is 10 ml, then anything up to 10 ml will be a reward, and after that it will stop being attractive / start being a punishment.

As a "theory of learning", this is sort of crappy, in that I was expecting stuff about Hebb and connectionism and how memories are stored in the brain. But if you're living in an era where everybody thinks "The response to a stimulus is predictable through patterns of reward and punishment" is an A+++ Nobel-Prize-worthy learning theory, then perceptual control-based theories of learning start sounding pretty good.

So I guess it's important to see this as a product of its times. And I don't understand those times – why Behaviorism ever seemed attractive is a mystery to me, maybe requiring more backwards-reading[10] than I can manage right now.

How useful is this book? I guess that depends on how metaphorical you want to be. Is the brain a control system? I don't know. Are police a control system trying to control crime? Are police a "response" to the "stimulus" of crime? Is a stimulus-response pairing a control system controlling for the quantity of always making sure the stimulus has the response? I think it's interesting and helpful to think of some psychological functions with these metaphors. But I'm not sure where to go from there. I think maybe there are some obvious parallels, maybe even parallels that bear fruit in empirical results, in lower level systems like motor control. Once you get to high-level systems like communism or social desirability, I'm not sure we're doing much better than the police as control-system metaphor. Still, I think that it's potentially a useful concept to have.

---

[10]https://slatestarcodex.com/2013/04/11/read-history-of-philosophy-backwards/

24

Book Review: Seeing Like A State

March 16, 2017

I

Seeing Like A State[1] is the book G.K. Chesterton would have written if he had gone into economic history instead of literature. Since he didn't, James Scott had to write it a century later. The wait was worth it.

Scott starts with the story of "scientific forestry" in 18th century Prussia. Enlightenment rationalists noticed that peasants were just cutting down whatever trees happened to grow in the forests, *like a chump*. They came up with a better idea: clear all the forests and replace them by planting identical copies of Norway spruce (the highest-lumber-yield-per-unit-time tree) in an evenly-spaced rectangular grid. Then you could just walk in with an axe one day and chop down like a zillion trees an hour and have more timber than you could possibly ever want.

This went poorly. The impoverished ecosystem couldn't support the game animals and medicinal herbs that sustained the surrounding peasant villages, and they suffered an economic collapse. The endless rows of identical trees were a perfect breeding ground for plant diseases and forest fires. And the complex ecological processes that sustained the soil stopped working, so after a generation the Norway spruces grew stunted and malnourished. Yet for some reason, everyone involved got promoted, and "scientific forestry" spread across Europe and the world.

---

[1] https://www.amazon.com/Seeing-like-State-Certain-Condition/dp/0300078153/ref=a s_li_ss_tl?ie=UTF8&qid=1489636888&sr=8-1&keywords=seeing+like+a+state&linkCode=ll 1&tag=slatestarcode-20&linkId=198e8051cd9d4c8c0cf118b6fd16f751

And this pattern repeats with suspicious regularity across history, not just in biological systems but also in social ones.

Natural organically-evolved cities tend to be densely-packed mixtures of dark alleys, tiny shops, and overcrowded streets. Modern scientific rationalists came up with a better idea: an evenly-spaced rectangular grid of identical giant Brutalist apartment buildings separated by wide boulevards, with everything separated into carefully-zoned districts. Yet for some reason, whenever these new rational cities were built, people hated them and did everything they could to move out into more organic suburbs. And again, for some reason the urban planners got promoted, became famous, and spread their destructive techniques around the world.

Ye olde organically-evolved peasant villages tended to be complicated confusions of everybody trying to raise fifty different crops at the same time on awkwardly shaped cramped parcels of land. Modern scientific rationalists came up with a better idea: giant collective mechanized farms growing purpose-bred high-yield crops and arranged in (say it with me) evenly-spaced rectangular grids. Yet for some reason, these giant collective farms had lower yields per acre than the old traditional methods, and wherever they arose famine and mass starvation followed. And again, for some reason governments continued to push the more "modern" methods, whether it was socialist collectives in the USSR, big agricultural corporations in the US, or sprawling banana plantations in the Third World.

Traditional lifestyles of many East African natives were nomadic, involving slash-and-burn agriculture in complicated jungle terrain according to a bewildering variety of ad-hoc rules. Modern scientific rationalists in African governments (both colonial and independent) came up with a better idea – resettlement of the natives into villages, where they could have modern amenities like schools, wells, electricity, and evenly-spaced rectangular grids. Yet for some reason, these villages kept failing: their crops died, their economies collapsed, and their native inhabitants disappeared back into the jungle. And again, for some reason the African governments kept trying to bring the natives back and make them stay, even if they had to blur the lines between villages and concentration camps to make it work.

A favorite *Seeing Like A State* image: a comparison of street maps for Bruges (a premodern organic city) with Chicago (a modern planned city)

Why did all of these schemes fail? And more importantly, why were they celebrated, rewarded, and continued, even when the fact of their failure became too obvious to ignore? Scott gives a two part answer.

The first part of the story is High Modernism, an aesthetic taste masquerading as a scientific philosophy. The High Modernists claimed to be about figuring out the most efficient and high-tech way of doing things, but most of them knew little relevant math or science and were basically just LARPing being rational by placing things in evenly-spaced rectangular grids.

But the High Modernists were pawns in service of a deeper motive: the centralized state wanted the world to be "legible", ie arranged in a way that made it easy to monitor and control. An intact forest might be more productive than an evenly-spaced rectangular grid of Norway spruce, but it was harder to legislate rules for, or assess taxes on.

The state promoted the High Modernists' platitudes about The Greater Good as cover, in order to implement the totalitarian schemes they wanted to implement anyway. The resulting experiments were usually failures by the humanitarian goals of the Modernists, but resounding successes by the command-and-control goals of the state. And so we gradually transitioned from systems that were messy but full of fine-tuned hidden order, to ones that were barely-functional but really easy to tax.

II

Suppose you're a premodern king, maybe one of the Louises who ruled France in the Middle Ages. You want to tax people to raise money for a Crusade or something. Practically everyone in your kingdom is a peasant, and all the peasants produce is grain, so you'll tax them in grain. Shouldn't be too hard, right? You'll just measure how many pints of grain everyone produces, and…

> The pint in eighteenth-century Paris was equivalent to 0.93 liters, whereas in Seine-en-Montane it was 1.99 liters and in Precy-sous-Thil, an astounding 3.33 liters. The aune, a measure of length used for cloth, varied depending on the material(the unit for silk, for instance, was smaller than that for linen) and across France there were at least seventeen different aunes.

Okay, this is stupid. Just give everybody evenly-sized baskets, and tell them that baskets are the new unit of measurement.

> Virtually everywhere in early modern Europe were endless micropolitics about how baskets might be adjusted through wear,

bulging, tricks of weaving, moisture, the thickness of the rim, and so on. In some areas the local standards for the bushel and other units of measurement were kept in metallic form and placed in the care of a trusted official or else literally carved into the stone of a church or the town hall. Nor did it end there. How the grain was to be poured (from shoulder height, which packed it somewhat, or from waist height?), how damp it could be, whether the container could be shaken down, and finally, if and how it was to be leveled off when full were subjects of long and bitter controversy.

Huh, this medieval king business is harder than you thought. Maybe you can just leave this problem to the feudal lords?

Thus far, this account of local measurement practices risks giving the impression that, although local conceptions of distance, area, volume, and so on were different from and more varied than the unitary abstract standards a state might favor, they were nevertheless aiming at objective accuracy. This impression would be false. [...]

A good part of the politics of measurement sprang from what a contemporary economist might call the "stickiness" of feudal rents. Noble and clerical claimants often found it difficult to increase feudal dues directly; the levels set for various charges were the result of long struggle, and even a small increase above the customary level was viewed as a threatening breach of tradition. Adjusting the measure, however, represented a roundabout way of achieving the same end.

The local lord might, for example, lend grain to peasants in smaller baskets and insist on repayment in larger baskets. He might surreptitiously or even boldly enlarge the size of the grain sacks accepted for milling (a monopoly of the domain lord) and reduce the size of the sacks used for measuring out flour; he might also collect feudal dues in larger baskets and pay wages in kind in smaller baskets. While the formal custom governing feudal dues and wages would thus remain intact (requiring, for example, the same number of sacks of wheat from the harvest of a given holding), the actual transaction might increasingly favor the lord. The results of such fiddling were far from trivial.

Kula estimates that the size of the bushel (boisseau) used to collect the main feudal rent (taille) increased by one-third between
1674 and 1716 as part of what was called the reaction feodale.

Okay, but nobody's going to make *too* big a deal about this, right?

This sense of victimization [over changing units of measure] was
evident in the cahiers of grievances prepared for the meeting of
the Estates General just before the Revolution. [...] In an un-
precedented revolutionary context where an entirely new political system was being created from first principles, it was surely
no great matter to legislate uniform weights and measures. As
the revolutionary decree read "The centuries old dream of the
masses of only one just measure has come true! The Revolution
has given the people the meter!"

Okay, so apparently (you think to yourself as you are being led to the
guillotine), it was a big deal after all.

Maybe you *shouldn't* have taxed grain. Maybe you should tax land. After
all, it's the land that grows the grain. Just figure out how much land everybody
owns, and you can calculate some kind of appropriate tax from there.

So, uh, peasant villagers, how much land does each of you own?

A hypothetical case of customary land tenure practices may help
demonstrate how difficult it is to assimilate such practices to the
barebones scheme of a modern cadastral map [land survey suitable for tax assessment] [...]

Let us imagine a community in which families have usufruct
rights to parcels of cropland during the main growing season.
Only certain crops, however, may be planted, and every seven
years the usufruct land is distributed among resident families
according to each family's size and its number of able-bodied
adults. After the harvest of the main-season crop, all cropland
reverts to common land where any family may glean, graze their
fowl and livestock, and even plant quickly maturing, dry-season
crops. Rights to graze fowl and livestock on pasture-land held in
common by the village is extended to all local families, but the
number of animals that can be grazed is restricted according to

family size, especially in dry years when forage is scarce. Families not using their grazing rights can give them to other villagers but not to outsiders. Everyone has the right to gather firewood for normal family needs, and the village blacksmith and baker are given larger allotments. No commercial sale from village woodlands is permitted.

Trees that have been planted and any fruit they may bear are the property of the family who planted them, no matter where they are now growing. Fruit fallen from such tree, however, is the property of anyone who gathers it. When a family fells one of its trees or a tree is felled by a storm, the trunk belongs to the family, the branches to the immediate neighbors, and the "tops" (leaves and twigs) to any poorer villager who carries them off. Land is set aside for use or leasing out by widows with children and dependents of conscripted males. Usufruct rights to land and trees may be let to anyone in the village; the only time they may be let to someone outside the village is if no one in the community wishes to claim them. After a crop failure leading to a food shortage, many of these arrangements are readjusted.

You know what? I'm just going to put you all down as owning ten. Ten land. Everyone okay with that? Cool. Let's say ten land for everyone and just move on to the next village.

Novoselok village had a varied economy of cultivation, grazing, and forestry... the complex welter of strips was designed to ensure that each village household received a strip of land in every ecological zone. An individual household might have as many as ten to fifteen different plots constituting something of a representative sample of the village's ecological zones and microclimates. The distribution spread a family's risks prudently, and from time to time the land was reshuffled as families grew or shrunk... The strips of land were generally straight and parallel so that a readjustment could be made by moving small stakes along just one side of a field, without having to think of areal dimensions. Where the other side of the field was not parallel, the stakes could be shifted to compensate for the fact that the strip lay toward the narrower or wider end of the field. Irregular fields were divided, not according to area, but according to yield.

…huh. Maybe this isn't going to work. Let's try it the other way around. Instead of mapping land, we can just get a list with the name of everyone in the village, and go from there.

> Only wealthy aristocrats tended to have fixed surnames… Imagine the dilemma of a tithe or capitation-tax collector [in England] faced with a male population, 90% of whom bore just six Christian names (John, William, Thomas, Robert, Richard, and Henry).

Okay, fine. That won't work either. Surely there's *something* else we can do to assess a tax burden on each estate. Think outside the box, scrape the bottom of the barrel!

> The door-and-window tax established in France [in the 18th century] is a striking case in point. Its originator must have reasoned that the number of windows and doors in a dwelling was proportional to the dwelling's size. Thus a tax assessor need not enter the house or measure it, but merely count the doors and windows.
>
> As a simple, workable formula, it was a brilliant stroke, but it was not without consequences. Peasant dwellings were subsequently designed or renovated with the formula in mind so as to have as few openings as possible. While the fiscal losses could be recouped by raising the tax per opening, the long-term effects on the health of the population lasted for more than a century.

Close enough.

III

The moral of the story is: premodern states had very limited ability to tax their citizens effectively. Along with the problems mentioned above – nonstandardized measurement, nonstandardized property rights, nonstandardized personal names – we can add a few others. At this point national languages were a cruel fiction; local "dialects" could be as different from one another as eg Spanish is from Portuguese, so villagers might not even be able to *understand* the tax collectors. Worst of all, there was no such thing as a census in France until the 17th century, so there wasn't even a good idea of how many people or villages there were.

Kings usually solved this problem by leaving the tax collection up to local lords, who presumably knew the idiosyncracies of their own domains. But one step wasn't always enough. If the King only knew Dukes, and the Dukes only knew Barons, and the Barons only knew village headmen, and it was only the village headmen who actually knew anything about the peasants, then you needed a four-step chain to get any taxes. Each link in the chain had an incentive to collect as much as they could and give up as little as they could get away with. So on the one end, the peasants were paying backbreaking punitive taxes. And on the other, the Royal Treasurer was handing the King half a loaf of moldy bread and saying "Here you go, Sire, apparently this is all the grain in France."

So from the beginning, kings had an incentive to make the country "legible" – that is, so organized and well-indexed that it was easy to know everything about everyone and collect/double-check taxes. Also from the beginning, nobles had an incentive to frustrate the kings so that they wouldn't be out of a job. And commoners, who figured that anything which made it easier for the State to tax them and interfere in their affairs was bad news, usually resisted too.

Scott doesn't bring this up, but it's interesting reading this in the context of Biblical history. It would seem that whoever wrote the Bible was not a big fan of censuses. From 1 Chronicles 21[2]:

> Satan rose up against Israel and caused David to take a census of the people of Israel. So David said to Joab and the commanders of the army, "Take a census of all the people of Israel—from Beersheba in the south to Dan in the north—and bring me a report so I may know how many there are."
>
> But Joab replied, "May the Lord increase the number of his people a hundred times over! But why, my lord the king, do you want to do this? Are they not all your servants? Why must you cause Israel to sin?"
>
> But the king insisted that they take the census, so Joab traveled throughout all Israel to count the people. Then he returned to

[2]https://www.biblegateway.com/passage/?search=1%20Chronicles%2021:1-16&version=NLT

Jerusalem and reported the number of people to David. There were 1,100,000 warriors in all Israel who could handle a sword, and 470,000 in Judah. But Joab did not include the tribes of Levi and Benjamin in the census because he was so distressed at what the king had made him do.

God was very displeased with the census, and he punished Israel for it. Then David said to God, "I have sinned greatly by taking this census. Please forgive my guilt for doing this foolish thing." Then the Lord spoke to Gad, David's seer. This was the message: "Go and say to David, 'This is what the Lord says: I will give you three choices. Choose one of these punishments, and I will inflict it on you.'"

So Gad came to David and said, "These are the choices the Lord has given you. You may choose three years of famine, three months of destruction by the sword of your enemies, or three days of severe plague as the angel of the Lord brings devastation throughout the land of Israel. Decide what answer I should give the Lord who sent me."

"I'm in a desperate situation!" David replied to Gad. "But let me fall into the hands of the Lord, for his mercy is very great. Do not let me fall into human hands."

So the Lord sent a plague upon Israel, and 70,000 people died as a result.

(related: Scott examined some of the same data about Holocaust survival rates as *Eichmann In Jerusalem*[3], but made them make a lot more sense: the greater the legibility of the state, the worse for the Jews. One reason Jewish survival in the Netherlands was so low was because the Netherlands had a very accurate census of how many Jews there were and where they lived; sometimes officials saved Jews by literally burning census records).

Centralized government projects promoting legibility have always been a two-steps-forward, one-step back sort of thing. The government very gradually expands its reach near the capital where its power is strongest, to peasants whom it knows will try to thwart it as soon as its back is turned, and then if its decrees survive it pushes outward toward the hinterlands.

---

[3] https://slatestarcodex.com/2017/01/30/book-review-eichmann-in-jerusalem/

Scott describes the spread of surnames. Peasants didn't like permanent surnames. Their own system was quite reasonable for them: John the baker was John Baker, John the blacksmith was John Smith, John who lived under the hill was John Underhill, John who was really short was John Short. The same person might be John Smith and John Underhill in different contexts, where his status as a blacksmith or place of origin was more important.

But the government insisted on giving everyone a single permanent name, unique for the village, and tracking who was in the same family as whom. Resistance was intense:

> What evidence we have suggests that second names of any kind became rare as distance from the state's fiscal reach increased. Whereas one-third of the households in Florence declared a second name, the proportion dropped to one-fifth for secondary towns and to one-tenth in the countryside. It was not until the seventeenth century that family names crystallized in the most remote and poorest areas of Tuscany – the areas that would have had the least contact with officialdom. [...]
>
> State naming practices, like state mapping practices, were inevitably associated with taxes (labor, military service, grain, revenue) and hence aroused popular resistance. The great English peasant rising of 1381 (often called the Wat Tyler Rebellion) is attributed to an unprecedented decade of registration and assessments of poll taxes. For English as well as for Tuscan peasants, a census of all adult males could not but appear ominous, if not ruinous.

The same issues repeated themselves a few hundred years later when Europe started colonizing other continents. Again they encountered a population with naming systems they found unclear and unsuitable to taxation. But since colonial states had more control over their subjects than the relatively weak feudal monarchies of the Middle Ages, they were able to deal with it in one fell swoop, sometimes comically so:

> Nowhere is this better illustrated than in the Philippines under the Spanish. Filipinos were instructed by the decree of November 21, 1849 to take on permanent Hispanic surnames. [...]
>
> Each local official was to be given a supply of surnames sufficient for his jurisdiction, "taking care that the distribution be made by

letters of the alphabet." In practice, each town was given a number of pages from the alphabetized [catalog], producing whole towns with surnames beginning with the same letter. In situations where there has been little in-migration in the past 150 years, the traces of this administrative exercise are still perfectly visible across the landscape. "For example, in the Bikol region, the entire alphabet is laid out like a garland over the provinces of Albay, Sorsogon, and Catanduanes which in 1849 belonged to the single jurisdiction of Albay. Beginning with A at the provincial capital, the letters B and C mark the towns along the cost beyond Tabaco to Wiki. We return and trace along the coast of Sorosgon the letters E to L, then starting down the Iraya Valley at Daraga with M, we stop with S to Polangui and Libon, and finish the alphabet with a quick tour around the island of Catanduas.

The confusion for which the decree is the antidote is largely that of the administrator and the tax collector. Universal last names, they believe, will facilitate the administration of justice, finance, and public order as well as make it simpler for prospective marriage partners to calculate their degree of consanguinity. For a utilitarian state builder of [Governor] Claveria's temper, however, the ultimate goal was a complete and legible list of subjects and taxpayers.

This was actually a lot less cute and funny than the alphabetization makes it sound:

What if the Filipinos chose to ignore their new last names? This possibility had already crossed Claveria's mind, and he took steps to make sure that the names would stick. Schoolteachers were ordered to forbid their students to address or even know one another by any name except the officially inscribed family name. Those teachers who did not apply the rule with enthusiasm were to be punished. More efficacious perhaps, given the minuscule school enrollment, was the proviso that forbade priests and military and civil officials from accepting any document, application, petition, or deed that did not use the official surnames. All documents using other names would be null and void

Similar provisions ensured the replacement of local dialects with the approved national language. Students were only allowed to learn the national language in school and were punished for speaking in vernacular. All formal documents had to be in the national language, which meant that peasants who had formally been able to manage their own legal affairs had to rely on national-language-speaking intermediaries. Scott talks about the effect in France:

> One can hardly imagine a more effective formula for immediately devaluing local knowledge and privileging all those who had mastered the official linguistic code. It was a gigantic shift in power. Those at the periphery who lacked competence in French were rendered mute and marginal. They were now in need of a local guide to the new state culture, which appeared in the form of lawyers, notaries, schoolteachers, clerks, and soldiers.

IV

So the early modern period is defined by an uneasy truce between states who want to be able to count and standardize everything, and citizens who don't want to let them. Enter High Modernism. Scott defines it as

> A strong, one might even say muscle-bound, version of the self-confidence about scientific and technical progress, the expansion of production, the growing satisfaction of human needs, the mastery of nature (including human nature), and above all, the rational design of social order commensurate with the scientific understanding of natural laws

...which is just a *bit* academic-ese for me. An extensional definition might work better: standardization, Henry Ford, the factory as metaphor for the best way to run everything, conquest of nature, New Soviet Man, people with college degrees knowing better than you, wiping away the foolish irrational traditions of the past, Brave New World, everyone living in dormitories and eating exactly 2000 calories of Standardized Food Product (TM) per day, anything that is For Your Own Good, gleaming modernist skyscrapers, The X Of The Future, complaints that the unenlightened masses are resisting The X Of The Future, demands that if the unenlightened masses reject The X Of

The Future they must be re-educated For Their Own Good, and (of course) evenly-spaced rectangular grids.

(maybe the best definition would be "everything G. K. Chesterton didn't like.")

It sort of sounds like a Young Adult Dystopia, but Scott shocked me with his research into just how strong this ideology was around the turn of the last century. Some of the greatest early 20th-century thinkers were High Modernist to the point of self-parody, the point where a Young Adult Dystopian fiction writer would start worrying they were laying it on a little too thick.

The worst of the worst was Le Corbusier, the French artist/intellectual/architect. The Soviets asked him to come up with a plan to redesign Moscow. He came up with one: kick out everyone, bulldoze the entire city, and redesign it from scratch upon rational principles. For example, instead of using other people's irrational systems of measurement, they would use a new measurement system invented by Le Corbusier himself, called Modulor[4], which combined the average height of a Frenchman with the Golden Ratio.

Also, evenly-spaced rectangular grids may have been involved.

The Soviets decided to pass: the plan was too extreme and destructive of existing institutions *even for Stalin*. Undeterred, Le Corbusier changed the word "Moscow" on the diagram to "Paris", then presented it to the French government (who also passed). Some aspects of his design eventually ended up as Chandigarh, India.

A typical building in Chandigarh. The Soviets and French must have been kicking themselves when they realized what they'd missed out on.

Le Corbusier was challenged on his obsession with keeping his plan in the face of different local conditions, pre-existing structures, residents who might want a say in the matter, et cetera. Wasn't it kind of dictatorial? He replied that:

> The despot is not a man. It is the Plan. The correct, realistic, exact plan, the one that will provide your solution once the problem has been posited clearly, in its entirety, in its indispensable harmony. This plan has been drawn up well away from the frenzy in the mayor's office or the town hall, from the cries of the elec-

---

[4]https://en.wikipedia.org/wiki/Modulor

torate or the laments of society's victims. It has been drawn up by serene and lucid minds. It has taken account of nothing but human truths. It has ignored all current regulations, all existing usages, and channels. It has not considered whether or not it could be carried out with the constitution now in force. It is a biological creation destined for human beings and capable of realization by modern techniques.

What was so great about this "biological creation" of "serene and lucid minds"? It… might have kind of maybe been evenly-spaced rectangular grids:

> People will say: "That's easily said! But all your intersections are right angles. What about the infinite variations that constitute the reality of our cities?" But that's precisely the point: I eliminate all these things. Otherwise we shall never get anywhere.

> I can already hear the storms of protest and the sarcastic gibes: "Imbecile, madman, idiot, braggart, lunatic, etc." Thank you very much, but it makes no difference: my starting point is still the same: I insist on right-angled intersections. The intersections shown here are all perfect.

Scott uses Le Corbusier as the epitome of five High Modernist principles.

First, there can be no compromise with the existing infrastructure. It was designed by superstitious people who didn't have architecture degrees, or at the very least got their architecture degrees in the past and so were insufficiently Modern. The more completely it is bulldozed to make way for the Glorious Future, the better.

Second, human needs can be abstracted and calculated. A human needs X amount of food. A human needs X amount of water. A human needs X amount of light, and prefers to travel at X speed, and wants to live within X miles of the workplace. These needs are easily calculable by experiment, and a good city is the one built to satisfy these needs and ignore any competing frivolities.

Third, the solution is the solution. It is universal. The rational design for Moscow is the same as the rational design for Paris is the same as the rational design for Chandigarh, India. As a corollary, all of these cities ought to look exactly the same. It is *maybe* permissible to adjust for obstacles like mountains or lakes. But only if you are on too short a budget to follow the rationally correct solution of leveling the mountain and draining the lake to make your city truly optimal.

Fourth, all of the relevant rules should be explicitly determined by technocrats, then followed to the letter by their subordinates. Following these rules is better than trying to use your intuition, in the same way that using the laws of physics to calculate the heat from burning something is better than just trying to guess, or following an evidence-based clinical algorithm is better than just prescribing whatever you feel like.

Fifth, there is nothing whatsoever to be gained or learned from the people involved (eg the city's future citizens). *You* are a rational modern scientist with an architecture degree who has already calculated out the precise value for all relevant urban parameters. *They* are yokels who probably cannot even *spell* the word architecture, let alone usefully contribute to it. They probably make all of their decisions based on superstition or tradition or something, and their input should be ignored For Their Own Good.

And lest I be unfair to Le Corbusier, a lot of his scientific rational principles made a lot of sense. Have wide roads so that there's enough room for traffic and all the buildings get a lot of light. Use rectangular grids to make cities easier to navigate. Avoid frivolous decoration so that everything is efficient and affordable to all. Use concrete because it's the cheapest and strongest material. Keep pedestrians off the streets as much as possible so that they don't get hit by cars. Use big apartment towers to save space, then use the open space for pretty parks and public squares. Avoid anything that looks like a local touch, because nationalism leads to war and we are all part of the same global community of humanity. It sounded pretty good, and for a few decades the entire urban planning community was convinced.

So, how did it go?

Scott uses the example of Brasilia. Brazil wanted to develop its near-empty central regions and decided to build a new capital in the middle of nowhere. They hired three students of Le Corbusier, most notably Oscar Niemeyer, to build them a perfect scientific rational city. The conditions couldn't have been better. The land was already pristine, so there was no need to bulldoze Paris first. There were no inconvenient mountains or forests in the way. The available budget was in the tens of billions. The architects rose to the challenge and built them the world's greatest High Modernist city.

It's... even more beautiful than I imagined

Yet twenty years after its construction, the city's capacity of 500,000 residents was only half-full. And it wasn't the location – a belt of suburbs grew up with a population of almost a million. People wanted to live in *the vicinity of* Brasilia. They just didn't want to live *in the parts that Niemeyer and the Corbusierites had built.*

Brasilia from above. Note both the evenly-spaced rectangular grid of identical buildings in the center, and the fact that most people aren't living in it.

What happened? Scott writes:

> Most of those who have moved to Brasilia from other cities are amazed to discover "that it is a city without crowds." People complain that Brasilia lacks the bustle of street life, that it has none of the busy street corners and long stretches of storefront facades that animate a sidewalk for pedestrians. For them, it is almost as if the founders of Brasilia, rather than having planned a city, have actually planned to prevent a city. The most common way they put it is to say that Brasilia "lacks street corners,"by which they mean that it lacks the complex intersections of dense neighborhoods comprising residences and public cafes and restaurants with places for leisure, work, and shopping.

> While Brasilia provides well for some human needs, the functional separation of work from residence and of both from commerce and entertainment, the great voids between superquadra, and a road system devoted exclusively to motorized traffic make the disappearance of the street corner a foregone conclusion. The plan did eliminate traffic jams; it also eliminated the welcome and familiar pedestrian jams that one of Holston's informants called "the point of social conviviality

> The term brasilite, meaning roughly Brasilia-itis,which was coined by the first-generation residents, nicely captures the trauma they experienced. As a mock clinical condition, it connotes a rejection of the standardization and anonymity of life in Brasilia. "They use the term brasilite to refer to their feelings about a daily life without the pleasures-the distractions, conversations, flirtations, and little rituals of outdoor life in other Brazilian cities." Meeting someone normally requires seeing them either at their apartment or at work. Even if we allow for the initial simpli-

fying premise of Brasilia's being an administrative city, there is nonetheless a bland anonymity built into the very structure of the capital. The population simply lacks the small accessible spaces that they could colonize and stamp with the character of their activity, as they have done historically in Rio and Sao Paulo. To be sure, the inhabitants of Brasilia haven't had much time to modify the city through their practices, but the city is designed to be fairly recalcitrant to their efforts.

"Brasilite," as a term, also underscores how the built environment affects those who dwell in it. Compared to life in Rio and Sao Paulo, with their color and variety, the daily round in bland, repetitive, austere Brasilia must have resembled life in a sensory deprivation tank. The recipe for high-modernist urban planning, while it may have created formal order and functional segregation, did so at the cost of a sensorily impoverished and monotonous environment—an environment that inevitably took its toll on the spirits of its residents.

The anonymity induced by Brasilia is evident from the scale and exterior of the apartments that typically make up each residential superquadra. For superquadra residents, the two most frequent complaints are the sameness of the apartment blocks and the isolation of the residences ("In Brasilia, there is only house and work"). The facade of each block is strictly geometric and egalitarian. Nothing distinguishes the exterior of one apartment from another; there are not even balconies that would allow residents to add distinctive touches and create semipublic spaces.

Brasilia is interesting only insofar as it was an entire High Modernist planned city. In most places, the Modernists rarely got their hands on entire cities at once. They did build a number of suburbs, neighborhoods, and apartment buildings. There was, however, a disconnect. Most people did not want to buy a High Modernist house or live in a High Modernist neighborhood. Most governments *did* want to fund High Modernist houses and neighborhoods, because the academics influencing them said it was the modern scientific rational thing to do. So in the end, one of High Modernists' main contributions to the United States was the projects – ie government-funded public housing for poor people who didn't get to choose where to live.

I never really "got" Jane Jacobs. I originally interpreted her as arguing that it was great for cities to be noisy and busy and full of crowds, and that we should build neighborhoods that are confusing and hard to get through to force people to interact with each other and prevent them from being able to have privacy, and no one should be allowed to live anywhere quiet or nice. As somebody who (thanks to the public school system, etc) has had my share of being forced to interact with people, and of being placed in situations where it is deliberately difficult to have any privacy or time to myself, I figured Jane Jacobs was just a jerk.

But Scott has kind of made me come around. He rehabilitates her as someone who was responding to the very real excesses of High Modernism. She was the first person who really said "Hey, maybe people *like* being in cute little neighborhoods". Her complaint wasn't really against privacy or order per se as it was against extreme High Modernist perversions of those concepts that people empirically hated. And her background makes this all too understandable – she started out as a journalist covering poor African-Americans who lived in the projects and had some of the same complaints as Brazilians.

Her critique of Le Corbusierism was mostly what you would expect, but Scott extracts some points useful for their contrast with the Modernist points earlier:

First, existing structures are evolved organisms built by people trying to satisfy their social goals. They contain far more wisdom about people's needs and desires than anybody could formally enumerate. Any attempt at urban planning should try to build on this encoded knowledge, not detract from it.

Second, man does not live by bread alone. People don't want the right amount of Standardized Food Product, they want social interaction, culture, art, coziness, and a host of other things nobody will ever be able to calculate. Existing structures have already been optimized for these things, and unless you're really sure you understand all of them, you should be reluctant to disturb them.

Third, solutions are local. Americans want different things than Africans or Indians. One proof of this is that New York looks different from Lagos and from Delhi. Even if you are the world's best American city planner, you should be very concerned that you have no idea what people in Africa need, and you should be very reluctant to design an African city without extensive consultation of people who understand the local environment.

Fourth, even a very smart and well-intentioned person who is on board with points 1-3 will never be able to produce a set of rules. Most of people's knowledge is implicit, and most rule codes are quickly replaced by informal systems of things that work which are much more effective (the classic example of this is work-to-rule strikes[5]).

Fifth, although well-educated technocrats may understand principles which give them some advantages in their domain, they are hopeless without the on-the-ground experience of the people they are trying to serve, whose years of living in their environment and dealing with it every day have given them a deep practical knowledge which is difficult to codify.

How did Jacobs herself choose where to live? As per her Wikipedia page:

> [Jacobs] took an immediate liking to Manhattan's Greenwich Village, which did not conform to the city's grid structure.

V

The same thing that happened with cities happened with farms. The American version was merely farce:

> We should recognize that the rationalization of farming on a huge, even national, scale was part of a faith shared by social engineers and agricultural planners throughout the world. And they were conscious of being engaged in a common endeavor... They kept in touch through journals, professional conferences, and exhibitions. The connections were strongest between American agronomists and their Russian colleagues – connections that were not entirely broken even during the Cold War. Working in vastly different economic and political environments, the Russians tended to be envious of the level of capitalization, particularly in mechanization, of American farms while the Americans were envious of the political scope of Soviet planning. The degree to which they were working together to create a new world of large-scale, rational, industrial agriculture can be judged by this brief account of their relationship [...]

> Many efforts were made to put this faith to the test. Perhaps the most audacious was the Thomas Campbell "farm" in Montana,

---

begun – or, perhaps I should say, founded – in 1918 It was an industrial farm in more than one respect. Shares were sold by prospectuses describing the enterprise as an "industrial opportunity"; J. P. Morgan, the financier, helped to raise $2 million from the public. The Montana Farming Corporation was a monster wheat farm of ninety-five thousand acres, much of it leased from four Native American tribes. Despite the private investment, the enterprise would never have gotten off the ground without help and subsidies from the Department of Interior and the United States Department of Agriculture (USDA).

Proclaiming that farming was about 90 percent engineering and only 10 percent agriculture, Campbell set about standardizing as much of his operation as possible. He grew wheat and flax, two hardy crops that needed little if any attention between planting and harvest time. The land he farmed was the agricultural equivalent of the bulldozed site of Brasilia. It was virgin soil, with a natural fertility that would eliminate the need for fertilizer. The topography also vastly simplified matters: it was flat, with no forests, creeks, rocks, or ridges that would impede the smooth course of machinery over its surface. In other words, the selection of the simplest, most standardized crops and the leasing of something very close to a blank agricultural space were calculated to favor the application of industrial methods [...]

This is not the place to chronicle the fortunes of the Montana Farming Corporation, and in any event Deborah Fitzgerald has done so splendidly. Suffice it to note that a drought in the second year and the elimination of a government support for prices the following year led to a collapse that cost J. P. Morgan $1 million. The Campbell farm faced other problems besides weather and prices: soil differences, labor turnover, the difficulty of finding skilled, resourceful workers who would need little supervision. Although the corporation struggled on until Campbell's death in 1966, it provided no evidence that industrial farms were superior to family farms in efficiency and profitability.

But the Soviet version was tragedy. Instead of raising some money to start a giant farm and seeing it didn't work, the USSR uprooted millions of peasants, forced them onto collective farms, and then watched as millions of people starved to death due to crop failure. What happened?

Scott really focuses on that claim (above) that farming was "90% engineering and only 10% agriculture". He says that these huge farms all failed – despite being better-funded, higher-tech, and having access to the wisdom of the top agricultural scientists – exactly because this claim was false. Small farmers may not know much about agricultural science, but they know a lot about farming. Their knowledge is intuitive and local – for example, what to do in a particular climate or soil. It is sometimes passed down over generations, and other times determined through long hours of trial-and-error.

He gave the example of Tanzania, where small farmers grew dozens of different crops together in seeming chaos. Western colonists tried to convince them – often by force – to switch to just growing one thing at a time to reap advantages of efficiency, standardization, and specialization of labor. Only growing one crop in the same field was Agricultural Science 101. But this turned out to be a bad idea in the difficult Tanzanian environment:

> The multistoried effect of polyculture has some distinct advantages for yields and soil conservation. "Upper-story" crops shade "lowerstory" crops, which are selected for their ability to thrive in the cooler soil temperature and increased humidity at ground level. Rainfall reaches the ground not directly but as a fine spray that is absorbed with less damage to soil structure and less erosion. The taller crops often serve as a useful windbreak for the lower crops. Finally, in mixed or relay cropping, a crop is in the field at all times, holding the soil together and reducing the leaching effects that sun, wind, and rain exert, particularly on fragile land. Even if polyculture is not to be preferred on the grounds of immediate yield, there is much to recommend it in terms of sustainability and thus long-term production.

> Our discussion of mixed cropping has thus far dealt only with the narrow issues of yield and soil conservation. It has overlooked the cultivators themselves and the various other ends that they seek by using such techniques. The most significant advantage of intercropping, Paul Richards claims, is its great flexibility, "the scope [it] offers for a range of combinations to match individual needs and preferences, local conditions, and changing circumstances within each season and from season to season." Farm-

ers may polycrop in order to avoid labor bottlenecks at planting and at harvest.44Growing many different crops is also an obvious way to spread risks and improve food security. Cultivators can reduce the danger of going hungry if they sow, instead of only one or two cultivars, crops of long and short maturity, crops that are drought resistant and those that do well under wetter conditions, crops with different patterns of resistance to pests and diseases, crops that can be stored in the ground with little loss (such as cassava), and crops that mature in the "hungry time" before other crops are gathered. Finally, and perhaps most important, each of these crops is embedded in a distinctive set of social relations. Different members of the household are likely to have different rights and responsibilities with respect to each crop. The planting regimen, in other words, is a reflection of social relations, ritual needs, and culinary tastes; it is not just a production strategy that a profit-maximizing entrepreneur took straight out of the pages of a text in neoclassical economics.

Nor could this be solved just by adding a pinch of empiricism. A lot of European farming specialists were into empiricism, sort of. What they ended up doing was creating crops that worked really well in a lab but not in actual Tanzania. If they were lucky, they created crops that worked really well on the one experimental farm in Tanzania they fenced off as a testing ground, but not on any other Tanzanian farms. If they were *really* lucky, they created crops that would grow on Tanzanian farms and be good on whatever single axis they were optimizing (like selling for lots of money) but not in other ways that were equally important to the populace (like being low-risk, or useful for non-food purposes, or resistant to disease, or whatever). And if they were *supremely* lucky, then they would go to the Tanzanians and say "Hey, we invented a new farming method that solves all your problems!" and the Tanzanians would say "Yeah, we heard rumors about that, so we tried it ourselves, and now we've been using it for five years and advanced it way beyond what you were doing."

There *were* some scientists who got beyond these failure modes, and Scott celebrates them (while all too often describing how they were marginalized and ignored by the rest of the scientific community). But at the point where you've transcended all this, you're no longer a domain-general agricultural scientist, you're a Tanzanian farming specialist who's only one white coat removed from being a Tanzanian farmer yourself.

Even in less exotic locales like Russia, the peasant farmers were extraordinary experts on the conditions of their own farms, their own climates, and their own crops. Take all of these people, transport them a thousand miles away, and give them a perfectly rectangular grid to grow Wheat Cultivar #6 on, and you have a recipe for disaster.

VI

So if this was such a bad idea, why did everyone keep doing it?

Start with the cities. Scott notes that although citizens generally didn't have a problem with earlier cities, governments did:

> Historically, the relative illegibility to outsiders of some urban neighborhoods has provided a vital margin of political safety from control by outside elites. A simple way of determining whether this margin exists is to ask if an outsider would have needed a local guide in order to find her way successfully. If the answer is yes, then the community or terrain in question enjoys at least a small measure of insulation from outside intrusion. Coupled with patterns of local solidarity, this insulation has proven politically valuable in such disparate contexts as eighteenth-and early nineteenth-century urban riots over bread prices in Europe, the Front de Liberation Nationale's tenacious resistance to the French in the Casbah of Algiers, and the politics of the bazaar that helped to bring down the Shah of Iran. Illegibility, then, has been and remains a reliable resource for political autonomy

This was a particular problem in Paris, which was famous for a series of urban insurrections in the 19th century (think *Les Miserables*, but about once every ten years or so). Although these generally failed, they were hard to suppress because locals knew the "terrain" and the streets were narrow enough to barricade. Slums full of poor people gathered together formed tight communities where revolutionary ideas could easily spread. The late 19th-century redesign of Paris had the explicit design of destroying these areas and splitting up poor people somewhere far away from the city center where they couldn't do any harm.

The Soviet collective farms had the same dubious advantage. The problem they "effectively" "solved" was the non-collectivized farmers becoming too powerful and independent a political bloc. They lived in tight-knit little villages that did their own thing, the Party officials who went to these villages to keep order often ended up "going native", and the Soviets had no way of knowing how much food the farmers were producing and whether they were giving enough of it to the Motherland:

> Confronting a tumultuous, footloose, and "headless" rural soci-
> ety which was hard to control and which had few political assets,
> the Bolsheviks, like the scientific foresters, set about redesigning
> their environment with a few simple goals in mind. They created,
> in place of what they had inherited, a new landscape of large,
> hierarchical, state-managed farms whose cropping patterns and
> procurement quotas were centrally mandated and whose popu-
> lation was, by law, immobile. The system thus devised served
> for nearly sixty years as a mechanism for procurement and con-
> trol at a massive cost in stagnation, waste, demoralization, and
> ecological failure.

The collectivized farms couldn't grow much, but people were thrown to-
gether in artificial towns designed to make it impossible to build any kind of community: there was nowhere to be except in bed asleep, working in the fields, or at the public school receiving your daily dose of state propaganda. The towns were identical concrete buildings on a grid, which left the locals maximally disoriented (because there are no learnable visual cues) and the officials maximally oriented (because even a foreigner could go to the intersection of Street D and Street 7). All fields were perfectly rectangular and produced Standardized Food Product, so it was (theoretically) easy to calcu-
late how much they should be producing and whether people were meeting that target. And everyone was in the same place, so if there were some sort of problem it was much easier to bring in the army or secret police than if they were split up among a million tiny villages in the middle of nowhere.

So although modernist cities and farms may have started out as attempts to help citizens with living and farming, they ended up as contributors to the great government project of legibility and taxing people effectively. *Seeing Like A State* summarizes the sort of on-the-ground ultra-empirical knowledge that citizens have of city design and peasants of farming as *metis*, a Greek term meaning "practical wisdom". I was a little concerned about this because they seem like two different things. The average citizen knows nothing about city design and in fact does not design cities; cities sort of happen in a weird way through cultural evolution or whatever. The average farmer knows a lot about farming (even if it is implicit and not as book learning) and applies that knowledge directly in how they farm. But Scott thinks these are more or less the same thing, that this thing is a foundation of successful communities and industries, and that ignoring and suppressing it is what makes collective farms and modernist planned cities so crappy. He generalizes this further to almost every aspect of a society – its language, laws, social norms, and economy. But this is all done very quickly, and I feel like there was a sleight of hand between "each farmer eventually figures out how to farm well" and "social norms converge on good values".

Insofar as Scott squares the above circle, he seems to think that many actors competing with each other will eventually carve out a beneficial equilibrium better than that of any centralized authority. This doesn't really mesh will with that many actors competing with each other will eventually shoot themselves in the foot and destroy everything, and I haven't really seen a careful investigation of when we get one versus the other.

VII

What are we to make of all of this?

Well, for one thing, Scott basically admits to stacking the dice against High Modernism and legibility. He admits that the organic livable cities of old had life expectancies in the forties because nobody got any light or fresh air and they were all packed together with no sewers and so everyone just died of cholera. He admits that at some point agricultural productivity multiplied by like a thousand times and the Green Revolution saved millions of lives and all that, and probably that has something to do with scientific farming methods and rectangular grids. He admits that it's pretty convenient having a unit of measurement that local lords can't change whenever they feel like it. Even modern timber farms seem pretty successful. After all those admissions, it's kind of hard to see what's left of his case.

(also, I grew up in Irvine, the most planned of planned cities, and I loved it.)

What Scott eventually says is that he's not against legibility and modernism per se, but he wants to present them as ingredients in a cocktail of state failure. You need a combination of four things to get a disaster like Soviet collective farming (or his other favorite example, compulsory village settlement in Tanzania). First, a government incentivized to seek greater legibility for its population and territory. Second, a High Modernist ideology. Third, authoritarianism. And fourth, a "prostrate civil society", like in Russia after the Revolution, or in colonies after the Europeans took over.

I think his theory is that the back-and-forth between centralized government and civil society allows scientific advances to be implemented smoothly instead of just plowing over everyone in a way that leads to disaster. I also think that maybe a big part of it is incremental versus sudden: western farming did well because it got to incrementally add advances and see how they worked, but when you threw the entire edifice at Tanzania it crashed and burned.

I'm still not really sure what's left. Authoritarianism is bad? Destroying civil society is bad? You shouldn't do things when you have no idea what you're doing and all you've got to go on is your rectangle fetish? The book contained some great historical tidbits, but I'm not sure what overarching lesson I learned from it.

It's not that I don't think Scott's preference for *metis* over scientific omnipotence has value. I think it has lots of value. I see this all the time in psychiatry, which always has been and to some degree still is really High Modernist. We are educated people who know a lot about mental health, dealing with a poor population who (in the case of one of my patients) refers to Haldol as "Hound Dog". It's *very* easy to get in the trap of thinking that you know better than these people, especially since you often do (I will never understand how many people are *shocked* when I diagnose their sleep disorder as having something to do with them drinking fifteen cups of coffee a day).

But psychiatric patients have a *metis* of dealing with their individual diseases the same way peasants have a *metis* of dealing with their individual plots of land. My favorite example of this is doctors who learn their patients are taking marijuana, refuse to keep prescribing them their vitally important drugs unless the patient promises to stop, and then gets surprised when the patients end up decompensating because the marijuana was keeping them together. I'm not saying smoking marijuana is a good thing. I'm saying that for some people it's a load-bearing piece of their mental edifice. And if you take it away without any replacement they will fall apart. And *they have explained this to you a thousand times and you didn't believe them.*

There are *so many* fricking patients who respond to sedative medications by becoming stimulated, or stimulant medications by becoming sedated, or who become more anxious whenever they do anti-anxiety exercises, or who hallucinate when placed on some super common medication that has never caused hallucinations in anyone else, or who become suicidal if you try to reassure them that things aren't so bad, or any other completely perverse and ridiculous violation of the natural order that you can think of. And the only redeeming feature of all of this is that the patients themselves know all of this stuff super-well and are usually happy to tell you if you ask.

I can totally imagine going into a psychiatric clinic armed with the Evidence-Based Guidelines the same way Le Corbusier went into Moscow and Paris armed with his Single Rational City Plan and the same way the agricultural scientists went into Tanzania armed with their List Of Things That Definitely Work In Europe. I expect it would have about the same effect for about the same reason.

(including the part where I would get promoted[6]. I'm not too sure what's going on there, actually.)

So fine, Scott is completely right here. But I'm only bringing this up because it's something I've already thought about. If I didn't already believe this, I'd be indifferent between applying the narrative of the wise Tanzanian farmers knowing more than their English colonizers, versus the narrative of the dumb yokels who refuse to get vaccines because they might cause autism. Heuristics work until they don't[7]. Scott provides us with these great historical examples of local knowledge outdoing scientific acumen, but other stories present us with great historical examples of the opposite, and when to apply which heuristic seems really unclear. Even "don't bulldoze civil society and try to change everything at once" goes astray sometimes; the Meiji Restoration was wildly successful by doing exactly that.

Maybe I'm trying to take this too far by talking about psychiatry and Meiji Restorations. Most of Scott's good examples involved either agriculture or resettling peasant villages. This is understandable; Scott is a scholar of colonialism in Southeast Asia and there was a lot of agriculture and peasant resettling going on there. But it's a pretty limited domain. The book amply proves that peasants know an astounding amount about how to deal with local microclimates and grow local varieties of crops and so on, and frankly I am shocked that anyone with an IQ of less than 180 has ever managed to be a peasant farmer, but how does that apply to the sorts of non-agricultural issues we think about more often?

The closest analogy I can think of right now – maybe because it's on my mind – is this story about check-cashing shops[8]. Professors of social science

---

[6]https://slatestarcodex.com/2016/12/29/book-review-mount-misery/

[7]https://slatestarcodex.com/2017/01/11/heuristics-work-until-they-dont/

[8]http://www.businessinsider.com/check-cashing-stores-good-deal-upenn-professor-2

think these shops are evil because they charge the poor higher rates, so they should be regulated away so that poor people don't foolishly shoot themselves in the foot by going to them. But on closer inspection, they offer a better deal for the poor than banks do, for complicated reasons that aren't visible just by comparing the raw numbers. Poor people's understanding of this seems a lot like the *metis* that helps them understand local agriculture. And progressives' desire to shift control to the big banks seems a lot like the High Modernists' desire to shift everything to a few big farms. Maybe this is a point in favor of something like libertarianism? Maybe especially a "libertarianism of the poor" focusing on things like occupational licensing, not shutting down various services to the poor because they don't meet rich-people standards, not shutting down various services to the poor because we think they're "price-gouging", et cetera?

Maybe instead of concluding that Scott is too focused on peasant villages, we should conclude that he's focused on confrontations between a well-educated authoritarian overclass and a totally separate poor underclass. Most modern political issues don't exactly map on to that – even things like taxes where the rich and the poor are on separate sides don't have a bimodal distribution. But in cases there are literally about rich people trying to dictate to the poorest of the poor how they should live their lives, maybe this becomes more useful.

Actually, one of the best things the book did to me was make me take cliches about "rich people need to defer to the poor on poverty-related policy ideas" more seriously. This has become so overused that I roll my eyes at it: "Could quantitative easing help end wage stagnation? Instead of asking macroeconomists, let's ask this 19-year old single mother in the Bronx!" But Scott provides a lot of situations where that was exactly the sort of person they should have asked. He also points out that Tanzanian natives using their traditional farming practices were more productive than European colonists using scientific farming. I've had to listen to so many people talk about how "we must respect native people's different ways of knowing" and "native agriculturalists have a profound respect for the earth that goes beyond logocentric Western ideals" and nobody had ever bothered to tell me before that they *actually produced more crops per acre*, at least some of the time. That would have put all of the other stuff in a pretty different light.

I understand Scott is an anarchist. He didn't really try to defend anarchism in this book. But I was struck by his description of peasant villages as this totally separate unit of government which was happily doing its own thing very effectively for millennia, with the central government's relevance being entirely negative – mostly demanding taxes or starting wars. They kind of reminded me of some pictures of hunter-gatherer tribes, in terms of being self-sufficient, informal, and just never encountering the sorts of economic and political problems that we take for granted. They make communism (the type with actual communes, not the type where you have Five Year Plans and Politburos and gulags) look more attractive. I think Scott was trying to imply that this is the sort of thing we could have if not for governments demanding legibility and a world of universal formal rule codes accessible from the center? Since he never actually made the argument, it's hard for me to critique it. And I wish there had been more about cultural evolution as separate from the more individual idea of *metis*.

A final note: Scott often used the word "rationalism" to refer to the excesses of High Modernism, and I've deliberately kept it. What relevance does this have for the LW-Yudkowsky-Bayesian rationalist project? I think the similarities are more than semantic; there certainly is a hope that learning domain-general skills will allow people to leverage raw intelligence and The Power Of Science to various different object-level domains. I continue to be doubtful that this will work in the sort of practical domains where people have spent centuries gathering *metis* in the way Scott describes; this is why I'm wary of any attempt of the rationality movement to branch into self-help. I'm more optimistic about rationalists' ability to open underexplored areas like existential risk – it's not like there's a population of Tanzanian peasants who have spent the last few centuries developing traditional x-risk research whom we are arrogantly trying to replace – and to focus on things that don't bring any immediate practical gain but which help build the foundations for new philosophies, better communities, and more positive futures. I also think that a good art of rationality would look a lot like *metis*, combining easily teachable mathematical rules with more implicit virtues which get absorbed by osmosis.

Overall I did like this book. I'm not really sure what I got from its thesis, but maybe that was appropriate. *Seeing Like A State* was arranged kind of like the premodern forests and villages it describes; not especially well-organized, not really directed toward any clear predetermined goal, but full of interesting things and lovely to spend some time in.

25

Guided By The Beauty Of Our Weapons

March 24, 2017

Content note: *kind of talking around Trump supporters and similar groups as if they're not there.*

I

Tim Harford writes The Problem With Facts[1], which uses Brexit and Trump as jumping-off points to argue that people are mostly impervious to facts and resistant to logic:

> All this adds up to a depressing picture for those of us who aren't ready to live in a post-truth world. Facts, it seems, are toothless. Trying to refute a bold, memorable lie with a fiddly set of facts can often serve to reinforce the myth. Important truths are often stale and dull, and it is easy to manufacture new, more engaging claims. And giving people more facts can backfire, as those facts provoke a defensive reaction in someone who badly wants to stick to their existing world view. "This is dark stuff," says Reifler. "We're in a pretty scary and dark time."

He admits he has no easy answers, but cites some studies showing that "scientific curiosity" seems to help people become interested in facts again. He thinks maybe we can inspire scientific curiosity by linking scientific truths to human interest stories, by weaving compelling narratives, and by finding "a Carl Sagan or David Attenborough of social science".

---

[1] http://timharford.com/2017/03/the-problem-with-facts/

I think this is generally a good article and makes important points, but there are three issues I want to highlight as possibly pointing to a deeper pattern.

First, the article makes the very strong claim that "facts are toothless" – then tries to convince its readers of this using facts. For example, the article highlights a study by Nyhan & Reifler which finds a "backfire effect" – correcting people's misconceptions only makes them cling to those misconceptions more strongly. Harford expects us to be impressed by this study. But how is this different from all of those social science facts to which he believes humans are mostly impervious?

Second, Nyhan & Reifler's work on the backfire effect is probably not true. The original study establishing its existence failed[2] to replicate (see eg Porter & Wood, 2016[3]). This isn't directly contrary to Harford's argument, because Harford doesn't cite the original study – he cites a slight extension of it done a year later by the same team that comes to a slightly different conclusion. But given that the entire field is now in serious doubt, I feel like it would have been judicious to mention some of this in the article. This is especially true given that the article itself is about the way that false ideas spread by people never double-checking their beliefs. It seems to me that if you believe in an epidemic of falsehood so widespread that the very ability to separate fact from fiction is under threat, it ought to inspire a state of CONSTANT VIGILANCE[4], where you obsessively question each of your beliefs. Yet Harford writes an entire article about a worldwide plague of false beliefs without mustering enough vigilance to see if the relevant studies are true or not.

Third, Harford describes his article as being about *agnotology*, "the study of how ignorance is deliberately produced". His key example is tobacco companies sowing doubt about the negative health effects of smoking – for example, he talks about tobacco companies sponsoring (accurate) research into all of the non-smoking-related causes of disease so that everyone focused on those instead. But his solution – telling engaging stories, adding a human interest element, enjoyable documentaries in the style of Carl Sagan – seems unusually unsuited to the problem. The National Institute of Health can make an engaging human interest documentary about a smoker who got lung

---

[2]https://www.poynter.org/2016/fact-checking-doesnt-backfire-new-study-suggests/43 6983/

[3]https://papers.ssrn.com/sol3/papers.cfm?abstract_id=2819073

[4]https://slatestarcodex.com/2014/06/09/constant-vigilance/

cancer. And the tobacco companies can make an engaging human interest documentary about a guy who got cancer because of asbestos, then was saved by tobacco-sponsored research. Opponents of Brexit can make an engaging documentary about all the reasons Brexit would be bad, and then proponents of Brexit can make an engaging documentary about all the reasons Brexit would be good. If you get good documentary-makers, I assume both will be equally convincing regardless of what the true facts are.

All three of these points are slightly unfair. The first because Harford's stronger statements about facts are probably exaggerations, and he just meant that in *certain cases* people ignore evidence. The second because the specific study cited wasn't the one that failed to replicate and Harford's thesis might be that it was different enough from the original that it's probably true. And the third because the documentaries were just one idea meant to serve a broader goal of increasing "scientific curiosity", a construct which has been shown in studies to be helpful in getting people to believe true things.

But I worry that taken together, they suggest an unspoken premise of the piece. It isn't that *people* are impervious to facts. Harford doesn't expect his reader to be impervious to facts, he doesn't expect documentary-makers to be impervious to facts, and he certainly doesn't expect *himself* to be impervious to facts. The problem is that there's some weird tribe of fact-immune troglodytes out there, going around refusing vaccines and voting for Brexit, and the rest of us have to figure out what to do about them. The fundamental problem is one of *transmission*: how can we make knowledge percolate down from the fact-loving elite to the fact-impervious masses?

And I don't want to condemn this too hard, because it's obviously true up to a point. Medical researchers have lots of useful facts about vaccines. Statisticians know some great facts about the link between tobacco and cancer (shame about Ronald Fisher[5], though). Probably there are even some social scientists who have a fact or two.

Yet as I've argued before[6], excessive focus on things like vaccine denialists teaches the wrong habits. It's a desire to take a degenerate case, the rare situation where one side is obviously right and the other bizarrely wrong, and make it into the flagship example for modeling all human disagreement. Imagine a theory of jurisprudence designed only to smack down sovereign citizens, or a government pro-innovation policy based entirely on warning inventors against perpetual motion machines.

---

[5] https://priceonomics.com/why-the-father-of-modern-statistics-didnt-believe/
[6] https://slatestarcodex.com/2014/04/15/the-cowpox-of-doubt/

And in this wider context, part of me wonders if the focus on transmission is part of the problem. Everyone from statisticians to Brexiteers knows that they are right. The only remaining problem is how to convince others. Go on Facebook and you will find a million people with a million different opinions, each confident in her own judgment, each zealously devoted to informing everyone else.

Imagine a classroom where everyone believes they're the teacher and everyone else is students. They all fight each other for space at the blackboard, give lectures that nobody listens to, assign homework that nobody does. When everyone gets abysmal test scores, one of the teachers has an idea: *I need a more engaging curriculum.* Sure. That'll help.

II

A new Nathan Robinson article: Debate Vs. Persuasion[7]. It goes through the same steps as the Harford article, this time from the perspective of the political Left. Deploying what Robinson calls "Purely Logical Debate" against Trump supporters hasn't worked. Some leftists think the answer is violence. But this may be premature; instead, we should try the tools of rhetoric, emotional appeal, and other forms of discourse that aren't Purely Logical Debate. In conclusion, Bernie Would Have Won.

> I think giving up on argumentation, reason, and language, just because Purely Logical Debate doesn't work, is a mistake. It's easy to think that if we can't convince the right with facts, there's no hope at all for public discourse. But this might not suggest anything about the possibilities of persuasion and dialogue. Instead, it might suggest that mere facts are rhetorically insufficient to get people excited about your political program.

The resemblance to Harford is obvious. You can't convince people with facts. But you *might* be able to convince people with facts carefully intermixed with human interest, compelling narrative, and emotional appeal.

Once again, I think this is generally a good article and makes important points. But I still want to challenge whether things are quite as bad as it says.

---

[7] https://www.currentaffairs.org/2017/03/debate-versus-persuasion

Google "debating Trump supporters is"[8], and you realize where the article is coming from. It's page after page of "debating Trump supporters is pointless", "debating Trump supporters is a waste of time", and "debating Trump supporters is like [funny metaphor for thing that doesn't work]". The overall picture you get is of a world full of Trump opponents and supporters debating on every street corner, until finally, after months of banging their heads against the wall, everyone collectively decided it was futile.

Yet I have the opposite impression. Somehow a sharply polarized country went through a historically divisive election with *essentially no debate taking place*.

Am I about to No True Scotsman[9] the hell out of the word "debate"? Maybe. But I feel like in using the exaggerated phrase "Purely Logical Debate, Robinson has given me leave to define the term as strictly as I like. So here's what I think are minimum standards to deserve the capital letters:

1. Debate where two people with opposing views are *talking* to each other (or writing, or IMing, or some form of bilateral communication). Not a pundit putting an article on *Huffington Post* and demanding Trump supporters read it. Not even a Trump supporter who comments on the article with a counterargument that the author will never read. Two people who have chosen to engage and to listen to one another.

2. Debate where both people want to be there, and have chosen to enter into the debate in the hopes of getting something productive out of it. So not something where someone posts a "HILLARY IS A CROOK" meme on Facebook, someone gets really angry and lists all the reasons Trump is an even bigger crook, and then the original poster gets angry and has to tell them why they're wrong. Two people who have made it their business to come together at a certain time in order to compare opinions.

3. Debate conducted in the spirit of mutual respect and collaborative truth-seeking. Both people reject personal attacks or 'gotcha' style digs. Both people understand that the other person is *around* the same level of intelligence as they are and may have some useful things to say. Both people understand that they themselves might have some false beliefs that the other person will be able to correct for them. Both people

---

[8] https://encrypted.google.com/search?q=%22debating+trump+supporters%22#q=%22deba ting+trump+supporters+is%22&*

[9] https://en.wikipedia.org/wiki/No_true_Scotsman

go into the debate with the hope of convincing their opponent, but not completely rejecting the possibility that their opponent might convince them also.

4. Debate conducted outside of a high-pressure point-scoring environment. No audience cheering on both participants to respond as quickly and bitingly as possible. If it can't be done online, at least do it with a smartphone around so you can open Wikipedia to resolve simple matters of fact.

5. Debate where both people agree on what's being debated and try to stick to the subject at hand. None of this "I'm going to vote Trump because I think Clinton is corrupt" followed by "Yeah, but Reagan was even worse and that just proves you Republicans are hypocrites" followed by " *We're* hypocrites? You Democrats claim to support women's rights but you love Muslims who make women wear headscarves!" Whether or not it's hypocritical to "support women's rights" but "love Muslims", it doesn't seem like anyone is even *trying* to change each other's mind about Clinton at this point.

These to me seem like the *bare minimum* conditions for a debate that could possibly be productive.

(and while I'm asking for a pony on a silver platter, how about both people have to read *How To Actually Change Your Mind*[10] first?)

Meanwhile, in reality…

If you search "debating Trump supporters" without the "is", your first result is this video[11], where some people with a microphone corner some other people at what looks like a rally. I can't really follow the conversation because they're all shouting at the same time, but I can make out somebody saying 'Republicans give more to charity!' and someone else responding 'That's cause they don't do anything at their jobs!'". Okay.

The second link is this podcast[12] where a guy talks about debating Trump supporters. After the usual preface about how stupid they were, he describes a typical exchange – "It's kind of amazing how they want to go back to the good old days… Well, when I start asking them 'You mean the good old days when 30% of the population were in unions'… they never seem to like to

---

[10] https://wiki.lesswrong.com/wiki/How_To_Actually_Change_Your_Mind

[11] https://www.youtube.com/watch?v=Fqm_Br1ywPY

[12] https://soundcloud.com/best-of-the-left/debating-trump-supporters-colin-from-cleveland-oh

hear that!… so all this unfettered free market capitalism has got to go bye-bye. They don't find comfort in that idea either. It's amazing. I can say I now know what cognitive dissonance feels like on someone's face." I'm glad time travel seems to be impossible, because otherwise I would be tempted to warp back and change my vote to Trump just to spite this person.

The third link is Vanity Fair's "Foolproof Guide To Arguing With Trump Supporters"[13], which suggests "using their patriotism against them" by telling them that wanting to "curtail the rights and privileges of certain of our citizens" is un-American.

I worry that people do this kind of thing every so often. Then, when it fails, they conclude "Trump supporters are immune to logic". This is much like observing that Republicans go out in the rain without melting, and concluding "Trump supporters are immortal".

Am I saying that if you met with a conservative friend for an hour in a quiet cafe to talk over your disagreements, they'd come away convinced? No. I've changed my mind on various things during my life, and it was never a single moment that did it. It was more of a series of different things, each taking me a fraction of the way. As the old saying goes, "First they ignore you, then they laugh at you, then they fight you, then they fight you half-heartedly, then they're neutral, then they then they grudgingly say you might have a point even though you're annoying, then they say on balance you're mostly right although you ignore some of the most important facets of the issue, then you win."

There might be a parallel here with the one place I see something like Purely Logical Debate on a routine basis: cognitive psychotherapy. I know this comparison sounds crazy, because psychotherapy is supposed to be the opposite of a debate, and trying to argue someone out of their delusions or depression inevitably fails. The rookiest of all rookie therapist mistakes is to say "FACT CHECK: The patient says she is a loser who everybody hates. PsychiaFact rates this claim: PANTS ON FIRE."

But in other ways it's a lot like the five points above. You have two people who disagree – the patient thinks she's a worthless loser who everyone hates, and the therapist thinks maybe not. They meet together in a spirit of voluntary mutual inquiry, guaranteed safe from personal attacks like "You're crazy!". Both sides go over the evidence together, sometimes even agreeing on explicit experiments like "Ask your boyfriend tonight whether he hates you

---

[13] http://www.vanityfair.com/news/2017/02/reza-aslan-debating-trump-supporters

or not, predict beforehand what you think he's going to say, and see if your prediction is accurate". And both sides approach the whole process suspecting that they're right but admitting the possibility that they're wrong (very occasionally, after weeks of therapy, I realize that frick, everyone really *does* hate my patient. Then we switch strategies to helping her with social skills, or helping her find better friends).

And contrary to what you see in movies, this doesn't usually give a single moment of blinding revelation. If you spent your entire life talking yourself into the belief that you're a loser and everyone hates you, no single fact or person is going to talk you out of it. But after however many months of intensive therapy, sometimes someone who was *sure* that they were a loser is now *sort of questioning* whether they're a loser, and has the mental toolbox to take things the rest of the way themselves.

This was also the response I got when I tried to make an anti-Trump case[14] on this blog. I don't think there were any sudden conversions, but here were some of the positive comments I got from Trump supporters:

- "This is a compelling case, but I'm still torn."[15]
- "This contains the most convincing arguments for a Clinton presidency I have ever seen. But, perhaps also unsurprisingly, while it did manage to shift some of my views, it did not succeed in convincing me to change my bottom line."[16]
- "This article is perhaps the best argument I have seen yet for Hillary. I found myself nodding along with many of the arguments, after this morning swearing that there was nothing that could make me consider voting for Hillary... the problem in the end was that it wasn't enough."[17]
- "The first coherent article I've read justifying voting for Clinton. I don't agree with your analysis of the dollar"value" of a vote, but other than that, something to think about."[18]

---

[14] https://slatestarcodex.com/2016/09/28/ssc-endorses-clinton-johnson-or-stein/
[15] https://slatestarcodex.com/2016/09/28/ssc-endorses-clinton-johnson-or-stein/#comment-415499
[16] https://slatestarcodex.com/2016/09/28/ssc-endorses-clinton-johnson-or-stein/#comment-415543
[17] https://slatestarcodex.com/2016/09/28/ssc-endorses-clinton-johnson-or-stein/#comment-415708
[18] https://slatestarcodex.com/2016/09/28/ssc-endorses-clinton-johnson-or-stein/#comment-415749

- "Well I don't like Clinton at all, and I found this essay reasonable enough. The argument from continuity is probably the best one for voting Clinton if you don't particularly love any of her policies or her as a person. Trump is a wild card, I must admit."[19]
- As an orthodox Catholic, you would probably classify me as part of your conservative audience... I certainly concur with both the variance arguments and that he's not conservative by policy, life, or temperament, and I will remain open to hearing what you have to say on the topic through November.[20]
- "I've only come around to the 'hold your nose and vote Trump' camp the past month or so... I won't say [you] didn't make me squirm, but I'm holding fast to my decision."[21]

These are the people you say are completely impervious to logic so don't even try? It seems to me like this argument was one of not-so-many straws that might have broken some camels' backs if they'd been allowed to accumulate. And the weird thing is, when I re-read the essay I notice a lot of flaws and things I wish I'd said differently. I don't think it was an exceptionally good argument. I think it was... an argument. It was something more than saying "You think the old days were so great, but the old days had labor unions, CHECKMATE ATHEISTS". This isn't what you get when you do a splendid virtuoso perfomance. This is what you get *when you show up*.

(and lest I end up 'objectifying' Trump supporters as prizes to be won, I'll add that in the comments some people made pro-Trump arguments, and two people who were previously leaning Clinton said that they were feeling uncomfortably close to being convinced)

Another SSC story. I keep trying to keep "culture war"-style political arguments from overrunning the blog and subreddit, and every time I add restrictions a bunch of people complain[22] that this is the only place they can go for that. Think about this for a second. A heavily polarized country of three hundred million people, split pretty evenly into two sides and obsessed with politics, blessed with the strongest free speech laws in the world, and

---

[19] https://slatestarcodex.com/2016/09/28/ssc-endorses-clinton-johnson-or-stein/#comment-415873

[20] https://slatestarcodex.com/2016/09/28/ssc-endorses-clinton-johnson-or-stein/#comment-416477

[21] https://slatestarcodex.com/2016/09/28/ssc-endorses-clinton-johnson-or-stein/#comment-417013

[22] https://www.reddit.com/r/slatestarcodex/comments/60gvph/culture_war_roundup_for_week_of_march_20_2017/df76d5z/

people are complaining that I can't change my comment policy because this one small blog is *the only place they know where they can debate people from the other side*.

Given all of this, I reject the argument that Purely Logical Debate has been tried and found wanting. Like GK Chesterton, I think it has been found difficult and left untried.

III

Therapy might change minds, and so might friendly debate among equals, but neither of them scales very well. Is there anything that big fish in the media can do beyond the transmission they're already trying?

Let's go back to that Nyhan & Reifler study which found that fact-checking backfired. As I mentioned above, a replication attempt by Porter & Wood found the opposite. This could have been the setup for a nasty conflict, with both groups trying to convince academia and the public that they were right, or even accusing the other of scientific malpractice.

Instead, something great happened. All four researchers decided to work together[23] on an "adversarial collaboration" – a bigger, better study where they all had input into the methodology and they all checked the results independently. The collaboration found that fact-checking generally didn't backfire in most cases. All four of them used their scientific clout to publicize the new result and launch further investigations into the role of different contexts and situations.

Instead of treating disagreement as demonstrating a need to transmit their own opinion more effectively, they viewed it as demonstrating a need to collaborate to investigate the question together.

And yeah, part of it was that they were all decent scientists who respected each other. But they didn't *have* to be. If one team had been total morons, and the other team was secretly laughing at them the whole time, the collaboration still would have worked. All required was an assumption of good faith.

A while ago I blogged about a journalistic spat between German Lopez and Robert VerBruggen on gun control. Lopez wrote a voxsplainer[24] citing

---

[23] http://nymag.com/scienceofus/2016/11/theres-more-hope-for-political-fact-checking.html

[24] http://www.vox.com/2015/10/3/9444417/gun-violence-united-states-america

some statistics about guns. VerBruggen wrote a piece at National Review[25] saying that some of the statistics were flawed. German fired back (pun not intended) with an article[26] claiming that VerBruggen was ignoring better studies.

(Then I yelled at both of them[27], as usual.)

Overall the exchange was in the top 1% of online social science journalism – by which I mean it included at least one statistic and at some point that statistic was superficially examined. But in the end, it was still just two people arguing with one another, each trying to transmit his superior knowledge to each other and the reading public. As good as it was, it didn't meet my five standards above – and nobody expected it to.

But now I'm thinking – what would have happened if Lopez and Ver-Bruggen had joined together in an adversarial collaboration? Agreed to work together to write an article on gun statistics, with nothing going into the article unless they both approved, and then they both published that article on their respective sites?

This seems like a mass media equivalent of shifting from Twitter spats to serious debate, from transmission mindset to collaborative truth-seeking mindset. The adversarial collaboration model is just the first one to come to mind right now. I've blogged about others before – for example, bets, prediction markets, and calibration training.

The media already spends a lot of effort *recommending* good behavior. What if they tried *modeling* it?

IV

The bigger question hanging over all of this: "Do we *have* to?"

Harford's solution – compelling narratives and documentaries – sounds easy and fun. Robinson's solution – rhetoric and emotional appeals – also sounds easy and fun. Even the solution Robinson rejects – violence – is easy, and fun for a certain type of person. All three work on pretty much anybody.

Purely Logical Debate is difficult and annoying. It doesn't scale. It only works on the subset of people who are willing to talk to you in good faith

---

[25] http://www.nationalreview.com/article/427967/guns-tk-robert-verbruggen?target=author&tid=1043

[26] http://www.vox.com/policy-and-politics/2015/12/8/9870240/gun-ownership-deaths-homicides

[27] https://slatestarcodex.com/2016/01/06/guns-and-states/

and smart enough to understand the issues involved. And even then, it only works glacially slowly, and you win only partial victories. What's the point?

Logical debate has one advantage over narrative, rhetoric, and violence: it's an *asymmetric weapon*. That is, it's a weapon which is stronger in the hands of the good guys than in the hands of the bad guys. In ideal conditions (which may or may not ever happen in real life) – the kind of conditions where everyone is charitable and intelligent and wise – the good guys will be able to present stronger evidence, cite more experts, and invoke more compelling moral principles. The whole point of logic is that, when done right, it can only prove things that are true.

Violence is a *symmetric weapon*; the bad guys' punches hit just as hard as the good guys' do. It's true that hopefully the good guys will be more popular than the bad guys, and so able to gather more soldiers. But this doesn't mean violence itself is asymmetric – the good guys will only be more popular than the bad guys insofar as their ideas have previously spread through some means other than violence. Right now antifascists outnumber fascists and so could probably beat them in a fight, but antifascists didn't come to outnumber fascists by winning some kind of primordial fistfight between the two sides. They came to outnumber fascists because people rejected fascism on the merits. These merits might not have been "logical" in the sense of Aristotle dispassionately proving lemmas at a chalkboard, but "fascists kill people, killing people is wrong, therefore fascism is wrong" is a sort of folk logical conclusion which is both correct and compelling. Even "a fascist killed my brother, so fuck them" is a placeholder for a powerful philosophical argument making a probabilistic generalization from indexical evidence to global utility. So insofar as violence is asymmetric, it's because it parasitizes on logic which allows the good guys to be more convincing and so field a bigger army. Violence itself doesn't enhance that asymmetry; if anything, it decreases it by giving an advantage to whoever is more ruthless and power-hungry.

The same is true of documentaries. As I said before, Harford can produce as many anti-Trump documentaries as he wants, but Trump can fund documentaries of his own. He has the best documentaries. Nobody has ever seen documentaries like this. They'll be absolutely huge.

And the same is true of rhetoric. Martin Luther King was able to make persuasive emotional appeals for good things. But Hitler was able to make persuasive emotional appeals for bad things. I've previously argued[28] that

---

[28] https://slatestarscratchpad.tumblr.com/post/103708539246/nostalgebraist-at-various-points-bostrom-like

Mohammed counts as the most successful persuader of all time. These three people pushed three very different ideologies, and rhetoric worked for them all. Robinson writes as if "use rhetoric and emotional appeals" is a novel idea for Democrats, but it seems to me like they were doing little else throughout the election (pieces attacking Trump's character, pieces talking about how inspirational Hillary was, pieces appealing to various American principles like equality, et cetera). It's just that they did a bad job, and Trump did a better one. The real takeaway here is "do rhetoric better than the other guy". But "succeed" is not a primitive action.

Unless you use asymmetric weapons, the best you can hope for is to win by coincidence.

That is, there's no reason to think that good guys are consistently better at rhetoric than bad guys. Some days the Left will have an Obama and win the rhetoric war. Other days the Right will have a Reagan and *they'll* win the rhetoric war. Overall you should average out to a 50% success rate. When you win, it'll be because you got lucky.

And there's no reason to think that good guys are consistently better at documentaries than bad guys. Some days the NIH will spin a compelling narrative and people will smoke less. Other days the tobacco companies will spin a compelling narrative and people will smoke more. Overall smoking will stay the same. And again, if you win, it's because you lucked out into having better videographers or something.

I'm not against winning by coincidence. If I stumbled across Stalin and I happened to have a gun, I would shoot him without worrying about how it's "only by coincidence" that he didn't have the gun instead of me. You should use your symmetric weapons if for no reason other than that the other side's going to use *theirs* and so you'll have a disadvantage if you don't. But you shouldn't confuse it with a long-term solution.

Improving the quality of debate, shifting people's mindsets from transmission to collaborative truth-seeking, is a painful process. It has to be done one person at a time, it only works on people who are already *almost* ready for it, and you will pick up far fewer warm bodies per hour of work than with any of the other methods. But in an otherwise-random world, even a little purposeful action can make a difference. Convincing 2% of people would have flipped three of the last four US presidential elections. And this is a capacity to win-for-reasons-other-than-coincidence that you can't build any other way.

(and my hope is that the people most willing to engage in debate, and the ones most likely to recognize truth when they see it, are disproportionately influential – scientists, writers, and community leaders who have influence beyond their number and can help others see reason in turn)

I worry that I'm not communicating how beautiful and inevitable all of this is. We're surrounded by a a vast confusion, "a darkling plain where ignorant armies clash by night", with one side or another making a temporary advance and then falling back in turn. And in the middle of all of it, there's this gradual capacity-building going on, where what starts off as a hopelessly weak signal gradually builds up strength, until one army starts winning a little more often than chance, then a lot more often, and finally takes the field entirely. Which seems strange, because surely you can't build any complex signal-detection machinery in the middle of all the chaos, surely you'd be shot the moment you left the trenches, but – *your enemies are helping you do it.* Both sides are diverting their artillery from the relevant areas, pooling their resources, helping bring supplies to the engineers, because until the very end they think it's going to ensure *their* final victory and not yours.

You're doing it right under their noses. They might try to ban your documentaries, heckle your speeches, fight your violence Middlebury-student-for-Middlebury-student – but when it comes to the long-term solution to ensure your complete victory, they'll roll down their sleeves, get out their hammers, and build it alongside you.

A parable: Sally is a psychiatrist. Her patient has a strange delusion: that *Sally* is the patient and *he* is the psychiatrist. She would like to commit him and force medication on him, but he is an important politician and if push comes to shove he might be able to commit *her* instead. In desperation, she proposes a bargain: they will *both* take a certain medication. He agrees; from within his delusion, it's the best way for him-the-psychiatrist to cure her-the-patient. The two take their pills at the same time. The medication works, and the patient makes a full recovery.

(well, half the time. The other half, the medication works and *Sally* makes a full recovery.)

V

Harford's article says that facts and logic don't work on people. The various lefty articles say they merely don't work on Trump supporters, ie 50% of the population.

If you genuinely believe that facts and logic don't work on people, you shouldn't be writing articles with potential solutions. You should be jettisoning everything you believe and entering a state of pure Cartesian doubt, where you try to rederive everything from *cogito ergo sum.*

If you genuinely believe that facts and logic don't work on at least 50% of the population, again, you shouldn't be writing articles with potential solutions. You should be worrying whether you're in that 50%. After all, how did you figure out you aren't? By using facts and logic? *What did we just say?* Nobody is doing either of these things, so I conclude that they accept that facts can sometimes work. Asymmetric weapons are not a pipe dream. As Gandhi used to say, "If you think the world is all bad, remember that it contains people like you."

You are not completely immune to facts and logic. But you have been wrong about things before. You may be a bit smarter than the people on the other side. You may even be a *lot* smarter. But fundamentally their problems are your problems, and the same kind of logic that convinced you can convince them. It's just going to be a long slog. You didn't develop *your* opinions after a five-minute shouting match. You developed them after years of education and acculturation and engaging with hundreds of books and hundreds of people. Why should they be any different?

You end up believing that the problem is deeper than insufficient documentary production. The problem is that Truth is a weak signal. You're trying to perceive Truth. You would like to hope that the other side is trying to perceive Truth too. But at least one of you is doing it wrong. It seems like perceiving Truth accurately is harder than you thought.

You believe your mind is a truth-sensing instrument that does at least a little bit better than chance. You *have* to believe that, or else what's the point? But it's like one of those physics experiments set up to detect gravitational waves or something, where it has to be in a cavern five hundred feet underground in a lead-shielded chamber atop a gyroscopically stable platform cooled to one degree above absolute zero, trying to detect fluctuations of a millionth of a centimeter. Except you don't have the cavern or the lead or the gyroscope or the coolants. You're on top of an erupting volcano being pelted by meteorites in the middle of a hurricane.

If you study psychology for ten years, you can remove the volcano. If you spend another ten years obsessively checking your performance in various *metis*-intensive domains, you can remove the meteorites. You can never remove the hurricane and you shouldn't try. But if there are a thousand trustworthy people at a thousand different parts of the hurricane, then the stray gusts of wind will cancel out and they can average their readings to get something approaching a signal.

All of this is too slow and uncertain for a world that needs more wisdom *now*. It would be nice to force the matter, to pelt people with speeches and documentaries until they come around. This will work in the short term. In the long term, it will leave you back where you started.

If you want people to be right more often than chance, you have to teach them ways to distinguish truth from falsehood. If this is in the face of enemy action, you will have to teach them so well that they cannot be fooled. You will have to do it person by person until the signal is strong and clear. You will have to raise the sanity waterline[29]. There is no shortcut.

---

[29] https://www.greaterwrong.com/lw/1e/raising_the_sanity_waterline/

26

The Atomic Bomb Considered As Hungarian High School Science Fair Project

May 26, 2017

I

A group of Manhattan Project physicists created[1] a tongue-in-cheek mythology where superintelligent Martian scouts landed in Budapest in the late 19th century and stayed for about a generation, after which they decided the planet was unsuitable for their needs and disappeared. The only clue to their existence were the children they had with local women.

The joke was that this explained why the Manhattan Project was led by a group of Hungarian supergeniuses, all born in Budapest between 1890 and 1920. These included Manhattan Project founder Leo Szilard[2], H-bomb creator Edward Teller[3], Nobel-Prize-winning quantum physicist Eugene Wigner[4], and legendary polymath John von Neumann[5], namesake of the List Of Things Named After John Von Neumann[6].

The coincidences actually pile up beyond this. Von Neumann, Wigner, and possibly Teller all went to the same central Budapest high school at about the same time, leading a friend to joke about the atomic bomb being *basically* a Hungarian high school science fair project.

But maybe we shouldn't be joking about this so much. Suppose we learned

[1] https://en.wikipedia.org/wiki/The_Martians_scientists

[2] https://en.wikipedia.org/wiki/Leo_Szilard

[3] https://en.wikipedia.org/wiki/Edward_Teller

[4] https://en.wikipedia.org/wiki/Eugene_Wigner

[5] https://en.wikipedia.org/wiki/John_von_Neumann

[6] https://en.wikipedia.org/wiki/List_of_things_named_after_John_von_Neumann

that Beethoven, Mozart, and Bach all had the same childhood piano tutor. It sounds less like "ha ha, what a funny coincidence" and more like "wait, who was this guy, and how quickly can we make everyone else start doing what he did?"

In this case, the guy was Laszlo Ratz[7], legendary Budapest high school math teacher. I didn't even know people *told* legends about high school math teachers, but apparently they do, and this guy features in a lot of them. There is apparently a Laszlo Ratz Memorial Congress for high school math teachers each year, and a Laszlo Ratz medal for services to the profession. There are plaques and statues to this guy. It's pretty impressive.

A while ago I looked into the literature on teachers and concluded[8] that they didn't have much effect overall. Similarly, Freddie deBoer writes that most claims that certain schools or programs have transformative effects on their students are the result of selection bias[9].

On the other hand, we have a Hungarian academy producing like half the brainpower behind 20th century physics, and Nobel laureates who literally keep a picture[10] of their high school math teacher on the wall of their office to inspire them. Perhaps even if teachers don't explain much of the *existing* variability, there are heights of teacherdom so rare that they don't show up in the statistics, but still exist to be aspired to?

II

I've heard this argument a few times, and I think it's wrong.

Yes, two of Ratz's students went on to become supergeniuses. But Edward Teller, another supergenius, went to the same high school but (as far as I know) was never taught by Ratz himself. That suggests that the school was good at producing supergeniuses regarldess of Ratz's personal qualities. A further point in support of this: John Harsanyi[11] also went to the school, also wasn't directly taught by Ratz, and also went on to win a Nobel Prize and invent various important fields of mathematics. So this school – the Fasori

[7] https://en.wikipedia.org/wiki/L%C3%A1szl%C3%B3_R%C3%A1tz

[8] https://slatestarcodex.com/2016/05/19/teachers-much-more-than-you-wanted-to-know/

[9] https://fredrikdeboer.com/2017/03/29/why-selection-bias-is-the-most-powerful-force-in-education/

[10] https://en.wikipedia.org/wiki/L%C3%A1szl%C3%B3_R%C3%A1tz#Eugene_Wigner_about_his_teacher_L.C3.A1szl.C3.B3_R.C3.A1tz

[11] https://en.wikipedia.org/wiki/John_Harsanyi

Gymnasium[12] – seems to have been about equally excellent for both its Ratz-taught and its non-Ratz-taught pupils.

Yet the Fasori Gymnasium *might not have even been the best high school in its neighborhood.* It competed with the Minta Gymnasium half a mile down the street, whose alumni include Manhattan Project physicists Nicholas Kurti[13] and Theodore von Karman[14] (von Karman went on to found the Jet Propulsion Laboratory), brilliant chemist-philosopher Michael Polanyi[15], economists Thomas Balogh[16] and Nicholas Kaldor[17] (of Kaldor-Hicks efficiency fame), and Peter Lax[18], who once said[19] "You don't have to be Hungarian to be a mathematician – but it helps". There are also some contradictory sources suggesting Teller attended this school and not Fasori; for all I know he might have attended both. Once again, most of these people were born in the 1890-1910 period when the Martian scouts were supposedly in Budapest.

Worse, I'm not even sure that the best high school in early 20th-century Hungary was *either* of the two mentioned above. The Berzsenyi Gymnasium, a two mile walk down Gyorgy Street from the others, boasts alumni including multizillionaire George Soros[20], Intel founder Andrew Grove[21], BASIC inventor John Kemeny[22], leading cancer biologist George Klein[23], great mathematician George Polya[24], and Nobel Prize winning physicist Dennis Gabor[25].

Given that the Fasori Gymnasium wasn't obviously better than either of these others, is it possible that the excellence was at a higher level – neither excellent teachers nor excellent principals, but some kind of generally excellent Hungarian culture of education?

This is definitely what the Hungarians want us to think. According to *Cultures of Creativity*[26]:

[12] https://en.wikipedia.org/wiki/Fasori_Gimn%C3%A1zium

[13] https://en.wikipedia.org/wiki/Nicholas_Kurti

[14] https://en.wikipedia.org/wiki/Theodore_von_K%C3%A1rm%C3%A1n

[15] https://en.wikipedia.org/wiki/Michael_Polanyi

[16] https://en.wikipedia.org/wiki/Thomas_Balogh,_Baron_Balogh

[17] https://en.wikipedia.org/wiki/Nicholas_Kaldor

[18] https://en.wikipedia.org/wiki/Peter_Lax

[19] http://www.hkame.org.hk/uploaded_files/magazine/15/274.pdf

[20] https://en.wikipedia.org/wiki/George_Soros

[21] https://en.wikipedia.org/wiki/Andrew_Grove

[22] https://en.wikipedia.org/wiki/John_G._Kemeny

[23] https://en.wikipedia.org/wiki/George_Klein_biologist

[24] https://en.wikipedia.org/wiki/George_P%C3%B3lya

[25] https://en.wikipedia.org/wiki/Dennis_Gabor

[26] https://books.google.com/books?id=g7nWSs5k7V8C&pg=PA167&lpg=PA167&dq=Szent-Gy%C

What's so special about Budapest's schools? A certain elitism and a spirit of competition partly explains the successes of their students. For example, annual competitions in mathematics and physics have been held since 1894. The instruction the students receive as well as these contests are an expression of a special pedagogy and a striving to encourage creativity. Mor Karman, founder of the Minta school, believed that everything should be taught by showing its relation to everyday life. Instead of learning rules by heart from books, students tried to formulate the rules themselves.

This paper on "The Hungarian Phenomenon"[27] makes similar claims, but adds a few more details:

> The Eotvos Contests were a powerful mean for the stimulation of mathematics on a large scale and were used to motivate mathematical culture in the society. It also provided a channel to search for talented youths. The contests, which have been open to Hungarian high school students in their last year since 1894, played a remarkable role in the development of mathematics.

Okay. But I want to challenge this. During this era, formal education in Hungary began at age 10. By age ten, John von Neumann, greatest of the Hungarian supergeniuses, already spoke English, French, German, Italian, and Ancient Greek, knew integral and differential calculus, and could multiply and divide 8-digit numbers in his head. Wikipedia notes that on his first meeting with his math teacher, the math teacher "was so astounded with the boy's mathematical talent that he was brought to tears". This doesn't sound like a guy whose potential was kindled by formal education. This sounds like a guy who would have become one of history's great mathematicians even if his teachers had slept through his entire high school career.

Likewise, the book above notes that Dennis Gabor, the Hungarian inventor of holography, "developed his passion for physics during his youth, but did so for the most part on his own". His biography[28] notes that "During

3%B6rgyi+Minta+gymnasium&source=bl&ots=kSbtumTe3C&sig=EHHwVerDrwxrIY0-hg2a6r10xGQ&h
l=en&sa=X&ved=0ahUKEwiLlsa6kYzUAhVnzFQKHVWWBuQQ6AEIIzAA#v=onepage&q=Szent-Gy%C3%B6rgy
i%20Minta%20gymnasium&f=false

[27] http://www.hkame.org.hk/uploaded_files/magazine/15/274.pdf
[28] http://www.madehow.com/inventorbios/48/Dennis-Gabor.html

his childhood in Budapest, Gabor and his brother would often duplicate the experiments they read about in scientific journals in their home laboratory."

Likewise, consider Paul Erdos[29], a brilliant mathematician born in Budapest around this time. As per his Wikipedia page, "Left to his own devices, he taught himself to read through mathematics texts that his parents left around their home. By the age of four, given a person's age, he could calculate, in his head, how many seconds they had lived."

I have no knock-down proof that Hungary's clearly excellent education system didn't contribute to this phenomenon. A lot of child prodigies burn out, and maybe Hungary was unusually good at making sure that didn't happen. But it sure seems like they had a lot of child prodigies to work with.

So what's going on? Should we just accept the Manhattan Project consensus that there was a superintelligent Martian scout force in early 20th-century Budapest?

III

Here's something interesting: every single person I mentioned above is of Jewish descent. *Every single one.* This isn't some clever setup where I only selected Jewish-Hungarians in order to spring this on you later. I selected all the interesting Hungarians I could find, then went back and checked, and every one of them was Jewish.

This puts the excellence of the Hungarian education system in a different light. Hungarian schools totally failed to work their magic on Gentiles. You can talk all you want about "elitism and a spirit of competition" and "striving to encourage creativity", yet for some reason this worked on exactly one of Hungary's many ethnic groups.

This reduces the difficult question of Hungarian intellectual achievement to the easier question of Jewish intellectual achievement.

I say "easier question" because I find the solution by Cochran, Hardy, and Harpending really compelling. Their paper is called A Natural History Of Ashkenazi Intelligence[30] ("Ashkenazi" means Eastern European Jew) and they start by expressing the extent of the issue:

> Ashkenazi Jews have the highest average IQ of any ethnic group
> for which there are reliable data. They score 0.75 to 1.0 standard

---

[29]https://en.wikipedia.org/wiki/Paul_Erd%C5%91s

[30]http://web.mit.edu/fustflum/documents/papers/AshkenaziIQ.jbiosocsci.pdf

deviations above the general European average, corresponding to an IQ 112 – 115. This fact has social significance because IQ (as measured by IQ tests) is the best predictor we have of success in academic subjects and most jobs. Ashkenazi Jews are just as successful as their tested IQ would predict, and they are hugely overrepresented in occupations and fields with the highest cognitive demands. During the 20th century, they made up about 3% of the US population but won 27% of the US Nobel science prizes and 25% of the Turing Awards [in computer science]. They account for more than half of world chess champions.

This doesn't seem to be due to any advantage in material privilege; Ashkenazi Jews frequently did well even in countries where they were persecuted. Nor is it obviously linked to Jewish culture; Jews from other regions of the world show no such advantage. So what's going on?

Doctors have long noted that Ashkenazi Jews are uniquely susceptible to various genetic diseases. For example, they're about a hundred times more likely to have Gaucher's Disease[31], a hundred times more likely to get Tay-Sachs Disease[32], ten times more likely to have torsion dystonia[33], et cetera. Genetic diseases are so common in this population that the are official recommendation[34] is that all Ashkenazi Jewish couples get screened for genetic disease before marriage. I'm Ashkenazi Jewish, I got screened, and I turn out to be a carrier for Riley-Day syndrome[35] – three hundred times as common in Ashkenazi Jews as in anyone else.

Evolution usually gets rid of genetic diseases pretty quickly. If they stick around, it's because they're doing something to earn their keep. One common pattern is "heterozygote advantage"[36] – two copies of the gene cause a disease, but one copy does something good. For example, people with two copies of the sickle cell gene get sickle cell anaemia, but people with one copy get some protection against malaria. In Africa, where malaria is relatively common, the tradeoff is worth it – so people of African descent have high rates of the sickle cell gene and correspondingly high rates of sickle cell anaemia. In other places, where malaria is relatively uncommon, the tradeoff isn't worth it and

---

[31] https://en.wikipedia.org/wiki/Gaucher%27s_disease

[32] https://en.wikipedia.org/wiki/Tay%E2%80%93Sachs_disease

[33] https://en.wikipedia.org/wiki/Torsion_dystonia

[34] http://www.jewishgeneticdiseases.org/

[35] https://en.wikipedia.org/wiki/Familial_dysautonomia

[36] https://en.wikipedia.org/wiki/Heterozygote_advantage

evolution eliminates the sickle cell gene. That's why sickle cell is about a hundred times more common in US blacks than US whites.

The moral of the story is: populations can have genetic diseases if they also provide a useful advantage to carriers. And if those genetic diseases are limited to a single group, we expect them to provide a useful advantage for that group, but not others. Might the Jewish genetic diseases provide some advantage? And why would that advantage be limited to Jews?

Most of the Jewish genetic diseases cluster into two biological systems – the sphingolipid system and the DNA repair system. This is suspicious. It suggests that they're not just random. They're doing something specific. Both of these systems are related to neural growth and neural branching. Might they be doing something to the brain?

Gaucher's disease, one of the Ashkenazi genetic diseases, appears to increase IQ. CHH obtained a list of all of the Gaucher's patients in Israel. They were about 15 times more likely than the Israeli average to be in high-IQ occupations like scientist or engineer; CHH calculate the probability that this is a coincidence to be 4×10^{-19}.

Torsion dystonia, another Ashkenazi genetic disease, shows a similar pattern. CHH find ten reports in the literature where doctors comment on unusual levels of intelligence in their torsion dystonia patients. Eldridge, Harlan, Cooper, and Riklan[37] tested 14 torsion dystonia patients and found an average IQ of 121; another similar study found an average of 117. Torsion dystonia is pretty horrendous, but sufferers will at least get the consolation prize of being really, really smart.

Moving from medicine to history, we find that Ashkenazi Jews were persecuted for the better part of a millennium, and the particular form of this persecution was locking them out of various jobs until the main career opportunities open to them were things like banker, merchant, and doctor. CHH write:

> For 800 to 900 years, from roughly 800 AD to 1650 or 1700 AD, the great majority of the Ashkenazi Jews had managerial and financial jobs, jobs of high complexity, and were neither farmers nor craftsmen. In this they differed from all other settled peoples of which we have knowledge.

They continue:

---

[37] http://www.thelancet.com/journals/lancet/article/PIIS0140-67367091848-9/abstract

Jews who were particularly good at these jobs enjoyed increased reproductive success. Weinryb (1972, see also Hundert 1992) comments: "More children survived to adulthood in affluent families than in less affluent ones. A number of genealogies of business leaders, prominent rabbis, community leaders, and the like – generally belonging to the more affluent classes – show that such people often had four, six, sometimes even eight or nine children who reached adulthood. On the other hands, there are some indications that poorer families tended to be small ones… as an example, in a census of the town of Brody in 1764 home-owner households had 1.2 children per adult member while ten-ant households had 0.6.

Now we can start to sketch out the theory in full. Due to persecution, Jews were pushed into cognitively-demanding occupations like banker or merchant and forced to sink or swim. The ones who swam – people who were intellectually up to the challenge – had more kids than the ones who sank, producing an evolutionary pressure in favor of intelligence greater than that in any other ethnic group. Just as Africans experiencing evolutionary pressure for malaria resistance developed the sickle cell gene, so Ashkenazim experiencing evolutionary pressure for intelligence developed a bunch of genes which increased heterozygotes' IQ but caused serious genetic disease in homozygotes. As a result, Ashkenazi ended up somewhat more intelligent – and somewhat more prone to genetic disease – than the rest of the European population.

If true, this would explain the 27% of Nobel Prizes and 50% of world chess champions thing. But one still has to ask – everywhere had Jews. Why Hungary in particular? What was so special about Budapest in the early 1900s?

IV

Okay, sure, everywhere had Jews. But it's surprising exactly how *many* Jews were in early 1900s Hungary.

The modern United States is about 2% Jewish. Hungary in 1900 was about 5%. The most Jewish city in America, New York, is about 15% Jewish. Budapest in 1900 was 25%. It was one of the most Jewish large cities anywhere in history, excepting only Israel itself. According to Wikipedia, the city's late 19th-century nickname was "Judapest".

So is it possible that all the Jews were winning Nobel Prizes, and Hungary just had more Jews and so more Nobelists?

No. This doesn't seem right. The 1933 European Jewish Population By Country[38] site lists the following size for each country's Jewish communities:

Country	Jewish Population
Poland	3,000,000
Russia	2,500,000
Romania	750,000
Germany	500,000
Hungary	500,000
Britain	300,000
France	250,000
Austria	200,000

It's hard to find a good list of all famous Manhattan Project physicists, but I tried this article[39] and got the following number of famous Jewish Manhattan Project physicists per country of origin:

Country	MP Physicists
Hungary	4
Germany	2
Poland	2
Austria	2
Italy	1
Netherlands	1
Switzerland	1

Here's[40] an alternative source with a different definition of "famous", broken down the same way:

Country	MP Physicists
Germany	5

[38] https://www.ushmm.org/wlc/en/article.php?ModuleId=10005161
[39] http://www.americanthinker.com/articles/2015/02/jewish_scientists_helped_america _build_the_atom_bomb.html
[40] http://www.atomicheritage.org/bios

Country	MP Physicists
Hungary	4
Poland	3
Italy	2
Austria	2

The main point seems to be disproportionately many people from Central European countries like Hungary and Germany, compared to either Eastern European countries like Poland and Russia or Western European countries like France and Britain.

The Central European advantage over Western Europe is unsurprising; the Western European Jews probably weren't Ashkenazim, and so didn't have the advantage mentioned in the CHH paper above. But is there any reason to think that Central European Jews were more intelligent than Polish and Russian Jews?

I'm not really sure what to think about this. This paper[41] finds that the sphingolipidoses and other Jewish genetic diseases are about twice as common in Central European Jews as in Eastern European Jews, but I have very low confidence in these results. Intra-Jewish gossip points out the Lithuanians as the geniuses among world Jewry, but doesn't have any similar suggestions about Hungarians. And torsion dystonia, maybe the most clearly IQ-linked disease, is unique to Lithuanians and absent in Hungarians.

Probably much more promising is just to focus on the obvious facts of the social situation. Early'1900s Hungary was a great nation and a prosperous center of learning. Remember, we're talking about the age of the Austro-Hungarian Empire, one of the most industrialized and dynamic economies of the time. It might have had advantages that Poland, Romania, and Russia didn't. My list of historical national GDPs per capita[42] is very unimpressed by the difference between Hungarian and Polish GDPs in 1900, but maybe it's wrong, or maybe Budapest was an especially modern part of Hungary, or maybe there's something else I'm missing.

Also, there could have been a difference in the position of Jews in these countries. Russia was still experiencing frequent anti-Jewish pogroms in 1900; in Hungary, Jews were among the country's most noble families. Actually, the extent of Jewish wealth and influence in Hungary sort of defies belief.

[41] http://www.cell.com/ajhg/fulltext/S0002-92970760605-3
[42] http://www.ggdc.net/maddison/historical_statistics/horizontal-file_03-2007.xls

According to Wikipedia, in 1920 Jews were 60% of Hungarian doctors, 50% of lawyers, 40% of engineers and chemists, and 90% of currency brokers and stock exchange members. "In interwar Hungary, more than half and perhaps as much as 90 percent of Hungarian industry was owned or operated by a few closely related Jewish banking families."

So Central European Jews – the Jews in Hungary and Germany – had a unique combination of intellectual and financial advantages. This means Hungary's only real rival here is Germany. Since they were rich, industrialized, and pretty liberal about Jewish rights at the beginning of the 20th century – and since they had just as many Jews as Hungary – we should expect to see the same phenomenon there too.

And we kind of do. Germany produced its share of Jewish geniuses. Hans Bethe[43] worked for the Manhattan Project and won a Nobel Prize. Max Born[44] helped develop quantum mechanics and also won a Nobel Prize. James Franck[45], more quantum physics, another Nobel Prize. Otto Stern[46], even *more* quantum physics, yet *another* Nobel Prize. John Polanyi[47], chemical kinetics, Nobel Prize (although he was half-Hungarian). And of course we probably shouldn't forget about that Einstein[48] guy. All of these people were born in the same 1880 – 1920 window as the Martians in Hungary.

I think what's going on is this: Germany and Hungary had about the same Jewish population. And they produced about the same number of genius physicists in the same window. But we think of Germany as a big rich country, and Hungary as a small poor country. And the German Jews were spread over a bunch of different cities, whereas the Hungarian Jews were all crammed into Budapest. So when we hear "there were X Nobel Prize winning German physicists in the early 1900s", it sounds only mildly impressive. But when we hear "there were X Nobel Prize winning physicists from Budapest in the early 1900s", it sounds kind of shocking. But the denominator isn't the number of Germans vs. Hungarians, it's the number of German Jews vs. Hungarian Jews, which is about the same.

---

[43] https://en.wikipedia.org/wiki/Hans_Bethe
[44] https://en.wikipedia.org/wiki/Max_Born
[45] https://en.wikipedia.org/wiki/James_Franck
[46] https://en.wikipedia.org/wiki/Otto_Stern
[47] https://en.wikipedia.org/wiki/John_Polanyi
[48] https://en.wikipedia.org/wiki/Albert_Einstein

V

This still leaves one question: why the period 1880 to 1920?

On further reflection, this isn't much of a mystery. The emancipation of the Jews in Eastern Europe was a difficult process that took place throughout the 19th century. Even when it happened, it took a while for the first generation of Jews to get rich enough that their children could afford to go to fancy schools and fritter away their lives on impractical subjects like physics and chemistry. In much of Eastern Europe, the Jews born around 1880 were the first generation that was free to pursue what they wanted and seek their own lot in the world.

The end date around 1920 is more depressing: any Jew born after this time probably wasn't old enough to escape the Nazis. Almost all the famous Hungarian Jews became physics professors in Europe, fled to America during WWII using channels open to famous physicists, and then made most of their achievements on this side of the Atlantic. There are a couple of stragglers born after 1920 who survived – George Soros' family lived because they bought identity documents saying they were Christian; Andrew Grove lived because he was hidden by righteous Gentiles[49]. But in general Jews born in Europe after 1920 didn't have a great life expectancy.

All of this suggests a pretty reasonable explanation of the Martian phenomenon. For the reasons suggested by Cochran, Hardy, and Harpending, Ashkenazi Jews had the potential for very high intelligence. They were mostly too poor and discriminated against to take advantage of it. Around 1880, this changed in a few advanced Central European economies like Germany, Austria, and Hungary. Austria didn't have many Jews. Germany had a lot of Jews, but it was a big country, so nobody really noticed. Hungary had a lot of Jews, all concentrated in Budapest, and so it was really surprising when all of a sudden everyone from Budapest started winning Nobel Prizes around the same time. This continued until World War II, and then all anyone remembered was "Hey, wasn't it funny that so many smart people were born in Budapest between 1880 and 1920?"

And this story is really, really, gloomy.

For centuries, Europe was sitting on this vast untapped resource of potential geniuses. Around 1880, in a few countries only, economic and political conditions finally became ripe for the potential to be realized. The result was one of the greatest spurts of progress in scientific history, bringing us relativ-

---

[49] https://en.wikipedia.org/wiki/Righteous_Among_the_Nations

ity, quantum mechanics, nuclear bombs, dazzling new mathematical systems, the foundations of digital computing, and various other abstruse ideas I don't even pretend to understand. This lasted for approximately one generation, after which a psychopath with a stupid mustache killed everyone involved.

I certainly can't claim that the Jews were the only people being crazy smart in Central Europe around this time. This was the age of Bohr, Schrodinger, Planck, Curie, etc. But part of me wonders even here. If you have one physicist in a town, he sits in an armchair and thinks. If you have five physicists in a town, they meet and talk and try to help each other with their theories. If you have fifty physicists in a town, they can get funding and start a university department. If you have a hundred, maybe some of them can go into teaching or administration and help support the others. Having this extra concentration of talent in central Europe during this period might have helped Jews and Gentiles alike.

I wonder about this because of a sentiment I hear a lot, from people who know more about physics than I do, that we just don't get people like John von Neumann or Leo Szilard anymore. That there was some weird magical productivity to the early 20th century, especially in Central Europe and Central European immigrants to the United States, that we're no longer really able to match. This can't be a pure numbers game – the Ashkenazi population has mostly recovered since the Holocaust, and people from all over the world are coming to American and European universities and providing more of a concentration of talent than ever. And even though it's impossible to measure, there's still a feeling that it's not enough.

I started down this particular research rabbit hole because a friend challenged me to explain what was so magical about early 20th century Hungary. I think the Jewish population calculations above explain a lot of the story. I'm not sure whether there's a missing ingredient, or, if so, what it might be. Maybe it really was better education. Maybe it really was math competitions and talent searches.

Or maybe it was superintelligent Martian scouts with an Earthling fetish.

27

Hungarian Education II: Four Nobel Truths

May 29, 2017

1. Israel historically has only a moderate number of Nobels per capita

On Friday, I discussed the phenomenon of Hungarian science geniuses[1], and conjectured it was because of Hungary's high concentration of Ashkenazi Jews. A commenter pointed out that Israel had an even higher concentration of Ashkenazi Jews, with less impressive results:

> By this logic, Israel should have become the hotbed of geniuses. And while it's true that there are a lot of smart people there, none of the Israeli universities are in the top 10 or maybe even in top 100. And the fraction of Nobel prize winners is not impressive, either.

The objection makes superficial sense. The list of Nobel winners per capita[2] puts Israel at a modest tenth place, after places like Norway and the United Kingdom.

This doesn't look promising for any Ashkenazi-Jew-based theory.

2. But their more modern numbers look much more impressive

On the other hand, that list counts total Nobels won, ever, and divides them by modern population. That gives an advantage to older countries. Nor way's been collecting Nobels since 1903; Israel wasn't even *founded* until 1948.

---

[1] https://slatestarcodex.com/2017/05/26/the-atomic-bomb-considered-as-hungarian-high-school-science-fair-project/#comment-504339

[2] https://en.wikipedia.org/wiki/List_of_countries_by_Nobel_laureates_per_capita

And for the first couple generations the Israelis were pretty busy starting kib-butzim, building infrastructure, fighting off enemies, et cetera. Setting up a good university system capable of churning out Nobels takes time. So Nor-way and the UK had an unfair head start.

I redid their analysis looking only at Nobels won since the year 2000 (be-cause it was big and round and serves as a signal that I'm trying to avoid optional stopping). My source was this list of Nobel laureates by country[3], and I deferred to Wikipedia's judgment about whether or not to count dual citizens, immigrants, et cetera. Here's the results:

We see that during this period, Israel has by far the highest number of Nobel prizes per capita.

3. This advantage increases if we look only at Ashkenazim

The original theory was about Ashkenazi Jews in particular. Only about a third of Israels are Ashkenazi (the rest are other types of Jews, or Palestinians, or other non-Jewish minorities). If we separate out the Ashkenazim, the graph looks like this.

ISAZ is Israeli Ashkenazi Jews, considered as a separate population. On the one hand, it's kind of unfair comparing Israel's most successful population group to other countries taken as a whole. On the other hand, if we were to take other countries' most successful population groups, those would be Ashkenazi Jews too, so whatever. Since Israeli Ashkenazim get about five times more Nobels per capita than any country, I'm going to consider the "what about Israel?" objection officially refuted.

4. But there's not a lot of evidence for benefits to concentration, and other factors might be involved

One more graph:

USAZ is US Ashkenazi Jews, who get twice as many Nobels per capita as their Israeli cousins (I'm not sure how seriously to take this; the Israeli data is based on eight Nobel laureates, so there's a lot of room for sampling issues.)

And although it's hard for me to get exact numbers, it looks like a lot of Israeli Nobelist (maybe more than half) did their best work abroad, usually in the US.

---

[3]https://en.wikipedia.org/wiki/List_of_Nobel_laureates_by_country

Israel went from 1948 to 2002 without winning a single science Nobel (it did win in Literature and Peace during that time). Now it's winning more of them – a lot more, more than any other country per capita – but mostly when its citizens go and study in foreign universities. This seems consistent with an Israeli educational system that's still struggling to get its act together.

Does this mean that once the educational system gets its act together more fully, the ISAZ Nobel rate will approximately double to match the USAZ Nobel rate? I'm not sure.

Just from this analysis, it doesn't look like the theory in the last post, where everyone gets benefits from concentrating closer together, is true. Israel has about ten times as many Ashkenazi Jews per capita than the US, but still does worse than they do.

These data don't challenge the conclusion from the last post that Ashkenazim might have been responsible for Hungary's sudden crop of great scientists. But they do potentially challenge the implicit conclusion that the education system didn't matter that much. I'll have more on that later this week.

28

Hungarian Education III: Mastering The Core Teachings Of The Budapestians

May 30, 2017

I

Someone summed up my prior essay as "Hungarian education isn't magic". I would amend that to read "Hungarian education isn't *systemically* magic". As far as I know, there's only one Hungarian educator with magic powers, and (like all good wizards) his secrets are maddeningly hard to find.

Laszlo Polgar studied intelligence in university, and decided he had discovered the basic principles behind raising any child to be a genius. He wrote a book called *Bring Up Genius* and recruited an interested woman to marry him so they could test his philosophy by raising children together. He said a bunch of stuff on how 'natural talent' was meaningless and so any child could become a prodigy with the right upbringing.

This is normally the point where I'd start making fun of him. Except that when he trained his three daughters in chess, they became the 1st, 2nd, and 6th best female chess players in the world, gaining honors like "youngest grandmaster ever" and "greatest female chess player of all time". Also they spoke seven languages, including Esperanto.

Their immense success suggests that education can have a major effect even on such traditional genius-requiring domains as chess ability. How can we reconcile that with the rest of our picture of the world, and how obsessed should we be with getting a copy of Laszlo Polgar's book?

II

Let's get this out of the way first: the Polgar sisters were probably genetically really smart. The whole family was Hungarian Jews, a group with a great track record. Their mother and father were both well-educated teachers interested in stuff like developmental psychology. They had every possible biological advantage and I'm sure that helped.

J Levitt proposes[1] an equation to estimate a chess player's IQ from their chess score. It suggests that chess grandmasters probably have IQs above 160. Plugging the Polgar sisters' chess scores into his equation, I get IQs in the range of 150, 160, and 170 for the three sisters.

~~This is biologically impossible. Even if both Polgar parents were 170-IQ themselves, regression to the mean predicts that their children would have IQs around 140 to 150. It's mathematically possible for there to be an IQ that predicts you would have three children of 150, 160, and 170, but I doubt any living people have it, and even if they did there's no way they would marry somebody else equally gifted.~~

EDIT: Thanks to a few people who pointed out some problems with my math here (1^2, 2^3, 3^4). I still think that having three supergenius-IQ kids when you and your spouse show no signs of being a supergenius yourself (Laszlo Polgar's daughters could beat him at chess by the time they were 8) is pretty unlikely, but I admit not impossible. I still think arguing about this is unnecessary thanks to the points below.

On the other hand, I'm not sure Levitt's right. Chess champion Gary Kasparov actually sat and took an IQ test[5] for the magazine *Der Spiegel*, and his IQ was 135. That's not bad – it's top 1% of the population – but it's not amazing either.

This is what we should expect given the correlation of about r = 0.24[6] between IQ and chess ability (see also this analysis[7], although I disagree with

---

[1] http://www.jlevitt.dircon.co.uk/iq.htm

[2] https://www.reddit.com/r/slatestarcodex/comments/6e92d1/hungarian_education_iii_m astering_the_core/di8m65y/

[3] https://slatestarcodex.com/2017/05/30/hungarian-education-iii-mastering-the-core -teachings-of-the-budapestians/#comment-505553

[4] https://slatestarcodex.com/2017/05/30/hungarian-education-iii-mastering-the-core -teachings-of-the-budapestians/#comment-505584

[5] http://www.spiegel.de/spiegel/print/d-13526693.html

[6] https://www.researchgate.net/profile/Fernand_Gobet/publication/307874653_The_rel ationship_between_cognitive_ability_and_chess_skill_A_comprehensive_meta-analysis/lin ks/57d15ea908ae601b39a1c60b.pdf

[7] https://pumpkinperson.com/2015/05/30/the-iq-of-garry-kasparov/comment-page-1/

the details). And the contrary claims – like the one[8] that Bobby Fischer's IQ was in the 180s – are less well-sourced (although Fischer was the son of a Hungarian-Jewish mathematician[9], so who knows?).

If it were possible to be a chess world champion with an IQ of 135, then maybe it's possible to be a "mere" grandmaster with IQs in the high 120s and low 130s. And it's just barely plausible that some sufficiently smart people might have three kids who all have IQs in the high 120s and low 130s.

But this just passes the buck on the mystery. 2% of people have IQs in the high 120s or low 130s, but 2% of people aren't the top-ranked female chess player in the world. The Polgar sisters' IQs might have been a *permissive* factor in allowing them to excel, but it didn't *necessitate* it. So what's going on there?

III

"Practice" seems like an obvious part of the picture. Malcolm Gladwell uses the Polgars as poster children for his famous '10,000 hours of practice makes you an expert at anything'[10] rule. The Polgars had 50,000 hours of chess practice each by the time they were adults, presumably enough to make them quintuple-experts.

Robert Howard has a paper Does High-Level Performance Depend On Practice Alone? Debunking The Polgar Sisters Case[11] in which he argues against the strong version of Gladwell's thesis. He points out that there are many chess masters who have practiced much less than the Polgar sisters but are better than they are. He also points out that even though the sisters themselves have all practiced similar amounts, youngest sister Judit is clearly better than the other two in a way that practice alone cannot explain.

I don't know if the case he's arguing against – that practice is literally everything and it's impossible for anything else to factor in – is a straw man or not. But it seems more important to consider a less silly argument – that practice is one of many factors, and that enough of it can make up for a lack of the others. This seems potentially true. This study[12] showing that amount of practice only explains 12% of the variance in skill level at various tasks, and

---

[8] http://bobbyfischer.net/bobby02.html

[9] https://en.wikipedia.org/wiki/Paul_Nemenyi#Bobby_Fischer.27s_father.3F

[10] http://www.newyorker.com/news/sporting-scene/complexity-and-the-ten-thousand-hour-rule

[11] http://www.sciencedirect.com/science/article/pii/S0885201411000335

[12] http://www.businessinsider.com/new-study-destroys-malcolm-gladwells-10000-rule-2014-7

is often summarized as "practice doesn't matter much". But it finds practice matters more (25% of the variance) in unchanging games with clear fixed rules, and uses chess as an example.

So suppose that the Polgar sisters are genetically smart, but maybe not as high up there as some other chess masters. We would expect them to need much more practice to achieve a level of proficiency similar to those chess masters, and indeed that seems like what happens.

(all of this is confounded by them being women and almost all the other equally-good chess masters being men. It's unclear if the Polgars deserve extra points for overcoming whatever factor usually keeps women out of the highest levels of chess.)

But I'm actually still not sure this suffices as an explanation. According to Wikipedia:

> Polgár began teaching his eldest daughter, Susan, to play chess when she was four years old. Six months later, Susan toddled into Budapest's smoke-filled chess club," which was crowded with elderly men, and proceeded to beat the veteran players.

The study linked above suggests that Susan practiced 48 hours a week. During those six months, she would have accumulated about 1200 hours of practice. Suppose the elderly Budapest chess players practiced only one hour a week, but had been doing so for the last twenty-five years. They would have more practice than Susan – plus the advantage of having older, more developed brains. So why did she beat them so easily?

Maybe there's a time-decay factor for practice? That is, maybe Susan had been practicing intensively, so she got a lot of chances to link it all together as she was learning, and also it was fresh in her mind when she went to the club to go play? I'm not sure. If some of those veterans had been playing more than one hour a week (and surely the sort of people who frequent Budapest chess clubs do) then her advantage seems too implausible to be due to freshness-of-material alone.

IV

That leaves two possibilities.

First, Susan could have benefitted from some form of malleability. A lot of people claim there's a "developmental window" during which children have a unique ability to learn language. If cats see only vertical stripes[13] for the first few weeks of their lives, they never learn to see in horizontal. Maybe if you teach your kid high-level chess at age 4, they'll be able to recruit systems that adults could never manage, or reorganize the fundamental structure of their brain to conform to chess better, or something like that.

Second, Polgar might actually have some really good educational methods besides just "start early and have a lot of practice". I assume this is true, but I'm having a lot of trouble finding them. Shockingly, Polgar's book *Bring Up Genius* is out of print and totally unavailable anywhere – I guess the book-reading community heard that someone wrote down a way to reliably turn any child into a genius which had a great real-world track record of success, and collectively decided "Nah, better read *Fifty Shades Of Grey* instead". I'm not sure at what point I should start positing a conspiracy of suppression, or whether that would be better or worse than the alternative.

The book seems to possibly be available in Hungarian under the title *Nevelj zsenit!*, but I can't tell for sure and a lot of the Hungarian sites suggest it's out of print even in that language. There *may* have been a recent republication in Esperanto called *Eduku geniulon!*, but I can't find that one either. If anybody knows where to find this book and wants to send it to me, I will figure out some way to translate it and review it. I'd also be willing to pay for costs and even pay extra for your time if it helps. Come on, Esperanto-speakers! This is the only chance you'll ever have to be useful!

V

One thing I know without reading the book: Polgar says that his method should work to create geniuses in any field, not just chess. He said he chose chess kind of on the whim of his eldest daughter. From Wikipedia:

> Polgár and his wife considered various possible subjects in which to drill their children, "including mathematics and foreign languages," but they settled on chess. "We could do the same thing with any subject, if you start early, spend lots of time and give great love to that one subject," Klara later explained. "But we chose chess. Chess is very objective and easy to measure." Susan described chess as having been her own choice: "Yes, he could

---

[13] https://www.psychologytoday.com/blog/brain-food/201404/the-cat-nobel-prize-part-ii

have put us in any field, but it was I who chose chess as a four-year-old…. I liked the chessmen; they were toys for me."

It's disappointing that he decided to stick with chess for his other two daughters. The study linked above suggests that chess is unusually amenable to practice. What would have happened if he'd tried to train his kids in art? In mathematics? In entrepreneurship? I'm not sure, and I'm really tempted to have some kids and find out.

(be right back, going to change my OKCupid profile to include "must be interested in n=1 developmental-psych experiments, have access to a rare book library, and speak either Hungarian or Esperanto")

I mentioned this plan to a friend, who protested that this was cruel and tantamount to child abuse. After all, how can you force someone to spend their entire childhood indoors, studying mind-numbing chess problems day in and day out, instead of enjoying themselves like normal kids?

First of all, this isn't how the Polgar children (or adults) describe their experiment. From *The Guardian*[14]:

> Starting with his eldest daughter, Susan, Polgár was careful to treat it as a playful activity, turning it into a fantasy of dramatic wins and losses. Whereas Earl and Kultida Woods had coerced perfection from Tiger, the Polgárs encouraged enjoyment, By the time Susan had turned five, she was excited by playing and spent hundreds of hours practising. She was entered into a local competition and treated it as fun, winning 10-0, causing a sensation.
>
> Meanwhile, her younger sisters were intrigued and László allowed them to feel the pieces, seeing them as toys, with no formal tuition until they were five. Interviewed recently, all three girls described playing the game as something that they loved doing – it never felt like a chore. Instead of messing about playing Monopoly, netball or going to the local swimming pool, chess was just what the Polgár family enjoyed… Polgár understood that coercion was less valuable than small children's need to enjoy fantasy play. Consequently, his daughters all seem to have grown into satiable, well-balanced people rather than success addicts.

---

[14]https://www.theguardian.com/lifeandstyle/2016/feb/27/how-to-raise-a-brilliant-child-without-screwing-them-up

But more important – I responded that the Polgars claim to have spent about 48 hours a week practicing chess. I spent seven hours a day in school, so if my teachers assigned two hours of homework a night then we spent about the same amount of time getting educated. Except what the *Polgars* got out of it was world-champion-level mastery of their favorite subject in the world, nationwide fame, and (by their own accounts) loving every second of it, and what *I* got was staring out a window all day as my teacher declared that we were going to make a collage about the meaning of Respect.

The Polgar sisters talk about how they loved their education, had a great childhood, thought their parents were always patient with them and never strict and harsh, and don't regret anything. How many kids who went to public school can say the same?

An article about Laszlo Polgar mentions that he had to fight the Hungarian authorities to be allowed to home school his children. Imagine being so certain of your own home-schooling techniques that you're afraid taking your kids to is going to stunt their intellectual growth. And imagine being *right*. And imagine my friend thinking that normal American public school might be better than that. It sort of boggles the imagination.

And I guess I shouldn't be too harsh, because the public school system tries to do the best it can with an impossible set of constraints. But I'm still suspicious. *Who else has the motivation to hide that book?*

EDIT: Thanks to readers, I've got an Esperanto copy and a person willing to translate it. I'll let you know as this develops.

— 29 —

SSC Journal Club: AI Timelines

June 8, 2017

I

A few years ago, Muller and Bostrom et al surveyed AI researchers to assess their opinion on AI progress and superintelligence. Since then, deep learning took off, AlphaGo beat human Go champions, and the field has generally progressed. I've been waiting for a new survey for a while, and now we have one.

Grace et al (*New Scientist* article[1], paper[2], see also the post on the author's blog AI Impacts[3]) surveyed 1634 experts at major AI conferences and received 352 responses. Unlike Bostrom's survey, this didn't oversample experts at weird futurist conferences and seems to be a pretty good cross-section of mainstream opinion in the field. What did they think?

Well, a lot of different things.

The headline result: the researchers asked experts for their probabilities that we would get AI that was "able to accomplish every task better and more cheaply than human workers". The experts thought on average there was a 50% chance of this happening by 2062 – and a 10% chance of it happening by 2026!

But on its own this is a bit misleading. They also asked by what year "for any occupation, machines could be built to carry out the task better and more cheaply than human workers". The experts thought on average that there was

---

[1] https://www.newscientist.com/article/2133188-ai-will-be-able-to-beat-us-at-everything-by-2060-say-experts/

[2] https://arxiv.org/pdf/1705.08807.pdf

[3] http://aiimpacts.org/some-survey-results/

a 50% chance of this happening by 2139, and a 20% chance of it happening by 2037.

As the authors point out, these two questions are basically the same – they were put in just to test if there was any framing effect. The framing effect was apparently strong enough to shift the median date of strong human-level AI from 2062 to 2139. This makes it hard to argue AI experts actually have a strong opinion on this.

Also, these averages are deceptive. Several experts thought there was basically a 100% chance of strong AI by 2035; others thought there was only a 20% chance or less by 2100. This is less "AI experts have spoken and it will happen in 2062" and more "AI experts have spoken, and everything they say contradicts each other and quite often themselves".

This *does* convey more than zero information. It conveys the information that AI researchers are *really unsure*. I can't tell you how many people I've heard say "there's no serious AI researcher who thinks there's any chance of human-level intelligence before 2050". Well actually, there are a few dozen conference-paper-presenting experts who think there's a *one hundred* percent chance of human-level AI before that year. I don't know what drugs they're on, but they exist. The moral of the story is: be less certain about this kind of thing.

II

The next thing we can take from this paper is a timeline of what will happen when. The authors give a bunch of different tasks, jobs, and milestones, and ask the researchers when AI will be able to complete them. Average answers range from nearly fifty years off (for machines being able to do original high-level mathematical research) to only three years away (for machines achieving the venerable accomplishment of being able to outperform humans at *Angry Birds*). Along the way they'll beat humans at poker (four years), writing high school essays (ten years), be able to outrun humans in a 5K foot race (12 years), and write a New York Times bestseller (26 years). What do these AI researchers think is the hardest and most quintessentially human of the tasks listed, the one robots will have the most trouble doing because of its Olympian intellectual requirements? That's right – AI research (80 years).

I make fun of this, but it's actually interesting to think about. Might the AI researchers have put their own job last not because of an inflated sense of their own importance, but because they engage with it every day in Near

Mode? That is, because they imagine writing a New York Times bestseller as "something something pen paper be good with words okay done" whereas they understand the complexity of AI research and how excruciatingly hard it would be to automate away every piece of what they do?

Also, since they rated AI research (80 years) as the hardest of all occupations, what do they mean when they say that "full automation of all human jobs" is 125 years away? Some other job not on the list that will take 40 years longer than AI research? Or just a combination of framing effects and not understanding the question?

(it's also unclear to what extent they believe that automating AI research will lead to a feedback loop and subsequent hard takeoff to superintelligence. This kind of theory would fit with it being the last job to be automated, but not with it taking another forty years before an unspecified age of full automation.)

III

The last part is the most interesting for me: what do AI researchers believe about risk from superintelligence?

This is very different from the earlier questions about timelines. It's possible to believe that AI will come very soon but be perfectly safe. And it's possible to believe that AI is a long time away but we really need to start preparing now, or else. A lot of popular accounts collapse these two things together, "oh, you're worried about AI, but that's dumb because there's no way it's going to happen anytime soon", but past research has shown that short timelines and high risk assessment are only modestly correlated. This survey asked about both separately.

There were a couple of different questions trying to get at this, but it looks like the most direct one was "does Stuart Russell's argument for why highly advanced AI might pose a risk, point at an important problem?". You can see the exact version of his argument quoted in the survey on the AI Impacts page[4], but it's basically the standard Bostrom/Yudkowsky argument for why AIs may end up with extreme values contrary to our own, framed in a very normal-sounding and non-threatening way. According to the experts, this was:

No, not a real problem	11%

[4]http://aiimpacts.org/some-survey-results/

No, not an important problem	19%
Yes, a moderately important problem	31%
Yes, an important problem	34%
Yes, among the most important problems in the field	5%

70% of AI experts agree with the basic argument that there's a risk from poorly-goal-aligned AI. But very few believe it's among "the most important problems in the field". This is pretty surprising; if there's a good chance AI could be hostile to humans, shouldn't that automatically be pretty high on the priority list?

The next question might help explain this: "Value of working on this problem now, compared to other problems in the field?"

Much less valuable	22%
Less valuable	41%
As valuable as other problems	28%
More valuable	7%
Much more valuable	1.4%

So charitably, the answer to this question was coloring the answer to the previous one: AI researchers believe it's plausible that there could be major problems with machine goal alignment, they just don't think that there's too much point in working on it now.

One more question here: "Chance intelligence explosion argument is broadly correct?"

Quite likely (81-100% chance)	12%
Likely (61-80% chance)	17%
About even (41-60% chance)	21%
Unlikely (21-40% chance)	24%
Quite unlikely (0-20% chance)	26%

Splitting the 41-60% bin in two, we might estimate that about 40% of AI researchers think the hypothesis is more likely than not.

Take the big picture here, and I worry there's sort of a discrepancy.

50% of experts think there's at least a ten percent chance of above-human-level AI coming within the next ten years.

And 40% of experts think that there's a better-than-even chance that, once we get above-human level AI, it will "explode" to suddenly become vastly more intelligent than humans.

And 70% of experts think that Stuart Russell makes a pretty good point when he says that without a lot of research into AI goal alignment, AIs will probably have their goals so misaligned with humans that they could become dangerous and hostile.

I don't have the raw individual-level data, so I can't prove that these aren't all anti-correlated in some perverse way that's the opposite of the direction I would expect. But if we assume they're not, and just naively multiply the probabilities together for a rough estimate, that suggests that about 14% of experts believe that all three of these things: that AI might be soon, superintelligent, and hostile.

Yet only a third of these – 5% – think this is "among the most important problems in the field". Only a tenth – 1.4% – think it's "much more valuable" than other things they could be working on.

IV

How have things changed since Muller and Bostrom's survey in 2012?

The short answer is "confusingly". Since almost everyone agrees that AI progress in the past five years has been much faster than expected, we would expect experts to have faster timelines – ie expect AI to be closer now than they did then. But Bostrom's sample predicted human-level AI in 2040 (median) or 2081 (mean). Grace et al don't give clear means or medians, preferring some complicated statistical construct which isn't exactly similar to either of these. But their dates – 2062 by one framing, 2139 by another – at least seem potentially a little bit later.

Some of this may have to do with a subtle difference in how they asked their question:

Bostrom: "Define a high-level machine intelligence as one that can carry out most human professions as well as a typical human…"

Grace: "High-level machine intelligence is achieved when unaided machines can accomplish every task better and more cheaply than human workers."

Bostrom wanted it equal to humans; Grace wants it better. Bostrom wanted "most professions", Grace wants "every task". It makes sense that experts would predict longer timescales for meeting Grace's standards.

But as we saw before, expecting AI experts to make sense might be giving them too much credit. A more likely possibility: Bostrom's sample included people from wackier subbranches of AI research, like a conference on Philosophy of AI and one on Artificial General Intelligence; Grace's sample was more mainstream. The most mainstream part of Bostrom's sample, a list of top 100 AI researchers, had an estimate a bit closer to Grace's (2050).

We can also compare the two samples on belief in an intelligence explosion. Bostrom asked how likely it was that AI went from human-level to "greatly surpassing" human level within two years. The median was 10%; the mean was 19%. The median of top AI researchers not involved in wacky conferences was 5%.

Grace asked the same question, with much the same results: a median 10% probability. I have no idea why this question – which details what an "intelligence explosion" would entail – was so much less popular than the one that used the words "intelligence explosion" (remember, 40% of experts agreed that "the intelligence explosion argument is broadly correct"). Maybe researchers believe it's a logically sound argument and worth considering but in the end it's not going to happen – or maybe they don't actually know what "intelligence explosion" means.

Finally, Bostrom and Grace both asked experts' predictions for whether the final impact of AI would be good or bad. Bostrom's full sample (top 100 subgroup in parentheses) was:

Extremely good	24%	(20)
On balance good	28%	(40)
More or less neutral	17%	(19)
On balance bad	3%	(13)
Extremely bad – existential catastrophe	18%	(8)

Grace's results for the same question:

Extremely good	20%
On balance good	25%
More or less neutral	40%
On balance bad	10%
Extremely bad – human extinction	5%

Grace's data looks pretty much the same as the TOP100 subset of Bostrom's data, which makes sense since both are prestigious non-wacky AI researchers.

V

A final question: "How much should society prioritize AI safety research"?

Much less	5%
Less	6%
About the same	41%
More	35%
Much more	12%

People who say that real AI researchers don't believe in safety research are now just empirically wrong. I can't yet say that most of them want more such research – it's only 47% on this survey. But next survey AI will be a little bit more advanced, people will have thought it over a little bit more, and maybe we'll break the 50% mark.

But we're not there yet.

I think a good summary of this paper would be that large-minorities-to-small-majorities of AI experts agree with the arguments around AI risk and think they're worth investigating further. But only a very small minority of experts consider it an emergency or think it's really important right now.

You could tell an optimistic story here – "experts agree that things will probably be okay, everyone can calm down".

You can also tell a more pessimistic story. Experts agree with a lot of the claims and arguments that suggest reason for concern. It's just that, having granted them, they're not *actually* concerned.

This seems like a pretty common problem in philosophy. "Do you believe it's more important that poor people have basic necessities of life than that you have lots of luxury goods?" "Yeah" "And do you believe that the money you're currently spending on luxury goods right now could instead be spent on charity that would help poor people get life necessities?" "Yeah." "Then shouldn't you stop buying luxury goods and instead give all your extra money beyond what you need to live to charity?" "Hey, what? Nobody does that! That would be a lot of work and make me look really weird!"

How many of the experts in this survey are victims of the same problem? "Do you believe powerful AI is coming soon?" "Yeah." "Do you believe it could be really dangerous?" "Yeah." "Then shouldn't you worry about this?" "Hey, what? Nobody does that! That would be a lot of work and make me look really weird!"

I don't know. But I'm encouraged to see people are even taking the arguments seriously. And I'm encouraged that researchers are finally giving us good data on this. Thanks to the authors of this study for being so diligent, helpful, intelligent, wonderful, and (of course) sexy.

(I might have forgotten to mention that the lead author is my girlfriend. But that's not biasing my praise above in any way.)

30

My IRB Nightmare

August 29, 2017

Epistemic status: Pieced together from memory years after the event. I may have mis-remembered some things or gotten them in the wrong order. Aside from that – and the obvious jokes – this is all true. I'm being deliberately vague in places because I don't want to condemn anything specific without being able to prove anything.

September 2014

There's a screening test for bipolar disorder. You ask patients a bunch of things like "Do you ever feel really happy, then really sad?". If they say 'yes' to enough of these questions, you start to worry.

Some psychiatrists love this test. I hate it. Patients will say "Yes, that absolutely describes me!" and someone will diagnose them with bipolar disorder. Then if you ask what they meant, they'd say something like "Once my local football team made it to the Super Bowl and I was really happy, but then they lost and I was really sad." I don't even want to tell you how many people get diagnosed bipolar because of stuff like this.

There was a study that supposedly proved this test worked. But parts of it confused me, and it was done on a totally different population that didn't generalize to hospital inpatients. Also, it said in big letters THIS IS JUST A SCREENING TEST IT IS NOT INTENDED FOR DIAGNOSIS, and everyone was using it for diagnosis.

So I complained to some sympathetic doctors and professors, and they asked "Why not do a study?"

Why *not* do a study? Why not join the great tradition of scientists, going back to Galileo and Newton, and make my mark on the world? Why not replace my griping about bipolar screening with an experiment about bipolar screening, an experiment done to the highest standards of the empirical tradition, one that would throw the entire weight of the scientific establishment behind my complaint? I'd been writing about science for so long, even doing my own informal experiments, why not move on to join the big leagues?

For (it would turn out) a whole host of excellent reasons that I was about to learn.

A spring in my step, I journeyed to my hospital's Research Department, hidden in a corner office just outside the orthopaedic ward. It was locked, as always. After enough knocking, a lady finally opened the door and motioned for me to sit down at a paperwork-filled desk.

"I want to do a study," I said.

She looked skeptical. "Have you done the Pre-Study Training?"

I had to admit I hadn't, so off I went. The training was several hours of videos about how the Nazis had done unethical human experiments. Then after World War II, everybody met up and decided to only do ethical human experiments from then on. And the most important part of being ethical was to have all experiments monitored by an Institutional Review Board (IRB) made of important people who could check whether experiments were ethical or not. I dutifully parroted all this back on the post-test ("Blindly trusting authority to make our ethical decisions for us is the *best* way to separate ourselves from the Nazis!") and received my Study Investigator Certification.

I went back to the corner office, Study Investigator Certification in hand.

"I want to do a study," I said.

The lady still looked skeptical. "Do you have a Principal Investigator?"

Mere resident doctors weren't allowed to do studies on their own. They would probably screw up and start building concentration camps or something. They needed an attending (high-ranking doctor) to sign on as Principal Investigator before the IRB would deign to hear their case.

I knew exactly how to handle this: one by one, I sought out the laziest attendings in the hospital and asked "Hey, would you like to have your name on a study as Principal Investigator for free while I do all the actual work?" Yet one by one, all of the doctors refused, as if I was offering them some kind of plague basket full of vermin. It was the weirdest thing.

Finally, there was only one doctor left – Dr. W, the hardest-working attending I knew, the one who out of some weird masochistic impulse took on every single project anyone asked of him and micromanaged it to perfection, the one who every psychiatrist in the whole hospital (including himself) had diagnosed with obsessive-compulsive personality disorder.

"Sure Scott," he told me. "I'd be happy to serve as your Principal Investigator".

A feeling of dread in my stomach, I walked back to the tiny corner office.

"I want to do a study," I said.

The lady still looked skeptical. "Have you completed the New Study Application?" She gestured to one of the stacks of paperwork filling the room.

It started with a section on my research question. Next was a section on my proposed methodology. A section on possible safety risks. A section on recruitment. A section on consent. A section on… wow. Surely this can't *all* be the New Study Application? Maybe I accidentally picked up the Found A New Hospital Application?

I asked the lady who worked in the tiny corner office whether, since I was just going to be asking bipolar people whether they ever felt happy and then sad, maybe I could get the short version of the New Study Application?

She told me that *was* the short version.

"But it's twenty-two pages!"

"You haven't done any studies before, have you?"

Rather than confess my naivete, I started filling out the twenty-two pages of paperwork. It started by asking about our study design, which was simple: by happy coincidence, I was assigned to Dr. W's inpatient team for the next three months. When we got patients, I would give them the bipolar screening exam and record the results. Then Dr. W. would conduct a full clinical interview and formally assess them. We'd compare notes and see how often the screening test results matched Dr. W's expert diagnosis. We usually got about twenty new patients a week; if half of them were willing and able to join our study, we should be able to gather about a hundred data points over the next three months. It was going to be easy-peasy.

That was the first ten pages or so of the Application. The rest was increasingly bizarre questions such as "Will any organs be removed from participants during this study?" (Look, I promise, I'm not a Nazi.)

And: "Will prisoners be used in the study?" (COME ON, I ALREADY SAID I WASN'T A NAZI.)

And: "What will you do if a participant dies during this research?" (If somebody dies while I'm asking them whether they sometimes feel happy and then sad, I really can't even promise so much as "not freaking out", let alone any sort of dignified research procedure).

And more questions, all along the same lines. I double-dog swore to give everybody really, really good consent forms. I tried my best to write a list of the risks participants were taking upon themselves (mostly getting paper cuts on the consent forms). I argued that these compared favorably to the benefits (maybe doctors will stop giving people strong psychiatric medications just because their football team made the Super Bowl).

When I was done, I went back to the corner office and submitted everything to the Institutional Review Board. Then I sat back and hoped for the best. Like an idiot.

October 2014

The big day arrived. The IRB debated the merits of my study, examined the risks, and... sent me a letter pointing out several irregularities in my consent forms.

IRREGULARITY #1: Consent forms traditionally included the name of the study in big letters where the patient could see it before signing. Mine didn't. Why not?

Well, because in questionnaire-based psychological research, you *never* tell the patient what you're looking for before they fill out the questionnaire. That's like Methods 101. The name of my study was "Validity Of A Screening Instrument For Bipolar Disorder". Tell the patient it's a study about bipolar disorder, and the gig is up.

The IRB listened patiently to my explanation, then told me that this was not a legitimate reason not to put the name of the study in big letters on the consent form. Putting the name of the study on the consent form was important. You know who *else* didn't put the name of the study on his consent forms? *Hitler.*

IRREGULARITY #2: Consent forms traditionally included a paragraph about the possible risks of the study and a justification for why we believed that the benefits were worth the risks. Everyone else included a paragraph about this on our consent forms, and read it to their patients before getting their consent. We didn't have one. Why not?

Well, for one thing, because all we were doing was asking them whether they felt happy and then sad sometimes. This is the sort of thing that goes on every day in a psychiatric hospital. Heck, the other psychiatrists were using this same screening test, except *for real*, and they never had to worry about whether it had risks. In the grand scheme of things, this just wasn't a very risky procedure.

Also, psychiatric patients are sometimes… how can I put this nicely?… a little paranoid. Sometimes you can offer them breakfast and they'll accuse you of trying to poison them. I had no illusions that I would get every single patient to consent to this study, but I felt like I could at least avoid handing them a paper saying "BY THE WAY, THIS STUDY IS FULL OF RISKS".

The IRB listened patiently to my explanation, then told me that this was not a legitimate reason not to have a paragraph about risks. We should figure out some risks, then write a paragraph explaining how those were definitely the risks and we took them very seriously. The other psychiatrists who used this test every day didn't have to do that *because they weren't running a study*.

IRREGULARITY #3: Signatures are traditionally in pen. But we said our patients would sign in pencil. Why?

Well, because psychiatric patients aren't allowed to have pens in case they stab themselves with them. I don't get why stabbing yourself with a pencil is any less of a problem, but the rules are the rules. We asked the hospital administration for a one-time exemption, to let our patients have pens just long enough to sign the consent form. Hospital administration said absolutely not, and they didn't care if this sabotaged our entire study, it was pencil or nothing.

The IRB listened patiently to all this, then said that it had to be in pen. You know who *else* had people sign consent forms in pencil…?

I'm definitely not saying that these were the only three issues the IRB sprung on Dr. W and me. I'm saying these are a *representative sample*. I'm saying I spent several weeks relaying increasingly annoyed emails and memos from myself to Dr. W to the IRB to the lady in the corner office to the IRB again. I began to come home later in the evening. My relationships suffered. I started having dreams about being attacked by giant consent forms filled out in pencil.

I was about ready to give up at this point, but Dr. W insisted on combing through various regulations and talking to various people, until he discovered some arcane rule that certain very safe studies with practically no risk were allowed to use an "expedited consent form", which was a lot like a normal consent form but didn't need to have things like the name of the study on it. Faced with someone even more obsessive and bureaucratic than they were, the IRB backed down and gave us preliminary permission to start our study.

The next morning, screening questionnaire in hand, I showed up at the hospital and hoped for the best. Like an idiot.

November 2014

Things progressed slowly. It turns out a lot of psychiatric inpatients are either depressed, agitated, violent, or out of touch with reality, and none of these are really conducive to wanting to participate in studies. A few of them already delusionally thought we were doing experiments on them, and got confused when we suddenly asked them to consent. Several of them made it clear that they hated us and wanted to thwart us in any way possible. After a week, I only had three data points, instead of the ten I'd been banking on.

"Data points" makes it sound abstract. It wasn't. I had hoped to put the results in the patients' easily accessible online chart, *the same place everyone else put the results of the exact same bipolar screening test* when they did it for real. They would put it in a section marked TEST RESULTS, which was there to have a secure place where you could put test results, and where everybody's secure test results were kept.

The IRB would have none of this. Study data are Confidential and need to be kept Secure. Never mind that all the patients' *other* secure test results were on the online chart. Never mind that the online chart contains all sorts of stuff about the patients' diagnoses, medications, hopes and fears, and even (remember, this is a psych hospital) secret fetishes and sexual perversions. Study data needed to be encrypted, then kept in a Study Binder in a locked drawer in a locked room that nobody except the study investigators had access to.

The first problem was that nobody wanted to give us a locked room that nobody except us had access to. There was a sort of All Purpose Psychiatry Paperwork room, but the janitors went in to clean it out every so often, and apparently this made it unacceptable. Hospitals aren't exactly drowning in spare rooms that not even janitors can get into. Finally Dr. W grudgingly agreed to keep it in his office. This frequently meant I couldn't access any of the study material because Dr. W was having important meetings that couldn't be interrupted by a resident barging into his office to rummage in his locked cabinets.

But whatever. The bigger problem was the encryption. There was a very specific way we had to do it. We would have a Results Log, that said things like "Patient 1 got a score of 11.5 on the test". And then we'd have a Secret Patient Log, which would say things like "Patient 1 = Bob Johnson from Oakburg." That way nobody could steal our results and figure out that Bob was sometimes happy, then sad.

(meanwhile, all of Bob's actual diagnoses, sexual fetishes, etc were in the easily-accessible secure online chart that we were banned from using)

And then – I swear this is true – we had to keep the Results Log and the Secret Patient Log right next to each other in the study binder in the locked drawer in the locked room.

I wasn't sure I was understanding this part right, so I asked Dr. W whether it made sense, to him, that we put a lot of effort writing our results in code, and then put the key to the code in the same place as the enciphered text. He cheerfully agreed this made no sense, but said we had to do it or else our study would fail an audit and get shut down.

January 2015

I'd planned to get a hundred data points in three months. Thanks to constant bureaucratic hurdles, plus patients being less cooperative than I expected, I had about twenty-five. Now I was finishing my rotation on Dr. W's team and going to a clinic far away. What now?

A bunch of newbies were going to be working with Dr. W for the next three months. I hunted them down and threatened and begged them until one of them agreed to keep giving patients the bipolar screening test in exchange for being named as a co-author. Disaster averted, I thought. Like an idiot.

Somehow news of this arrangement reached the lady in the corner office, who asked whether the new investigator had completed her Pre-Study Training. I protested that she wasn't designing the study, she wasn't conducting any analyses, all she was doing was asking her patients the same questions that she would be asking them anyway as part of her job for the next three months. The only difference was that she was recording them and giving them to me.

The lady in the corner office wasn't impressed. You know who *else* hadn't thought his lackeys needed to take courses in research ethics?

So the poor newbie took a course on how Nazis were bad. Now she could help with the study, right?

Wrong. We needed to submit a New Investigator Form to the IRB and wait for their approval.

Two and a half months later, the IRB returned their response: Newbie was good to go. She collected data for the remaining two weeks of her rotation with Dr. W before being sent off to another clinic just like I was.

July 2015

Dr. W and I planned ahead. We had figured out which newbies would be coming in to work for Dr. W three months ahead of time, and gotten them through the don't-be-a-Nazi course and the IRB approval process just in time for them to start their rotation. Success!

Unfortunately, we received another communication from the IRB. Apparently we were allowed to use the expedited consent form to get consent for our *study*, but not to get consent to *access protected health information*. That one required a whole different consent form, list-of-risks and all. We were right back where we'd started from.

I made my case to the Board. My case was: we're not looking at any protected health information, f@#k you.

The Board answered that we were accessing the patient's final diagnosis. It said right in the protocol, we were giving them the screening test, then comparing it to the patient's final diagnosis. "Psychiatric diagnosis" sure *sounds* like protected health information.

I said no, you don't understand, we're the psychiatrists. Dr. W is the one making the final diagnosis. When I'm on Dr. W's team, I'm in the room when he does the diagnostic interview, half the time I'm the one who types the final diagnosis into the chart. These are *our patients*.

The Board said this didn't matter. We, as the patient's doctors, would make the diagnosis and write it down on the chart. But we (as study investigators) needed a full signed consent form before we were allowed to access the diagnosis we had just made.

I said wait, you're telling us we have to do this whole bureaucratic rigamarole with all of these uncooperative patients before we're allowed to see something we wrote ourselves?

The Board said yes, exactly.

I don't remember this part very well, except that I think I half-heartedly trained whichever poor newbie we were using that month in how to take a Protected Health Information Consent on special Protected Health Information Consent Forms, and she nodded her head and said she understood. I think I had kind of clocked out at this point. I was going off to work all the way over in a different town for a year, and I was just sort of desperately hoping that Dr. W and various newbies would take care of things on their own and then in a year when I came back to the hospital I would have a beautiful pile of well-sorted data to analyze. Surely trained doctors would be able to ask simple questions from a screening exam on their own without supervision, I thought. Like an idiot.

July 2016

I returned to my base hospital after a year doing outpatient work in another town. I felt energized, well-rested, and optimistic that the bipolar screening study I had founded so long ago had been prospering in my absence.

Obviously nothing remotely resembling this had happened. Dr. W had vaguely hoped that I was taking care of it. I had vaguely hoped that Dr. W was taking care of it. The various newbies whom we had strategically enlisted had either forgotten about it, half-heartedly screened one or two patients before getting bored, or else mixed up the growing pile of consent forms and releases and logs so thoroughly that we would have to throw out all their work. It had been a year and a half since the study had started, and we had 40 good data points.

The good news was that I was back in town and I could go back to screening patients myself again. Also, we had some particularly enthusiastic newbies who seemed really interested in helping out and getting things right. Over the next three months, our sample size shot up, first to 50, then to 60, finally to 70. Our goal of 100 was almost in sight. The worst was finally behind me, I hoped. Like an idiot.

November 2016

I got an email saying our study was going to be audited.

It was nothing personal. Some higher-ups in the nationwide hospital system had decided to audit every study in our hospital. We were to gather all our records, submit them to the auditor, and hope for the best.

Dr. W, who was obsessive-compulsive at the best of times, became unbearable. We got into late-night fights over the number of dividers in the study binder. We hunted down every piece of paper that had ever been associated with anyone involved in the study in any way, and almost came to blows over how to organize it. I started working really late. My girlfriend began to doubt I actually existed.

The worst part was all the stuff the newbies had done. Some of them would have the consent sheets numbered in the upper left-hand-corner instead of the upper-right-hand corner. Others would have written the patient name down on the Results Log instead of the Secret Code Log right next to it. One even wrote something in green pen on a formal study document. It was hopeless. Finally we just decided to throw away all their data and pretend it had never existed.

With that decision made, our work actually started to look pretty good. As bad as it was working for an obsessive-compulsive boss in an insane bureaucracy, at least it had the advantage that – when nitpicking push came to ridiculous shove – you were going to be super-ready to be audited. I hoped. Like an idiot.

December 2016

The auditor found twenty-seven infractions.

She was very apologetic about it. She said that was actually a pretty good number of infractions for a study this size, that we were actually doing pretty well compared to a lot of the studies she'd seen. She said she absolutely wasn't going to shut us down, she wasn't even going to censure us. She just wanted us to make twenty-seven changes to our study and get IRB approval for each of them.

I kept the audit report as a souvenier. I have it in front of me now. Here's an example infraction:

> The data and safety monitoring plan consists of 'the Principal Investigator will randomly check data integrity'. This is a prospective study with a vulnerable group (mental illness, likely to have diminished capacity, likely to be low income) and, as such, would warrant a more rigorous monitoring plan than what is stated above. In addition to the above, a more adequate plan for this study would also include review of the protocol at regular inter-

vals, on-going checking of any participant complaints or difficulties with the study, monitoring that the approved data variables are the only ones being collected, regular study team meetings to discuss progress and any deviations or unexpected problems. Team meetings help to assure participant protections, adherence to the protocol. Having an adequate monitoring plan is a federal requirement for the approval of a study. See Regulation 45 CFR 46.111 Criteria For IRB Approval Of Research. IRB Policy: PI Qualifications And Responsibility In Conducting Research. Please revise the protocol via a protocol revision request form. Recommend that periodic meetings with the research team occur and be documented.

Among my favorite other infractions:

1. The protocol said we would stop giving the screening exam to patients if they became violent, but failed to rigorously define "violent".
2. We still weren't educating our patients enough about "Alternatives To Participating In This Study". The auditor agreed that the only alternative was "not participating in this study", but said that we had to tell every patient that, then document that we'd done so.
3. The consent forms were still getting signed in pencil. We are never going to live this one down. If I live to be a hundred, representatives from the IRB are going to break into my deathbed room and shout "YOU LET PEOPLE SIGN CONSENT FORMS IN PENCIL, HOW CAN YOU JUSTIFY THAT?!"
4. The woman in the corner office who kept insisting everybody take the Pre-Study Training... hadn't taken the Pre-Study Training, and was therefore unqualified to be our liaison with the IRB. I swear I am not making this up.

Faced with submitting twenty-seven new pieces of paperwork to correct our twenty-seven infractions, Dr. W and I gave up. We shredded the patient data and the Secret Code Log. We told all the newbies they could give up and go home. We submitted the Project Closure Form to the woman in the corner office (who as far as I know still hasn't completed her Pre-Study Training). We told the IRB that they had won, fair and square; we surrendered unconditionally.

They didn't seem the least bit surprised.

August 2017

I've been sitting on this story for a year. I thought it was unwise to publish it while I worked for the hospital in question. I still think it's a great hospital, that it delivers top-notch care, that it has amazing doctors, that it has a really good residency program, and even that the Research Department did everything it could to help me given the legal and regulatory constraints. I don't want this to reflect badly on them in any way. I just thought it was wise to wait a year.

During that year, Dr. W and I worked together on two less ambitious studies, carefully designed not to require any contact with the IRB. One was a case report, the other used publicly available data.

They won 1st and 2nd prize at a regional research competition. I got some nice certificates for my wall and a little prize money. I went on to present one of them at the national meeting of the American Psychiatric Association, a friend helped me write it up formally, and it was recently accepted for publication by a medium-tier journal.

I say this not to boast, but to protest that I'm not as much of a loser as my story probably makes me sound. I'm capable of doing research, I think I have something to contribute to Science. I still think the bipolar screening test is inappropriate for inpatient diagnosis, and I still think that patients are being harmed by people's reliance on it. I still think somebody should look into it and publish the results.

I'm just saying it's not going to be me. I am *done* with research. People keep asking me "You seem really into science, why don't you become a researcher?" Well…

I feel like a study that realistically could have been done by one person in a couple of hours got dragged out into hundreds of hours of paperwork hell for an entire team of miserable doctors. I think its scientific integrity was screwed up by stupid requirements like the one about breaking blinding, and the patients involved were put through unnecessary trouble by being forced to sign endless consent forms screaming to them about nonexistent risks.

I feel like I was dragged almost to the point of needing to be in a psychiatric hospital myself, while my colleagues who just *used* the bipolar screening test – without making the mistake of trying to check if it works – continue to do so without anybody questioning them or giving them the slightest bit of aggravation.

I feel like some scientists do amazingly crappy studies that couldn't possibly prove anything, but get away with it because they have a well-funded team of clerks and secretaries who handle the paperwork for them. And that I, who was trying to do everything right, got ground down with so many pointless security-theater-style regulations that I'm never going to be able to do the research I would need to show they're wrong.

In the past year or so, I've been gratified to learn some other people are thinking along the same lines. Somebody linked me to The Censor's Hand[1], a book by a law/medicine professor at the University of Michigan. A summary from a review[2]:

> Schneider opens by trying to tally the benefits of IRB review. "Surprisingly," he writes, a careful review of the literature suggests that "research is not especially dangerous. Some biomedical research can be risky, but much of it requires no physical contact with patients and most contact cannot cause serious injury. Ill patients are, if anything, safer in than out of research." As for social-science research, "its risks are trivial compared with daily risks like going online or on a date."
>
> Since the upsides of IRB review are likely to be modest, Schneider argues, it's critical to ask hard questions about the system's costs. And those costs are serious. To a lawyer's eyes, IRBs are strangely unaccountable. They don't have to offer reasons for their decisions, their decisions can't be appealed, and they're barely supervised at the federal level. That lack of accountability, combined with the gauzy ethical principles that govern IRB deliberations, is a recipe for capriciousness. Indeed, in Schneider's estimation, IRBs wield coercive government power—the power to censor university research—without providing due process of law.
>
> And they're not shy about wielding that power. Over time, IRB review has grown more and more intrusive. Not only do IRBs waste thousands of researcher hours on paperwork and elaborate consent forms that most study participants will never understand. Of greater concern, they also superintend research methods to minimize perceived risks. Yet IRB members often aren't

---

[1] https://mitpress.mit.edu/books/censors-hand
[2] http://theincidentaleconomist.com/wordpress/should-irbs-be-dismantled/

experts in the fields they oversee. Indeed, some know little or nothing about research methods at all.

IRBs thus delay, distort, and stifle research, especially research on vulnerable subgroups that may benefit most from it. It's hard to precise about those costs, but they're high: after canvassing the research, Schneider concludes that "IRB regulation annually costs thousands of lives that could have been saved, unmeasurable suffering that could have been softened, and uncountable social ills that could have been ameliorated."

This view seems to be growing more popular lately, and has gotten support from high-profile academics like Richard Nisbett and Steven Pinker:

Should IRBs (human subjects research approval committees) be dismantled? [Probably yes.] http://t.co/5mxhEycEA5

— Steven Pinker (@sapinker), July 24, 2015[3]

And there's been some recent reform, maybe. The federal Office for Human Research Protections made a vague statement[4] that perhaps studies that obviously aren't going to hurt anybody might not need the full IRB treatment. There's still a lot of debate about how this will be enforced and whether it's going to lead to any real-life changes. But I'm glad people are starting to think more about these things.

(I'm also glad people are starting to agree that getting rid of a little oversight for the lowest-risk studies is a good compromise, and that we don't have to start with anything more radical.)

I sometimes worry that people misunderstand the case against bureaucracy. People imagine it's Big Business complaining about the regulations preventing them from steamrolling over everyone else. That hasn't been my experience. Big Business – heck, Big Anything – loves bureaucracy. They can hire a team of clerks and secretaries and middle managers to fill out all the necessary forms, and the rest of the company can be on their merry way. It's everyone else who suffers. The amateurs, the entrepreneurs, the hobbyists, the people doing something as a labor of love. Wal-Mart is going to keep

---

[3]https://twitter.com/sapinker/status/624603026997706752

[4]https://www.nytimes.com/2017/05/22/science/social-science-research-institutional
-review-boards-common-rule.html

selling groceries no matter how much paperwork and inspections it takes; the poor immigrant family with the backyard vegetable garden might not.

Bureaucracy in science does the same thing: limit the field to big institutional actors with vested interests. No amount of hassle is going to prevent the Pfizer-Merck-Novartis Corporation from doing whatever study will raise their bottom line. But enough hassle *will* prevent a random psychiatrist at a small community hospital from pursuing his pet theory about bipolar diagnosis. The more hurdles we put up, the more the scientific conversation skews in favor of Pfizer-Merck-Novartis. And the less likely we are to hear little stuff, dissenting voices, and things that don't make anybody any money.

I'm not just talking about IRBs here. I could write a book about this. There are so many privacy and confidentiality restrictions around the most harmless of datasets that research teams won't share data with one another (let alone with unaffiliated citizen scientists) lest they break some arcane regulation or other. Closed access journals require people to pay thousands of dollars in subscription fees before they're allowed to read the scientific literature; open-access journals just shift the burden by requiring scientists to pay thousands of dollars to publish their research. Big research institutions have whole departments to deal with these kinds of problems; unaffiliated people who just want to look into things on their own are out of luck.

And this is happening at the same time we're becoming increasingly aware of the shortcomings of big-name research. Half of psychology studies[5] fail replication; my own field of psychiatry is even worse[6]. And citizen-scientists and science bloggers are playing a big part in debunking bad research: here I'm thinking especially of statistics bloggers like Andrew Gelman[7] and Daniel Lakens[8], but there are all sorts of people in this category. And both Gelman and Lakens are PhDs with institutional affiliations – "citizen science" doesn't mean random cavemen who don't understand the field – but they're both operating outside their day job, trying to contribute a few hours per project instead of a few years. I know many more people like them – smart, highly-qualified, but maybe not going to hire a team of paper-pushers and spend thousands of dollars in fees in order to say what they have to say. Even now these people are doing great work – but I can't help but feel like more is possible.

---

[5] https://www.nature.com/news/over-half-of-psychology-studies-fail-reproducibility-test-1.18248

[6] http://journals.plos.org/plosone/article?id=10.1371/journal.pone.0158064

[7] http://andrewgelman.com/

[8] http://daniellakens.blogspot.com/

IRB overreach is a small part of the problem. But it's the part which sunk my bipolar study, a study I really cared about. I'm excited that there's finally more of a national conversation about this kind of thing, and hopeful that further changes will make scientific efforts easier and more rewarding for the next generation of doctors.

31

Book Review: Surfing Uncertainty

September 5, 2017

Related to: , *Why Are Transgender People Immune To Optical Illusions?*[1], *Can We Link Perception And Cognition?*[2]

I

Sometimes I have the fantasy of being able to glut myself on Knowledge. I imagine meeting a time traveler from 2500, who takes pity on me and gives me a book from the future where all my questions have been answered, one after another. What's consciousness? That's in Chapter 5. How did something arise out of nothing? Chapter 7. It all makes perfect intuitive sense and is fully vouched by unimpeachable authorities. I assume something like this is how everyone spends their first couple of days in Heaven, whatever it is they do for the rest of Eternity.

And every so often, my fantasy comes true. Not by time travel or divine intervention, but by failing so badly at paying attention to the literature that by the time I realize people are working on a problem it's already been investigated, experimented upon, organized into a paradigm, tested, and then placed in a nice package and wrapped up with a pretty pink bow so I can enjoy it all at once.

The predictive processing model is one of these well-wrapped packages. Unbeknownst to me, over the past decade or so neuroscientists have come up with a real *theory* of how the brain works – a real unifying framework theory like Darwin's or Einstein's – and it's beautiful and it makes complete sense.

---

[1] https://slatestarcodex.com/2017/06/28/why-are-transgender-people-immune-to-optical-illusions/

[2] https://slatestarcodex.com/2017/07/14/can-we-link-perception-and-cognition/

Surfing Uncertainty[3] isn't pop science and isn't easy reading. Sometimes it's on the border of possible-at-all reading. Author Andy Clark (a professor of logic and metaphysics, of all things!) is clearly brilliant, but prone to going on long digressions about various esoteric philosophy-of-cognitive-science debates. In particular, he's obsessed with showing how "embodied" everything is all the time. This gets kind of awkward, since the predictive processing model isn't really a natural match for embodiment theory, and describes a brain which is pretty embodied in some ways but not-so-embodied in others. If you want a hundred pages of apologia along the lines of "this may not *look* embodied, but if you squint you'll see how super-duper embodied it really is!", this is your book.

It's also your book if you want to learn about predictive processing at all, since as far as I know this is the only existing book-length treatment of the subject. And it's comprehensive, scholarly, and very good at giving a good introduction to the theory and why it's so important. So let's be grateful for what we've got and take a look.

II

Stanislas Dehaene writes of our senses:

> We never see the world as our retina sees it. In fact, it would be a pretty horrible sight: a highly distorted set of light and dark pixels, blown up toward the center of the retina, masked by blood vessels, with a massive hole at the location of the "blind spot" where cables leave for the brain; the image would constantly blur and change as our gaze moved around. What we see, instead, is a three-dimensional scene, corrected for retinal defects, mended at the blind spot, stabilized for our eye and head movements, and massively reinterpreted based on our previous experience of similar visual scenes. All these operations unfold unconsciously— although many of them are so complicated that they resist computer modeling. For instance, our visual system detects the presence of shadows in the image and removes them. At a glance, our brain unconsciously infers the sources of lights and deduces the shape, opacity, reflectance, and luminance of the objects.

---

[3] https://www.amazon.com/Surfing-Uncertainty-Prediction-Action-Embodied/dp/0190217 014/ref=as_li_ss_tl?ie=UTF8&qid=1504662125&sr=8-1&keywords=surfing+uncertainty&linkC ode=lll&tag=slatestarcode-20&linkId=d47d594afe626208fa832b3243391316

Predictive processing begins by asking: how does this happen? By what process do our incomprehensible sense-data get turned into a meaningful picture of the world?

The key insight: the brain is a multi-layer prediction machine. All neural processing consists of two streams: a bottom-up stream of sense data, and a top-down stream of predictions. These streams interface at each level of processing, comparing themselves to each other and adjusting themselves as necessary.

The bottom-up stream starts out as all that incomprehensible light and darkness and noise that we need to process. It gradually moves up all the cognitive layers that we already knew existed – the edge-detectors that resolve it into edges, the object-detectors that shape the edges into solid objects, et cetera.

The top-down stream starts with everything you know about the world, all your best heuristics, all your priors, everything that's ever happened to you before – everything from "solid objects can't pass through one another" to "e = mc^2" to "that guy in the blue uniform is probably a policeman". It uses its knowledge of concepts to make predictions – not in the form of verbal statements, but in the form of expected sense data. It makes some guesses about what you're going to see, hear, and feel next, and asks "Like this?" These predictions gradually move *down* all the cognitive layers to generate lower-level predictions. If that uniformed guy was a policeman, how would that affect the various objects in the scene? Given the answer to that question, how would it affect the distribution of edges in the scene? Given the answer to *that* question, how would it affect the raw-sense data received?

Both streams are probabilistic in nature. The bottom-up sensory stream has to deal with fog, static, darkness, and neural noise; it knows that whatever forms it tries to extract from this signal might or might not be real. For its part, the top-down predictive stream knows that predicting the future is inherently difficult and its models are often flawed. So both streams contain not only data but estimates of the precision of that data. A bottom-up percept of an elephant right in front of you on a clear day might be labelled "very high precision"; one of a a vague form in a swirling mist far away might be labelled "very low precision". A top-down prediction that water will be wet might be labelled "very high precision"; one that the stock market will go up might be labelled "very low precision".

As these two streams move through the brain side-by-side, they continually interface with each other. Each level receives the predictions from the level above it and the sense data from the level below it. Then each level uses Bayes' Theorem[4] to integrate these two sources of probabilistic evidence as best it can. This can end up a couple of different ways.

First, the sense data and predictions may more-or-less match. In this case, the layer stays quiet, indicating "all is well", and the higher layers never even hear about it. The higher levels just keep predicting whatever they were predicting before.

Second, low-precision sense data might contradict high-precision predictions. The Bayesian math will conclude that the predictions are still probably right, but the sense data are wrong. The lower levels will "cook the books" – rewrite the sense data to make it look as predicted – and then continue to be quiet and signal that all is well. The higher levels continue to stick to their predictions.

Third, there might be some unresolvable conflict between high-precision sense-data and predictions. The Bayesian math will indicate that the predictions are probably wrong. The neurons involved will fire, indicating "surprisal" – a gratuitiously-technical neuroscience term for surprise. The higher the degree of mismatch, and the higher the supposed precision of the data that led to the mismatch, the more surprisal – and the louder the alarm sent to the higher levels.

When the higher levels receive the alarms from the lower levels, *this is their equivalent of bottom-up sense-data*. They ask themselves: "Did the even-higher-levels predict this would happen?" If so, they themselves stay quiet. If not, they might try to change their own models that map higher-level predictions to lower-level sense data. Or they might try to cook the books themselves to smooth over the discrepancy. If none of this works, they send alarms to the even-higher-levels.

All the levels really hate hearing alarms. Their goal is to *minimize surprisal* – to become so good at predicting the world (conditional on the predictions sent by higher levels) that nothing ever surprises them. Surprise prompts a frenzy of activity adjusting the parameters of models – or deploying new models – until the surprise stops.

All of this happens several times a second. The lower levels constantly shoot sense data at the upper levels, which constantly adjust their hypotheses and shoot them down at the lower levels. When surprise is registered, the relevant levels change their hypotheses or pass the buck upwards. After

---

[4]http://yudkowsky.net/rational/bayes

umpteen zillion cycles, everyone has the right hypotheses, nobody is surprised by anything, and the brain rests and moves on to the next task. As per the book:

> To deal rapidly and fluently with an uncertain and noisy world, brains like ours have become masters of prediction – surfing the waves and noisy and ambiguous sensory stimulation by, in effect, trying to stay just ahead of them. A skilled surfer stays 'in the pocket': close to, yet just ahead of the place where the wave is breaking. This provides power and, when the wave breaks, it does not catch her. The brain's task is not dissimilar. By constantly attempting to predict the incoming sensory signal we become able – in ways we shall soon explore in detail – to learn about the world around us and to engage that world in thought and action.

The result is perception, which the PP theory describes as "controlled hallucination". You're not seeing the world as it is, exactly. You're seeing your predictions about the world, cashed out as expected sensations, then shaped/constrained by the actual sense data.

III

Enough talk. Let's give some examples. Most of you have probably seen these before, but it never hurts to remind:

This demonstrates the degree to which the brain depends on top-down hypotheses to make sense of the bottom-up data. To most people, these two pictures start off looking like incoherent blotches of light and darkness. Once they figure out what they are (spoiler[5]) the scene becomes obvious and co-herent. According to the predictive processing model, this is how we per-ceive everything all the time – except usually the concepts necessary to make the scene fit together come from our higher-level predictions instead of from clicking on a spoiler link.

This demonstrates how the top-down stream's efforts to shape the bottom-up stream and make it more coherent can sometimes "cook the books" and alter sensation entirely. The real picture says "PARIS IN THE THE SPRINGTIME" (note the duplicated word "the"!). The top-down stream predicts this should be a meaningful sentence that obeys English grammar,

---

[5] https://slatestarcodex.com/blog_images/dalmatian_cow2.png

and so replaces the the bottom-up stream with what it thinks that it *should* have said. This is a very powerful process – how many times have I repeated the the word "the" in this paragraph alone without you noticing?

A more ambiguous example of "perception as controlled hallucination". Here your experience doesn't quite *deny* the jumbled-up nature of the letters, but it superimposes a "better" and more coherent experience which appears naturally alongside.

```
https://www.youtube.com/embed/Ftdb5EKqjIo?rel=0&controls=0&showinf
o=0&start=42
```

Next up – this low-quality video of an airplane flying at night. Notice how after an instant, you start to predict the movement and characteristics of the airplane, so that you're no longer surprised by the blinking light, the movement, the other blinking light, the camera shakiness, or anything like that – in fact, if the light *stopped* blinking, you would be surprised, even though naively nothing could be less surprising than a dark portion of the night sky staying dark. After a few seconds of this, the airplane continuing on its (pretty complicated) way just reads as "same old, same old". Then when something else happens – like the camera panning out, or the airplane making a slight change in trajectory – you focus entirely on that, the blinking lights and movement entirely forgotten or at least packed up into "airplane continues on its blinky way". Meanwhile, other things – like the feeling of your shirt against your skin – have been completely predicted away and blocked from consciousness, freeing you to concentrate entirely on any subtle changes in the airplane's motion.

```
https://www.youtube.com/embed/66tQR7koR_Q
```

In the same vein: this is Rick Astley's "Never Going To Give You Up" repeated again and again for ten hours (you can find some *weird* stuff on YouTube). The first hour, maybe you find yourself humming along occasionally. By the second hour, maybe it's gotten kind of annoying. By the third hour, you've completely forgotten it's even on at all.

But suppose that one time, somewhere around the sixth hour, it skipped two notes – just the two syllables "never", so that Rick said "Gonna give you up." Wouldn't the silence where those two syllables should be sound as jarring as if somebody set off a bomb right beside you? Your brain, having predicted sounds consistent with "Never Gonna Give You Up" going on forever, suddenly finds its expectations violated and sends all sorts of alarms to the higher levels, where they eventually reach your consciousness and make you go "What the *heck* ?"

IV

Okay. You've read a lot of words. You've looked at a lot of pictures. You've listened to "Never Gonna Give You Up" for ten hours. Time for the payoff. Let's use this theory to explain everything.

1. Attention

In PP, attention measures "the confidence interval of your predictions". Sense-data within the confidence intervals counts as a match and doesn't register surprisal. Sense-data outside the confidence intervals fails and alerts higher levels and eventually consciousness.

This modulates the balance between the top-down and bottom-up streams. High attention means that perception is mostly based on the bottom-up stream, since every little deviation is registering an error and so the overall perceptual picture is highly constrained by sensation. Low attention means that perception is mostly based on the top-down stream, and you're perceiving only a vague outline of the sensory image with your predictions filling in the rest.

There's a famous experiment which you can try below – if you're trying it, make sure to play the whole video before moving on:

```
https://www.youtube.com/embed/vJG698U2Mvo?rel=0&controls=0&showinf
o=0
```

...

...

About half of subjects, told to watch the players passing the ball, don't notice the gorilla. Their view of the ball-passing is closely constrained by the bottom-up stream; they see mostly what is there. But their view of the gorilla is mostly dependent on the top-down stream. Their confidence intervals are wide. Somewhere in your brain is a neuron saying "is that a guy in a gorilla suit?" Then it consults the top-down stream, which says "This is a basketball game, you moron", and it smooths out the anomalous perception into something that makes sense like another basketball player.

But if you watch the video with the prompt "Look for something strange happening in the midst of all this basketball-playing", you see the gorilla immediately. Your confidence intervals for unusual things are razor-thin; as soon as that neuron sees the gorilla it sends alarms to higher levels, and the higher levels quickly come up with a suitable hypothesis ("there's a guy in a gorilla suit here") which makes sense of the new data.

There's an interesting analogy to vision here, where the center of your vision is very clear, and the outsides are filled in in a top-down way – I have a vague sense that my water bottle is in the periphery right now, but only because I kind of already know that, and it's more of a mental note of "water bottle here as long as you ask no further questions" than a clear image of it. The extreme version of this is the blind spot[6], which gets filled in entirely with predicted imagery despite receiving no sensation at all.

2. Imagination, Simulation, Dreaming, Etc.

Imagine a house. Now imagine a meteor crashing into the house. Your internal mental simulation was probably pretty good. Without even thinking about it, you got it to obey accurate physical laws like "the meteor continues on a constant trajectory", "the impact happens in a realistic way", "the impact shatters the meteorite", and "the meteorite doesn't bounce back up to space like a basketball". Think how surprising this is.

In fact, think how surprising it is that you can imagine the house at all. This really high level concept – "house" – has been transformed in your visual imaginarium into a pretty good picture of a house, complete with various features, edges, colors, et cetera (if it hasn't, read). This is near-miraculous. Why do our brains have this apparently useless talent?

PP says that the highest levels of our brain make predictions *in the form of sense data*. They're not just saying "I predict that guy over there is a policeman", they're generating the image of a policeman, cashing it out in terms of sense data, and colliding it against the sensory stream to see how it fits. The sensory stream gradually modulates it to fit the bottom-up evidence – a white or black policeman, a mustached or clean-shaven policeman. But the top-down stream is doing a lot of work here. We are able to imagine the meteor, using the same machinery that would guide our perception of the meteor if we saw it up in the sky.

All of this goes double for dreaming. If "perception is controlled hallucination" caused by the top-down drivers of perception constrained by bottom-

[6]https://visionaryeyecare.wordpress.com/2008/08/04/eye-test-find-your-blind-spot-in-each-eye/

up evidence, then dreams are those top-down drivers playing around with themselves unconstrained by anything at all (or else very weakly constrained by bottom-up evidence, like when it's really cold in your bedroom and you dream you're exploring the North Pole).

A lot of people claim higher levels of this – lucid dreaming, astral projection, you name it, worlds exactly as convincing as our own but entirely imaginary. Predictive processing is very sympathetic to these accounts. The generative models that create predictions are really good; they can simulate the world well enough that it rarely surprises us. They also connect through various layers to our bottom-level perceptual apparatus, cashing out their predictions in terms of the lowest-level sensory signals. Given that we've got a top-notch world-simulator plus perception-generator in our heads, it shouldn't be surprising when we occasionally perceive ourselves in simulated worlds.

3. Priming

I don't mean the weird made-up kinds of priming that don't replicate. I mean the very firmly established ones, like the one where, if you flash the word "DOCTOR" at a subject, they'll be much faster and more skillful in decoding a series of jumbled and blurred letters into the word "NURSE".

This is classic predictive processing. The top-down stream's whole job is to assist the bottom-up stream in making sense of complicated fuzzy sensory data. After it hears the word "DOCTOR", the top-down stream is already thinking "Okay, so we're talking about health care professionals". This creeps through all the lower levels as a prior for health-care related things; when the sense organs receive data that can be associated in a health-care related manner, the high prior helps increase the precision of this possibility until it immediately becomes the overwhelming leading hypothesis.

4. Learning

There's a philosophical debate – which I'm not too familiar with, so sorry if I get it wrong – about how "unsupervised learning" is possible. Supervised reinforcement learning is when an agent tries various stuff, and then someone tells the agent if it's right or wrong. Unsupervised learning is when nobody's around to tell you, and it's what humans do all the time.

PP offers a compelling explanation: we create models that generate sense data, and keep those models if the generated sense data match observation.

Models that predict sense data well stick around; models that fail to predict the sense data accurately get thrown out. Because of all those lower layers adjusting out contingent features of the sensory stream, any given model is left with exactly the sense data necessary to tell it whether it's right or wrong.

PP isn't *exactly* blank slatist, but it's compatible with a slate that's pretty fricking blank. Clark discusses "hyperpriors" – extremely basic assumptions about the world that we probably need to make sense of anything at all. For example, one hyperprior is sensory synchronicity – the idea that our five different senses are describing the same world, and that the stereo we see might be the source of the music we hear. Another hyperprior is object permanence – the idea that the world is divided into specific objects that stick around whether or not they're in the sensory field. Clark says that some hyperpriors *might* be innate – but says they don't have to be, since PP is strong enough to learn them on its own if it has to. For example, after enough examples of, say, seeing a stereo being smashed with a hammer at the same time that music suddenly stops, the brain can infer that connecting the visual and auditory evidence together is a useful hack that helps it to predict the sensory stream.

I can't help thinking here of Molyneux's Problem[7], a thought experiment about a blind-from-birth person who navigates the world through touch alone. If suddenly given sight, could the blind person naturally connect the visual appearance of a cube to her own concept "cube", which she derived from the way cubes feel? In 2003, some researchers took advantage of a new cutting-edge blindness treatment to test this out[8] ; they found that no, the link isn't intuitively obvious to them. Score one for learned hyperpriors.

But learning goes all the way from these kinds of really basic hyperpriors all the way up to normal learning like what the capital of France is – which, if nothing else, helps predict what's going to be on the other side of your geography flashcard, and which high-level systems might keep as a useful concept to help it make sense of the world and predict events.

5. Motor Behavior

About a third of *Surfing Uncertainty* is on the motor system, it mostly didn't seem that interesting to me, and I don't have time to do it justice here (I might make another post on one especially interesting point). But this has

---

[7] https://en.wikipedia.org/wiki/Molyneux%27s_problem

[8] https://en.wikipedia.org/wiki/Molyneux%27s_problem#Responses

been kind of ignored so far. If the brain is mostly just in the business of making predictions, what exactly is the motor system doing?

Based on a bunch of really excellent experiments that I don't have time to describe here, Clark concludes: it's predicting action, which causes the action to happen.

This part is almost funny. Remember, the brain really hates prediction error and does its best to minimize it. With failed predictions about eg vision, there's not much you can do except change your models and try to predict better next time. But with predictions about proprioceptive sense data (ie your sense of where your joints are), there's an easy way to resolve prediction error: just move your joints so they match the prediction. So (and I'm asserting this, but see Chapters 4 and 5 of the book to hear the scientific case for this position) if you want to lift your arm, your brain just predicts *really really strongly* that your arm has been lifted, and then lets the lower levels' drive to minimize prediction error do the rest.

Under this model, the "prediction" of a movement isn't just the idle thought that a movement might occur, it's *the actual motor program*. This gets unpacked at all the various layers – joint sense, proprioception, the exact tension level of various muscles – and finally ends up in a particular fluid movement:

> Friston and colleagues... suggest that precise proprioceptive predictions directly elicit motor actions. This means that motor commands have been replaced by (or as I would rather say, implemented by) proprioceptive predictions. According to active inference, the agent moves body and sensors in ways that amount to actively seeking out the sensory consequences that their brains expect. Perception, cognition, and action – if this unifying perspective proves correct – work together to minimize sensory prediction errors by selectively sampling and actively sculpting the stimulus array. This erases any fundamental computational line between perception and the control of action. There remains [only] an obvious difference in direction of fit. Perception here matches hural hypotheses to sensory inputs... while action brings unfolding proprioceptive inputs into line with neural predictions. The difference, as Anscombe famously remarked, is akin to that between consulting a shopping list (thus letting the list determine the contents of the shopping basket) and listing

some actually purchased items (thus letting the contents of the shopping basket determine the list). But despite the difference in direction of fit, the underlying form of the neural computations is now revealed as the same.

6. Tickling Yourself

One consequence of the PP model is that organisms are continually adjusting out their own actions. For example, if you're trying to predict the movement of an antelope you're chasing across the visual field, you need to adjust out the up-down motion of your own running. So one "hyperprior" that the body probably learns pretty early is that if it itself makes a motion, it should expect to feel the consequences of that motion.

There's a really interesting illusion called the force-matching task. A researcher exerts some force against a subject, then asks the subject to exert exactly that much force against something else. Subjects' forces are usually biased upwards – they exert more force than they were supposed to – probably because their brain's prediction engines are "cancelling out" their own force. Clark describes one interesting implication:

> The same pair of mechanisms (forward-model-based prediction and the dampening of resulting well-predicted sensation) have been invoked to explain the unsettling phenomenon of 'force escalation'. In force escalation, physical exchanges (playground fights being the most common exemplar) mutually ramp up via a kind of step-ladder effect in which each person believes the other one hit them harder. Shergill et al describe experiments that suggest that in such cases each person is truthfully reporting their own sensations, but that those sensations are skewed by the attenuating effects of self-prediction. Thus, 'self-generated forces are perceived as weaker than externally generated forces of equal magnitude.'

This also explains why you can't tickle yourself – your body predicts and adjusts away your own actions, leaving only an attenuated version.

7. The Placebo Effect

We hear a lot about "pain gating" in the spine, but the PP model does a good job of explaining what this is: adjusting pain based on top-down priors. If you believe you should be in pain, the brain will use that as a filter to interpret ambiguous low-precision pain signals. If you believe you shouldn't, the brain will be more likely to assume ambiguous low-precision pain signals are a mistake. So if you take a pill that doctors assure you will cure your pain, then your lower layers are more likely to interpret pain signals as noise, "cook the books" and prevent them from reaching your consciousness.

Psychosomatic pain is the opposite of this; see Section 7.10 of the book for a fuller explanation.

8. Asch Conformity Experiment[9]

More speculative, and not from the book. But remember this one? A psychologist asked subjects which lines were the same length as other lines. The lines were all *kind of* similar lengths, but most subjects were still able to get the right answer. Then he put the subjects in a group with confederates; all of the confederates gave the same wrong answer. When the subject's turn came, usually they would disbelieve their eyes and give the same wrong answer as the confederates.

The bottom-up stream provided some ambiguous low-precision bottom-up evidence pointing toward one line. But in the final Bayesian computation, those were swamped by the strong top-down prediction that it would be another. So the middle layers "cooked the books" and replaced the perceived sensation with the predicted one. From Wikipedia:

> Participants who conformed to the majority on at least 50% of trials reported reacting with what Asch called a "distortion of perception". These participants, who made up a distinct minority (only 12 subjects), expressed the belief that the confederates' answers were correct, and were apparently unaware that the majority were giving incorrect answers.

---

[9]https://en.wikipedia.org/wiki/Asch_conformity_experiments

9. Neurochemistry

PP offers a way to a psychopharmacological holy grail – an explanation of what different neurotransmitters really *mean*, on a human-comprehensible level. Previous attempts to do this, like "dopamine represents reward, serotonin represents calmness", have been so wildly inadequate that the whole question seems kind of disreputable these days.

But as per PP, the NMDA glutamatergic system mostly carries the top-down stream, the AMPA glutamatergic system mostly carries the bottom-up stream, and dopamine mostly carries something related to precision, confidence intervals, and surprisal levels. This matches a lot of observational data in a weirdly consistent way – for example, it doesn't take a lot of imagination to think of the slow, hesitant movements of Parkinson's disease as having "low motor confidence".

10. Autism

Various research in the PP tradition has coalesced around the idea of autism as an unusually high reliance on bottom-up rather than top-down information, leading to "weak central coherence" and constant surprisal as the sensory data fails to fall within pathologically narrow confidence intervals.

Autistic people classically can't stand tags on clothing[10] – they find them too scratchy and annoying. Remember the example from Part III about how you successfully predicted away the feeling of the shirt on your back, and so manage never to think about it when you're trying to concentrate on more important things? Autistic people can't do that as well. Even though they have a layer in their brain predicting "will continue to feel shirt", the prediction is too precise; it predicts that next second, the shirt will produce *exactly* the same pattern of sensations it does now. But realistically as you move around or catch passing breezes the shirt will change ever so slightly – at which point autistic people's brains will send alarms all the way up to consciousness, and they'll perceive it as "my shirt is annoying".

Or consider the classic autistic demand for routine, and misery as soon as the routine is disrupted. Because their brains can only make very precise predictions, the slightest disruption to routine registers as strong surprisal, strong prediction failure, and "oh no, all of my models have failed, nothing is true, anything is possible!" Compare to a neurotypical person in the same

---

[10] http://kerrymagro.com/when-your-child-wont-wear-clothes-that-have-tags-on-them/

situation, who would just relax their confidence intervals a little bit and say "Okay, this is basically 99% like a normal day, whatever". It would take something genuinely unpredictable – like being thrown on an unexplored continent or something – to give these people the same feeling of surprise and unpredictability.

This model also predicts autistic people's strengths. We know that polygenic risk for autism is positively associated with IQ[11]. This would make sense if the central feature of autism was a sort of increased mental precision. It would also help explain why autistic people seem to excel in high-need-for-precision areas like mathematics and computer programming.

11. Schizophrenia

Converging lines of research suggest this also involves weak priors, apparently at a different level to autism and with different results after various compensatory mechanisms have had their chance to kick in. One especially interesting study asked neurotypicals and schizophrenics to follow a moving light, much like the airplane video in Part III above. When the light moved in a predictable pattern, the neurotypicals were much better at tracking it; when it was a deliberately perverse video specifically designed to frustrate expectations, the schizophrenics actually did better. This suggests that neurotypicals were guided by correct top-down priors about where the light would be going; schizophrenics had very weak priors and so weren't really guided very well, but also didn't screw up when the light did something unpredictable. Schizophrenics are also famous for not being fooled by the "hollow mask" (below) and other illusions where top-down predictions falsely constrain bottom-up evidence. My guess is they'd be more likely to see both 'the's in the "PARIS IN THE THE SPRINGTIME" image above.

The exact route from this sort of thing to schizophrenia is really complicated, and anyone interested should check out Section 2.12 and the whole of Chapter 7 from the book. But the basic story is that it creates waves of anomalous prediction error and surprisal, leading to the so-called "delusions of significance" where schizophrenics believe that eg the fact that someone is wearing a hat is some sort of incredibly important cosmic message. Schizophrenics' brains try to produce hypotheses that explain all of these prediction errors and reduce surprise – which is impossible, because the prediction errors are random. This results in incredibly weird hypotheses, and eventually in

---

[11] http://www.biorxiv.org/content/early/2016/11/23/089342

schizophrenic brains being willing to ignore the bottom-up stream entirely – hence hallucinations.

All this is treated with antipsychotics, which antagonize dopamine, which – remember – represents confidence level. So basically the medication is telling the brain "YOU CAN IGNORE ALL THIS PREDICTION ERROR, EVERYTHING YOU'RE PERCEIVING IS TOTALLY GARBAGE SPURIOUS DATA" – which turns out to be exactly the message it needs to hear.

An interesting corollary of all this – because all of schizophrenics' predictive models are so screwy, they lose the ability to use the "adjust away the consequences of your own actions" hack discussed in Part 5 of this section. That means their own actions *don't* get predicted out, and seem like the actions of a foreign agent. This is why they get so-called "delusions of agency", like "the government beamed that thought into my brain" or "aliens caused my arm to move just now". And in case you were wondering – yes, schizophrenics can tickle themselves[12].

12. Everything else

I can't possibly do justice to the whole of *Surfing Uncertainty*, which includes sections in which it provides lucid and compelling PP-based explanations of hallucinations, binocular rivalry, conflict escalation, and various optical illusions. More speculatively, I can think of really interesting connections to things like phantom limbs, creativity (and its association with certain mental disorders), depression, meditation, etc, etc, etc.

The general rule in psychiatry is: if you think you've found a theory that explains everything, diagnose yourself with mania and check yourself into the hospital. Maybe I'm not at that point yet – for example, I don't think PP does anything to explain what mania itself is. But I'm pretty close.

IV

This is a really poor book review of *Surfing Uncertainty*, because I only partly understood it. I'm leaving out a *lot* of stuff about the motor system, debate over philosophical concepts with names like "enactivism", descriptions of how neurons form and unform coalitions, and of course a hundred pages of apolo-

---

[12]http://www.iflscience.com/brain/people-schizophrenic-traits-are-able-tickle-the mselves/

gia along the lines of "this may not *look* embodied, but if you squint you'll see how super-duper embodied it really is!". As I reread and hopefully come to understand some of this better, it might show up in future posts.

But speaking of philosophical debates, there's one thing that really struck me about the PP model. Voodoo psychology[13] suggests that culture and expectation tyrannically shape our perceptions. Taken to an extreme, objective knowledge is impossible, since all our sense-data is filtered through our own bias. Taken to a *very far* extreme, we get things like What The !@#$ Do We Know?[14]'s claim that the Native Americans literally couldn't see Columbus' ships, because they had no concept of "caravel" and so the percept just failed to register. This sort of thing tends to end by arguing that science was invented by straight white men, and so probably just reflects straight white maleness, and so we should ignore it completely and go frolic in the forest or something.

Predictive processing is sympathetic to all this. It takes all of this stuff like priming and the placebo effect, and it predicts it handily. But it doesn't give up. It (theoretically) puts it all on a sound mathematical footing, explaining exactly how *much* our expectations should shape our reality, and in which *ways* our expectation should shape our reality. I feel like someone armed with predictive processing and a bit of luck should have been able to predict that placebo effect and basic priming would work, but stereotype threat and social priming wouldn't. Maybe this is total retrodictive cheating. But I feel like it should be possible.

If this is true, it gives us more confidence that our perceptions should correspond – at least a little – to the external world. We can accept that we may be misreading "PARIS IN THE THE SPRINGTIME" while remaining confident that we *wouldn't* misread "PARIS IN THE THE THE THE THE THE THE THE THE THE THE THE THE THE THE THE THE THE THE THE THE THE THE THE THE THE THE THE THE THE THE THE THE THE THE THE THE THE THE THE THE THE THE THE THE THE THE THE THE THE THE SPRINGTIME" as containing only one "the". Top-down processing very occasionally meddles in bottom-up sensation, but (as long as you're not schizophrenic), it sticks to an advisory role rather than being able to steamroll over arbitrary amounts of reality.

The rationalist project is overcoming bias, and that requires both an ad-

[13] https://slatestarcodex.com/2016/08/25/devoodooifying-psychology/
[14] https://en.wikipedia.org/wiki/What_the_Bleep_Do_We_Know!%3F

mission that bias is possible, and a hope that there's something *other* than bias which we can latch onto as a guide. Predictive processing gives us more confidence in both, and helps provide a convincing framework we can use to figure out what's going on at all levels of cognition.

32

Predictive Processing And Perceptual Control

September 6, 2017

Yesterday's review of *Surfing Uncertainty* mentioned how predictive processing attributes movement to strong predictions about proprioceptive sensations. Because the brain tries to minimize predictive error, it moves the limbs into the positions needed to produce those sensations, fulfilling its own prophecy.

This was a really difficult concept for me to understand at first. But there were a couple of passages that helped me make an important connection. See if you start thinking the same thing I'm thinking:

> To make [bodily] action come about, the motor plant behaves (Friston, Daunizeau, et al, 2010) in ways that cancel out proprioceptive prediction errors. This works because the proprioceptive prediction errors signal the difference between how the bodily plant is currently disposed and how it would be disposed were the desired actions being performed. Proprioceptive prediction error will yield (moment-by-moment) the projected proprioceptive inputs. In this way, predictions of the unfolding proprioceptive patterns that would be associated with the performance of some action actually bring that action about. This kind of scenario is neatly captured by Hawkins and Blakeslee (2004), who write that: "As strange as it sounds, when your own behavior is involved, your predictions not only precede sensation, they determine sensation."

And:

PP thus implements the distinctive circular dynamics described by Cisek and Kalaska using a famous quote from the American pragmatist John Dewey. Dewey rejects the 'passive' model of stimuli evoking responses in favour of an active and circular model in which 'the motor response determines the stimulus, just as truly as sensory stimulus determines movement'

Still not getting it? What about:

According to active inference, the agent moves body and sensors in ways that amount to actively seeking out the sensory consequences that their brains expect.

This is the model from Will Powers'.
Clark knows this. A few pages after all these quotes, he writes:

One signature of this kind of grip-based non-reconstructive dance is that it suggests a potent reversal of our ordinary way of thinking about the relations between perception and action. Instead of seeing perception as the control of action, it becomes fruitful to think of action as the control of perception [Powers 1973, Powers et al, 2011].

But I feel like this connection should be given more weight. Powers' perceptual control theory presages predictive processing theory in a lot of ways. In particular, both share the idea of cogntitive "layers", which act at various levels (light-intensity-detection vs. edge-detection vs. object-detection, or movements vs. positions-in-space vs. specific-muscle-actions vs. specific-muscle-fiber-tensions). Upper layers decide what stimuli they want lower levels to be perceiving, and lower layers arrange themselves in the way that produce those stimuli. PCT talks about "set points" for cybernetic systems, and PP talks about "predictions", but they both seem to be groping at the same thing.

I was least convinced by the part of PCT which represented the uppermost layers of the brain as control systems controlling various quantities like "love" or "communism", and which sometimes seemed to veer into self-parody. PP offers an alternative by describing those layers as making predictions (sometimes "active predictions" of the sort that guide behavior) and trying to minimize predictive error. This allows lower level systems to "control for" deviation from a specific plan, rather than just monitoring the amount of some scalar quantity.

My review of *Behavior: The Control Of Perception* ended by saying:

> It does seem like there's something going on where my decision to drive activates a lot of carefully-trained subsystems that handle the rest of it automatically, and that there's probably some neural correlate to it. But I don't know whether control systems are the right way to think about this... I think maybe there are some obvious parallels, maybe even parallels that bear fruit in empirical results, in lower level systems like motor control. Once you get to high-level systems like communism or social desirability, I'm not sure we're doing much better than [strained control-related metaphors].

I think my instincts were right. PCT is a good model, but what's good about it is that it approximates PP. It approximates PP best at the lower levels, and so is most useful there; its thoughts on the higher levels remain useful but start to diverge and so become less profound.

The Greek atomists like Epicurus have been totally superseded by modern atomic theory, but they still get a sort of "how did they do that?" award for using vague intuition and good instincts to cook up a scientific theory that couldn't be proven or universally accepted until centuries later. If PP proves right, then Will Powers and PCT deserve a place in the pantheon besides them. There's something kind of wasteful about this – we can't properly acknowledge the cutting-edgeness of their contribution until it's obsolete – but at the very least we can look through their other work and see if they've got even *more* smart ideas that might be ahead of their time.

(Along with his atomic theory, Epicurus gathered a bunch of philosophers and mathematicians[1] into a small cult[2] around him, who lived together in co-ed group houses[3] preaching atheism and materialism and – as per the rumors

---

[1] https://en.wikipedia.org/wiki/Polyaenus_of_Lampsacus

[2] https://en.wikipedia.org/wiki/Epicurus#Hero_cult

[3] http://classicalwisdom.com/epicureanism-original-hippie-commune-birth-american-dream/

– having orgies[4]. If we'd just agreed he was right about everything[5] from the start, we wouldn't have had to laboriously reinvent his whole system.)

---

[4]https://books.google.com/books?id=ZdlXAQAAQBAJ&pg=PA19&lpg=PA19&dq=Epicurus+gar den+orgies&source=bl&ols=Nb5k2ZN7-8&sig=_5DvQmEkDT1NC4t2iIY2XsDpu-s&hl=en&sa=X&ved=0 ahUKEwj7mJqwk43WAhVErVQKHScPD30Q6AEIPTAE#v=onepage&q=Epicurus%20garden%20orgies&f=fal se

[5]https://slatestarcodex.com/2015/07/23/the-general-factor-of-correctness/

33

How Did New Atheism Fail So Miserably?

October 24, 2017

The Baffler publishes a long article[1] against "idiot" New Atheists. It's interesting only in the context of so many similar articles[2], and an inability to imagine the opposite opinion showing up in an equally fashionable publication. New Atheism has lost its battle for the cultural high ground. r/atheism will shamble on as some sort of undead abomination, chanting "BRAAAAAAIIINSSSS... are what fundies don't have" as the living run away shrieking. But everyone else has long since passed them by.

The New Atheists accomplished the seemingly impossible task of alienating a society that agreed with them about everything. The Baffler-journalists of the world don't believe in God. They don't disagree that religion contributes to homophobia, transphobia, and the election of some awful politicians – and these issues have only grown more visible in the decade or so since New Atheism's apogee. And yet in the bubble where nobody believes in God and everyone worries full-time about sexual minorities and Trump, you get less grief for being a Catholic than a Dawkins fan. When Trump wins an election on the back of evangelicals, and the alt-right is shouting "DEUS VULT" and demanding "throne and altar conservativism", the *real* scandal is rumors that some New Atheist might be reading /pol/. How did the New Atheists become so loathed so quickly?

The second article presents a theory:

> It has something to do with a litany of grievances against the believoisie so rote that it might well (or ironically) be styled a catechism. These New Atheists and their many fellow travelers

---

[1] https://donotlink.it/l/glxv
[2] https://thebaffler.com/salvos/degrasse-tyson-kriss-atheists

all share an unpleasant obsessive tic: they mouth some obvious banality—there is no God, the holy books were all written by human beings—and then act as if it is some kind of profound insight. This repetition-compulsion seems to be baked right into their dogma.

It compares New Atheists to Kierkegaard's lunatic:

> Soren Kierkegaard, the great enemy of all pedants, offers a story that might shed considerable light. In his Concluding Unscientific Postscript, he describes a psychiatric patient who escapes from the asylum, climbing out a window and running through the gardens to rejoin the world at large. But the madman worries: out in the world, if anyone discovers that he is insane, he will instantly be sent back. So he has to watch what he says, and make sure none of it betrays his inner imbalance—in short, as the not-altogether unmad Danish genius put it, to "convince everyone by the objective truth of what he says that all is in order as far as his sanity is concerned." Finding a skittle-bowl on the ground and popping it in his pocket, he has an ingenious idea: who could possibly deny that the world is round? So he goes into town and starts endlessly repeating that fact, proffering it over and over again as he wanders about with his small furious paces, the skittle-bowl in his coat clanking, in strict conformity with Newton's laws, against what Kierkegaard euphemistically refers to as his "a–." Of course, the poor insistent soul is then sent right back to the asylum [...]

Kierkegaard's villagers saw someone maniacally repeating that the world is round and correctly sent him back to the asylum. We watched [Neil de Grasse] Tyson doing exactly the same thing, and instead of hiding him away from society where nobody would have to hear such pointless nonsense, thousands cheer him on for fighting for truth and objectivity against the forces of backwardness. We do the same when Richard Dawkins valiantly fights for the theory of evolution against the last hopeless stragglers of the creationist movement, with their dinky fiberglass dinosaurs munching leaves in a museum-piece Garden of Eden. We do it when Sam Harris prises deep into the human brain and announces that there's no little vacuole there containing a soul.

So the problem with New Atheism was that its whole shtick was repeating obviously true things that everyone already knew? But about 80% of Americans identify as religious, 63% claim to be "absolutely certain" that there is a God, and 46% think the world was literally created in seven days. This is a surprising number of people disagreeing with a thing that everybody already knows.

I could be misreading the article. The article could be wrong. But I don't think so. This is *my* intuitive feeling of what was wrong with New Atheism as well. It wasn't that they were wrong. Just that they were right in a loud, boring, and pointless way.

A charitable reading: New Atheists weren't reaching their intellectual opponents. They were coming into educated urban liberal spaces, saying things that educated urban liberals already believed, and demanding social credit for it. Even though 46% of America is creationist, zero percent of my hundred-or-so friends are. If New Atheists were preaching evolution in social circles like mine, they were wasting their time.

This seems like an accurate criticism of New Atheism, one that earns them all the condescension they have since received. But the New Atheist still ought to feel betrayed. Why isn't this an equally correct criticism of *everything else*?

While the atheists were going around saying there was no God, the environmentalists were going around saying climate change was real. The feminists were going around saying sexism was bad. And the Democrats were going around saying Donald Trump was an awful person. All of these statements might be controversial *somewhere*, but meet basically zero resistance in educated urban liberal spaces. All get repeated day-in and day-out by groups of people who make entire careers out of repeating them. And all get said in the same condescending way, a sort of society-wide plague of Voxsplaining.

This is 90% of popular intellectual culture these days: progressives regurgitating progressivism to other progressives for nothing but the warm glow of being told "Yup, that was some good progressiving there". Conservatives make fun of this incessantly, and they are right to do so. But for some reason, in the case of New Atheism and *only* in the case of New Atheism, Progressivism itself suddenly turned and said "Hey, you're just repeating our own platitudes back to us!" And New Atheism, caught flat-footed, mouth open wide: "But... but... we thought we were supposed to... we thought...".

Think of one of those corrupt kleptocracies where the dictator takes bribes, all his ministers take bribes, all their assistants take bribes, the anti-corruption task force takes bribes, etc. Then one day some shmuck manages to get on the dictator's bad side and – bam – the secret police nab him for taking bribes. The look on his face the moment before the firing squad shoots – that's how I imagine New Atheists feeling too.

So who's the dictator in this analogy? And what did New Atheism do to get on their bad side?

Maybe New Atheism failed to make the case that it was socially important. All these movements have a mix of factual claims and social calls to action – climate change activism combines "we should accept the scientifically true fact that the climate is changing" with "we should worry about climate change causing famines, hurricanes, etc", just as atheism combines "we should accept the scientifically true fact that God does not exist" with "we should worry about religion's promotion of terrorism, homophobia, et cetera". But the climate change people seem better at sounding like they care about the people involved, compared to atheists usually sounding more concerned with Truth For Its Own Sake and bringing in the other stuff as a justification.

Or maybe the New Atheists just didn't know how to stay relevant. Trump resistance always has new tweets to keep its attention. Social justice always has a new sexist celebrity to be angry about. Sure, a few New Atheists tried to keep up with the latest secretly-gay televangelist, but most of them kept going about intricacies of the kalam argument that had been done to death by 1400 AD. This is just an example – maybe there are other asymmetries that are more important?

Maybe the New Atheists accidentally got on board just before a nascent and tried to get Blue Tribe credibility by sending Grey Tribe signals. At some point there was a cultural fissure between Acela Corridor thinkfluencers with humanities degrees and Silicon Valley bloggers with STEM degrees, and the former got a head start on hating the latter while the latter still thought everybody was on the same anti-Republican side.

And the cynic in me wonders whether New Atheism wasn't pointless and obvious *enough*. There are more church-goers in educated liberal circles than Trump supporters, climate deniers, or self-identified racists. Maybe that made the "repeat platitudes to people who already believe them" game a little less fun, caused some friction – "You're talking about my dear grandmother!"

I don't know. The whole problem is so strange. For a brief second, modern culture looked at New Atheism, saw itself, and said "Huh, this is really stupid and annoying". Then it cast New Atheism into the outer darkness while totally failing to generalize that experience to anything else. Why would it do that? Could it happen again? *Please* can it happen again? *Pretty* please?

34

Ars Longa, Vita Brevis

November 9, 2017

The Alchemist asked if I wanted a drink. I did, but no amount of staring could make my eyes settle on the color of the liquid in the flask. And the gold the alchemists paid the taxmen smelled funny and made crackling noises. I declined.

I took the summons and set it on the table between us. The King's son was dying. The doctors, astrologers, witches, and other assorted wise people of the kingdom could not save him. The King had asked for an alchemist, and been given one. He, too, had failed. But he had let on that there were other alchemists in the guild, greater alchemists, who knew far more than he. So the king had demanded that all the guild's top alchemists come to the palace and try to save his son's life. And the alchemists' guild had refused, saying their studies could not be interrupted.

So here I was, come to make the request again, more formally but less politely.

The Alchemist pretended to read the parchment. I could tell he was faking; his eyes stayed still the whole time. Finally he gave me the same answer he had given the king's courier: the alchemists' studies could not be interrupted.

"Why is a few weeks subtracted from your studies more important than the prince's life?" I demanded, staring straight into his creepy too-still eyes.

He spent too long not answering. I worried I'd broken him, that he was some kind of intricate clockwork machine and I'd yelled too loud and shifted a gear out of place. Finally he asked: "How long would you have to study architecture before you could build a castle like this one?"

"I'm no architect," I said. "I'm a man of war."

"Yes. So how long would you have to study, before you were an architect?"

"Ten years?" I asked. "Twenty?"

"Why so? There are books of architecture, some of them written by men far greater than the planner of this castle. Some are five hundred pages long, others a thousand. Are you so slow a reader, that it would take you ten years to read a thousand pages?"

"You can't just read a book and know architecture."

"But why not?"

"Because… you wouldn't…" I had been annoyed when he first asked, but now I found the question interesting, at least amusing. Why *couldn't* a great architect write his knowledge down in a book? And why *couldn't* I read it and become as good as he?

"Because you'd have to memorize it all," I finally concluded.

"Not so. I will let you carry the book with you as you build the castle."

"It wouldn't help. It wouldn't be… indexed properly in my head. I would want to build a wall, and I wouldn't even know what things to consider when building a wall, and I would have to search the whole book for them each time."

"You are a man of war," repeated the Alchemist. "Do you know Caesar's histories?"

"Almost by heart."

"Are you as good a general as Caesar?"

"No."

"Why not?"

I took his point. Caesar had written down everything he could about war. I had mastered all of it. But I was no Caesar. It couldn't just be the difficulty of memorizing books.

"Knowledge," said the Alchemist, "is harder to transmit than anyone appreciates. One can write down the structure of a certain arch, or the tactical considerations behind a certain strategy. But above those are higher skills, skills we cannot name or appreciate. Caesar could glance at a battlefield and know precisely which lines were reliable and which were about to break. Vitruvius could see a great basilica in his mind's eye, every wall and column snapping into place. We call this wisdom. It is not unteachable, but neither can it be taught. Do you understand?"

I did. If I trained with Caesar for years, some of his skill at reading a battlefield might rub off on me; I might dimly see the outlines of his genius. But he couldn't just tell me. It wasn't a secret which he hid from other men to remain above them. It was a power belonging to him alone, only partially transferable.

"So imagine," continued the Alchemist, "that you wanted to build the simplest of structures. A cottage for peasants. How long would you have to study architecture under Vitruvius before you could do it?"

This time I didn't bother protesting that I didn't know. I just guessed. "A year?"

"And suppose you want to build something more complex. An aqueduct, every bit the equal of the Romans'. How long?"

"Five years?"

"Some grand building, a palace or temple?"

"…ten years?"

"The grandest building in the world. St. Peter's Basilica, or the Pantheon, or Chartres Cathedral, or something new that combines the virtues of all three."

"How should I know? Twenty years? Thirty?"

"Would you believe me if I said it was two hundred years?"

"No. The human lifespan is three score and ten. If you needed more than seventy years of studying architecture to design St. Peter's, it would never have gotten designed."

"Then," said the Alchemist, "we have discovered something surprising. The art of architecture is limited by the human lifespan. The greatest building that can ever be designed is the one that would take seventy years of studying architecture to master; God has drawn a line in the sand forever closing off buildings grander than these."

I thought for a second. "That doesn't seem right. There are new innovations every year. The flying buttress, stained glass, the pointed arch. The Romans had none of these. We progress not only by studying the works of Vitruvius, but by pushing beyond him. Perhaps it takes a century for someone to invent the buttress, but once it is invented, only weeks for other architects to observe it and understand it well enough to incorporate into their own buildings. Architecture does not advance only architect by architect, but also civilization by civilization."

"Are you skilled at mathematics?" asked the Alchemist.

I shook my head.

"Then we will talk this over, though rightfully it should be an equation. The first term is the speed at which a student can absorb already-discovered architectural knowledge. The second term is the speed at which a master can discover new knowledge. The third term represents the degree to which one must already be on the frontier of knowledge to make new discoveries; at zero, everyone discovers equally regardless of what they already know; at one, one must have mastered every previously-discovered fact before one can discover anything new. The fourth term represents potential for specialization; at one, it is impossible to understand any part without understanding the whole; at zero, it can be subdivided freely. The fifth…"

"I don't think saying it in words makes the math easier to understand."

"Ah. Well, imagine a science that takes one-tenth as long for a student to understand, as it did a master to discover. And imagine that one cannot advance the science until one understands everything that has already been discovered. And one cannot split the burden; tell one architect 'Oh, you learn how to make walls, I will learn how to make roofs' – a single genius must understand the whole building, every part must fit together perfectly. We can calculate how far the art can advance."

"How?"

"The first student has no master, and must discover everything himself. He researches for 70 years, then writes his wisdom into a book before he dies. The second student reads the book, and in 7 years, he has learned 70 years of research. Then he does his own original research for 63 years and writes a book containing 133 years of research. The third student reads for 13.3 years, then does his own research for 66.7 years, ending up with 200 years. Imagine going further and further. After many generations, 690 years of research have been done, and it takes a student 69 years to master them. The student only has one year left of life to research further, leaving the world with 691 years of research total. So the cycle creeps onward, always approaching but never quite reaching 700 years of architectural research."

"It doesn't work that way," I protested, partly because it didn't, and partly because something about the story distressed me more than I could say.

"Not in architecture. An architect who has not yet mastered the entire field can still make discoveries. And the field can be split – I can work on walls while you work on windows. It would only work that way if there were an Art so unified, so perfect, that a seeker had to know the totality of what had been discovered before, if he wanted to know anything at all."

"Then you really could never advance past 700 years of knowledge."

"You would have to be clever. We imagine each master writing down his knowledge in a book for the student who comes after, and each student reading it at a rate of ten times as quickly as the master discovered it. But what if there was a third person in between, an editor, who reads the book not to learn the contents, but to learn how to rewrite it better and more clearly? Someone whose job it is to figure out perfect analogies, clever shortcuts, new ways of graphing and diagramming the information involved. After he has processed the master's notes, he redacts them into a textbook which can teach in only a twentieth the time it took the master to discover."

"Then we could double the amount of research that could eventually be completed, to 1400 years' worth."

"Not easily. Remember, the editors face the same problem as the students: they can only redact knowledge they themselves understand. We are adding many new people, and many generations of work, to the problem. But in the end, yes, you could accumulate 1400 years of knowledge. What if you wanted more?"

"More?"

"I'm afraid so."

"Hm. You... could get more layers of redactors. Redactors of redactors, to make the textbooks truly perfect."

"Perhaps what you are trying to say is that redaction is an Art."

The Alchemist made the the capital letter unmistakeable.

"Every Art has its own structure. Architecture, with enough study, can allow you to accumulate seven hundred years of collected knowledge. How many years could redactors and tutors accumulate? Would some first redactor have to spend seventy years coming up with principles of redaction to pass down to his student, who advances the art by sixty-three more years, which he passes down in turn? Would a 1400-year redactor be an incomprehensible master, able to build whole basilicas of redaction, a master teacher who could frame any concepts to make it intuitive and memorable?"

"I changed my mind. I'm going to have that drink."

The Alchemist poured me the liquid of indeterminate color. I took a sip. It reminded me of nothing I had ever tasted before, but very slightly of the letter "N". More important, I was pretty sure it was alcoholic.

"You're talking about an infinite regress", I said, when I had finished the glass.

"Not infinite. Architects. Teachers. Teachers of teachers, but the art of teaching teaching is much the same as the art of teaching. Three levels is enough. Though the levels have to mix. The teacher who trains the next architect must be a master both of teaching and of architecture. I will spare you the math, but one needs a series of teachers at different points on the teaching-skill/architecture-skill tradeoff-curve. One will be a master teacher who has devoted decades to learning the textbook-writing skill, and who can write a brilliant Introduction To Architecture textbook that makes the first ten years of architecture ability seem perfectly natural and easy to master. Another will be a mediocre teacher who knows enough advanced architecture to write a passable textbook on the subject. Still another will do nothing but study pure Teaching itself, in the hopes that he can one day pass on this knowledge to others who will use it to write architecture textbooks. In practice we are limited to a few strategic points on the tradeoff curve."

"In practice?"

He motioned for me to get up. We walked through dark corridors until we reached a courtyard, bathed in the glow of the full moon. It took me a second to see it. Then the dull shapes took form. Obelisks, covered in hieroglyphs. A garden of obelisks.

"The word 'alchemy' comes from 'al-Kemi', the Arabic word from Egypt. It was the ancient Egyptians who first considered the project. They didn't want the Philosophers' Stone, not at first. They just wanted normal philosophers. But philosophy, more than other subjects, requires the wisdom that comes with age. More than other subjects, a philosophy book cannot merely be read; it must be digested, intermingled with life experience, wrestled with. The Egyptians scholars ran into precisely the problem as our hypothetical architects – there were secrets that evaded the human lifespan.

"So they wondered whether a way to cheat death might be found. The answer was both exciting and discouraging. Through the mysteries of spiritual chemistry, an elixir might be created which would grant immortality. But the Work itself would take far more knowledge than any one man could accumulate. The symbol of alchemists is the ouroboros because our task loops back upon itself. In order to become immortal, you must first become immortal.

"All we could do was go the slow way, the same as the architects working on their great basilica, for generation after generation. So Egypt fell, but we did not fall. Rome passed away, but we did not pass. A few lines, the remnants of the old priestly families of Hierakonopolis and Memphis, continued the work. To stop would be to reset a process requiring four thousand years of gradual asymptotic improvement all the way to the beginning – texts are not worthless, but only the true tutors trained by tutor-tutors trained by tutor-tutor-tutors are fit to tutor an alchemist. A misstep is too terrible to contemplate. But any victory – a single vial of the Elixir, a single fragment of the stone – would end the nightmare forever. We would have an immortal, a philosopher whose lifespan finally matches the depth of the challenges Nature throws at us.

"That is our guild's mission. A few of us, those who pass all their tests, do the alchemic research that moves the Work onwards. Others train to be teachers, or teachers-of-teachers. Those who fail a test somewhere along the way stay in the guild, managing its worldly affairs. Some scour the countryside for prodigies to take in and train as apprentices. Others manage our finances. And the very least capable, like me, have time to waste talking to outsiders, trying to convince them of our mission. A few centuries more, and we will have the Stone. Does that satisfy your curiosity?"

"All except my original question. Are you so busy that you cannot spare a few weeks for the prince?"

"God does not make the Great Work easy. We have done all we can to train our alchemists, our tutors, our tutor-tutors, and so on, yet in the end, the limit of human skill is the same place the possibility of success begins. It is His will to grind us up to the very asymptote."

"I still don't get it."

"Do you remember the architects who learned at ten times the rate they researched, the ones who would never accumulate more than 700 years of learning? The fiftieth alchemist in the sequence has 696 years of learning, and is able to do a scant five months' original research before his death. The hundredth alchemist has 699.98 years of learning, and is able to do about a day's research before dying. We are not so far along as all that, but we are far. We do not have the Stone, but we have tinctures that can stabilize the lifespan, make sure nobody dies before their time. The last few generations – on their deathbed, they say they can almost *taste* the Stone, that it lies only a few hours of further thought beyond their level. They say of my grandfather that he realized the recipe for the Stone on his deathbed, that he started speaking it, but that his eyes closed forever before he could complete the ingredient list."

"So?"

"You ask that we pause a few weeks from our studies to save the prince's life. Pausing a few weeks would set us back generations. This far into the project, only the last few hours of an Alchemist's life are of any value at all. We cannot spare the prince hours. We cannot even spare him seconds."

"Then your teachers… or your teacher-teachers?"

"Know some alchemy, but are in the same situation. Our textbooks have been so perfectly written and rewritten over the years that it is only in the last few days of a teacher's life that he is skilled enough to write a better one. And our teacher-training has become so perfect that it is only in the last few days of a teacher-trainer's life that he is qualified to create teachers better than the ones who already exist."

"There's no slack in the system at all?"

"Only me, and those like me. Those judged unfit for research and con-demned to worldly matters. We sent you one already. He failed you, as he did us. We have nothing more to give."

"The king will not be happy. And the Prince will die."

"Everyone dies," said the Alchemist. "If the prince does not die this year, he will die the next, or fifty years hence. The question is not when we die, but what our life adds to the Work which accumulates in spite of time. Quicksilver evaporates to nothing unless reacted with aqua fortis; but the part which is reacted endures forever. Those lives not part of any Work mean as little to me as they will one day mean to their possessors; those which add to the Work are more precious than gold. Tell the King this."

"He won't understand," I said.

"Then you will have to teach him," said the Alchemist, "as I taught you, and my tutors taught me, and as their tutors taught them, all the way back to the first philosophers of Egypt."

He stared at me as he spoke, and the blackness in his too-still pupils was the depth of Time.

35

Book Review: Legal Systems Very Different From Ours

November 13, 2017

I

Medieval Icelandic crime victims would sell the right to pursue a perpetrator to the highest bidder. 18th century English justice replaced fines with criminals bribing prosecutors to drop cases. Somali judges compete on the free market; those who give bad verdicts get a reputation that drives away future customers.

"Anarcho-capitalism" evokes a dystopian cyberpunk future. But maybe that's wrong. Maybe we've always been anarcho-capitalist. Maybe a state-run legal system isn't a fact of nature, but a historical oddity as contingent as collectivized farming or nationalized railroads. *Legal Systems Very Different From Ours*[1], by anarcho-capitalist/legal scholar/medieval history buff David Friedman, successfully combines the author's three special interests into a whirlwind tour of exotic law.

Law is a public good. Crime victims have little economic incentive to punish the perpetrator; if you burn my house down, jailing you won't unburn the house. If you steal my gold, I have some interest in catching you and taking it back, but no more than I do in catching some other poor shmuck and taking *his* gold. It's only society as a whole that wants to make sure criminals are reliably punished and the innocent consistently safe. This is the classic situation where economists usually recommend government intervention.

But sometimes that doesn't work. Maybe you live in an area like Somalia or medieval Ireland without a strong centralized government. Maybe you

---

[1] http://www.daviddfriedman.com/Academic/Course_Pages/legal_systems_very_different_12/LegalSystemsDraft.html

live in a strato-klepto-kakocracy run by warlords who can't even pronounce "jurisprudence", let alone enforce it. Maybe you're a despised minority group whom the State wants nothing to do with, or who wants nothing to do with the State.

Gypsies living scattered in foreign countries have generally wanted to run their own communities by their own rules. Nothing stops some of them from calling themselves a "legislature" or a "court" and claiming to make laws or pass sentences. But something does stop them from trying to enforce them: from the State's point of view, a "court" that executes an offender is just a bunch of Gypsies who got together and committed murder. So the Vlach Rom – Romanian Gypsies – organize courts called *kris* which enforce their sentences with threat of banishment from the community.

Gypsies traditionally believe in *marime*, a sort of awful pollution that infects people who don't follow the right rituals; anyone who interacts with polluted people will become polluted themselves. *Kris* courts can declare the worst offenders polluted, ensuring their speedy ostracization from Gypsy society. And since non-Gypsies are polluted by default, the possibility of ostracism and forced integration into non-Gypsy society will seem intolerable:

> The effectiveness of that threat [of ostracism] depends on how easily the exiled gypsy can function outside of his community. The marimé rules (and similar rules in other societies) provide a mechanism for isolating the members of the community. Gaije, non-gypsies, do not know the marimé rules and so do not and cannot obey them. It follows that they are all polluted, unclean, carriers of a contagious disease, people whom no Rom in his right mind would willingly choose to associate with; when and if such association is unavoidable it must be taken with great care. The gypsy view of gaije, reinforced by the gaije view of gypsies as uneducated and illiterate thieves and swindlers, eliminates the exit option and so empowers the kris to enforce gypsy law by the threat of exclusion from the only tolerable human society.

This reminds me of The Use And Abuse Of Witchdoctors For Life[2]: once your culture has a weird superstition, it can get plugged into various social needs to become a load-bearing part of the community structure.

---

[2] https://samzdat.com/2017/06/19/the-use-and-abuse-of-witchdoctors-for-life/

Amish also live under the authority of a foreign culture and have settled on a similar system, with a twist. The basic unit of Amish society is the church congregation; Amish settlements big enough to support multiple churches will have many congregations mixed together. Each congregation will have its own rules, especially about which technologies their members are or aren't allowed to use. Amish people who violate their congregation's rules, either by using forbidden technology or by the usual litany of sins, are punished with public confession or temporary ostracism. Amish people who refuse to abide by lesser punishments are excommunicated, though they can be un-excommunicated if they change their minds and agree to follow the court's orders.

Amish congregations are nominally democratic, but in practice Friedman calls them dictatorship-like because everyone votes the way the bishop wants. But they are a "competitive dictatorship"; since there are so many different congregations in the same town, an Amish family who doesn't like their con-gregation's leadership or legal system can move to another congregation and agree to be bound by their laws instead. This makes it a rare remaining ex-ample of a polycentric legal system outside anarcho-capitalist fantasies or *Too Like The Lightning*[3]:

> Such a system can be viewed as a competitive market for legal rules, constrained, like other competitive markets, to produce about the product that the customers want. Competitive dic-tatorship is the mechanism we routinely use to control hotels and restaurants; the customers have no vote on what color the walls are painted or what is on the menu, but an absolute vote on which one they patronize.

They do encounter the same problem as the Gypsies: can you just com-mit a crime, then accept your ostracism and integrate with another society somewhere else? The Amish have some internal mechanisms to prevent this: congregations are usually on good terms with each other, but if Congregation A accepts a member being shunned by Congregation B, then all of Congre-gation B's members will shun all of Congregation A's members. In practice, this makes it easy to switch rules as a member in good standing who honestly doesn't like the laws, but hard to break the laws and get away with it.

---

[3]https://www.amazon.com/Too-Like-Lightning-Terra-Ignota/dp/0765378019/ref=as_li_s
s_tl?ie=UTF8&qid=1510541976&sr=8-1&keywords=Too+Like+The+Lightning&linkCode=lll&tag
=slatestarcode-20&linkId=7713a379e783403fc0516c126b984177

Of course, you can still leave the Amish community and go join broader American society. But have you *seen* broader American society?

18th century England had a government, a court system, and some minimal law enforcement – but it really sucked. There were no public prosecutors; anyone who felt like it could bring a criminal to court and start prosecuting him, but if nobody felt like it then the crime remained unpunished. Prosecuting took a lot of time and money and was generally a thankless task. And the government didn't want to go to the expense of imprisoning people, so they usually just hanged convicted offenders (if the crime seemed really bad) or pardoned them (if it didn't seem to merit hanging). The exotic anarcho-capitalist part comes in as English civil society creates its own structures to work around these limitations.

Merchants, landowners, and other people with wealth banded together in mutual-protection-insurance-groups. Everyone in the group would pay a fixed amount yearly, and if one of them got robbed the group would use the money to hire a prosecutor to try the criminal. Group members would publish their names in the newspaper to help inform thieves whom it was a bad idea to rob. But this wasn't about leaving poor people out to dry. The groups would also help indigents who couldn't afford their own prosecutors, partly out of a desire to crack down on crime before it reached the point where it could inconvenience them. They wouldn't help people who could have afforded insurance but declined anyway, though – otherwise there would be no incentive to buy in.

(if this sounds familiar, it's from another, very different David Friedman book[4])

What about the lack of good punishments? Once a trial was underway, prosecutors would usually cut a deal: the offender would bribe the prosecutor with a certain amount, and the prosecutor would drop the case. The size of the bribe would vary based on how much the offender could pay, the extent of their crime, and the facts of the case (and therefore the likelihood of the magistrate choosing hanging vs. pardon). This not only helped tailor the punishment more precisely to the crime, but helped defer the cost of prosecution: victims (or their mutual-protection-insurance-groups) were incentivized to press charges because they could recoup their costs through the bribes paid to drop them:

What both modern and contemporary commentators seem to

---

have missed is that, however corrupt such arrangements might be from a legal standpoint, they helped solve the fundamental problem of private prosecution. The possibility of compounding provided an incentive to prosecute-it converted the system into something more like a civil system, where a victim sues in the hope of collecting money damages. And while compounding might save the criminal from the noose, he did not get off scott free. He ended up paying, to the prosecutor, what was in effect a fine.

10th through 13th century Iceland was in the same position as the Vlach Rom: a legislature (the Althing), some courts, but no executive branch. Unlike the Rom, the Icelanders' problem wasn't foreign oppressors – it was that they were the Viking equivalent of those hard-core libertarians who live in compounds in Montana where the Feds can't reach them. In this case "the Feds" were the forces of King Harald Fairhair, who had just taken over and centralized power in Norway. Some Norwegians decided they would rather live on a remote and frequently-exploding piece of rock on the edge of the world than be anyone's subject: thus, medieval Iceland.

If an Icelander thought a crime had happened, they would go to court and plead the case themselves. If the court pronounced a guilty verdict, it would demand a penalty from the criminal. Usually this was a fine paid to the victim; even murders were punished with wergeld. If the criminal paid the fine voluntarily, all was well. If they refused – or didn't even come to court – then the court could declare the criminal an outlaw, meaning it was legal to kill him and take his stuff. And:

> One obvious objection to a system of private enforcement is that the poor (or weak) would be defenseless. The Icelandic system dealt with this problem by giving the victim a property right – the right to be reimbursed by the criminal – and making that right transferable. The victim could turn over his case to someone else, either gratis or in return for a consideration. A man who did not have sufficient resources to prosecute a case or enforce a verdict could sell it to another who did and who expected to make a profit in both money and reputation by winning the case and collecting the fine. This meant that an attack on even the poorest victim could lead to eventual punishment.

A second objection is that the rich (or powerful) could commit crimes with impunity, since nobody would be able to enforce judgment against them. Where power is sufficiently concentrated this might be true; this was one of the problems which led to the eventual breakdown of the Icelandic legal system in the thirteenth century. But so long as power was reasonably dispersed, as it seems to have been for the first two centuries after the system was established, this was a less serious problem. A man who refused to pay his fines was outlawed and would probably not be supported by as many of his friends as the plaintiff seeking to enforce judgment, since in case of violent conflict his defenders would find themselves legally in the wrong. If the lawbreaker defended himself by force, every injury inflicted on the partisans of the other side would result in another suit, and every refusal to pay another fine would pull more people into the coalition against him.

There is a scene in Njal's Saga that provides striking evidence of the stability of this system. Conflict between two groups has become so intense that open fighting threatens to break out in the middle of the court. A leader of one faction asks a benevolent neutral what he will do for them in case of a fight. He replies that if they are losing he will help them, and if they are winning he will break up the fight before they kill more men than they can afford! Even when the system seems so near to breaking down, it is still assumed that every enemy killed must eventually be paid for. The reason is obvious enough; each man killed will have friends and relations who are still neutral–and will remain neutral if and only if the killing is made up for by an appropriate wergeld.

I think this is asking: are we sure you can't end up with outlaw cascades, where everyone just agrees to be outlaws together? Suppose Warren Buffett cuts off my arm. The court asks him to pay a fine, and he refuses, so the court declares him an outlaw and legally killable. I gather some of my friends to form a posse to kill him, but he hires a hundred bodyguards to resist me. There's a fight, the bodyguards kill my friends, and the court fines the bodyguards. They don't pay, so the court declares the bodyguards outlaws. I gather a thousand people to kill Buffett and/or his hundred bodyguards, and Buffett and his bodyguards pool their money to hire a whole force of mercenaries to resist us. The mercenaries kill lots of us, the court fines them, and the mercenaries don't pay. Now the court declares the mercenaries outlaws. But it seems like at some point maybe more than half the population of Iceland will be outlaws, and then maybe they just have to declare a new legal system or something.

An Icelander might retort: why doesn't that happen in modern America? A policeman catches you dealing drugs, so you offer the policeman $10,000 to let it pass. The policeman refuses because it's illegal and he would get in trouble. Well, you say, what's the worst thing that could happen if you got in trouble? The police would come after you? But police would hesitate to arrest a fellow officer, plus we've already established that they can be deflected with bribes. Sure, there's a stable equilibrium where you arrest me right now. But there's *also* a stable equilibrium where 51%+ of the nation's police join our sordid bribery chain, accumulate more power than the law-abiding police, and end up as some weird mercenary army that takes over the country and rewrites the law to their own advantage.

This is a good place to remember that David Friedman is also the author of A Positive Account Of Property Rights[5], maybe the single most mind-opening essay I've ever read. No summary can do it justice, but the basic outline is that governmental "legitimacy" is the government's position as a conspicuous Schelling point for everybody who wants to avoid civil war/the state of nature/a worse government. Once it's common knowledge that a government is legitimate, everyone expects everyone else to enforce its rules, and so they'll enforce its rules in turn until it becomes common knowledge that the government isn't legitimate anymore. This works just as well in medieval Icelandic anarcho-capitalism as it does in modern America. Just because our government dresses all of its enforcers-of-state-sanctioned violence in snazzy uniforms and makes them work out of the same building doesn't make the whole system any less of a mass hallucination.

II

This book works well alongside James Scott's and the whole discourse around cultural[6] evolution[7].

---

[5] http://www.daviddfriedman.com/Academic/Property/Property.html

[6] https://slatestarcodex.com/2015/07/07/the-argument-from-cultural-evolution/

[7] https://slatestarcodex.com/2015/07/08/cultural-evolution-2-thanks-for-the-meme-rise/

In *Seeing Like A State*, ordinary people living their daily lives blunder into highly advanced systems for doing whatever it is they do. Primitive farmers will know every tiny detail about exactly when to plant which crops, and how to exploit microvariations in soil quality, and know ridiculous tricks like planting fish heads in the ground as fertilizer. Ordinary city-dwellers will organically build houses and stores and streets in exactly the right fractal patterns to maximize some measure of quality of life. Scott dubs this "metis", an evolved intuitive sense of practical wisdom that often outperforms seemingly more scientific solutions.

Many of the societies Friedman profiles in *Legal Systems Very Different From Ours* seem to operate on *metis*. Most don't know who developed their legal system; in a few of them, it is explicitly declared to have been the work of God. Most don't really know why their legal system works – in some cases, Friedman only gives an economic analysis of why some rule might exist after admitting that previous scholarship (both modern academic, and within the society in question) has failed to come up with answers. And a lot of them are too brilliant, and need too many weird interlocking parts, to be the work of any single person.

"Cultural evolution" is the idea that cultures evolve in a way analogous to biological organisms. The definition gets kind of fuzzy – if I come up with a good idea and my culture adopts it, is that the result of "cultural evolution" or ordinary human ingenuity? 'But a lot of people find the concept to have some value – and if it has any at all, *Legal Systems Very Different From Ours* has to include some of the best examples.

Friedman frames this in economic terms. Social "entrepreneurs" come up with some new system that solves a need, and it catches on by raising the utility of everyone involved. The mutual-protection-insurance-groups of 18th century England work this way: somebody invents them and offers the opportunity for other people to sign on, everyone who does ends up better off than the people who doesn't, and they eventually reach fixation. Same with the criminal-prosecutor bribes; someone thinks it up, it leaves both sides better off, so everybody who hears about it does it. Viewed very optimistically, wherever there's a problem in your culture, institutions to solve the problem will magically appear and spread until everybody does them.

Conflict is an especially fertile ground for cultural innovation. Friedman stresses how many legal systems, including advanced ones with lawyers and codes and everything, show signs of originating from feud systems, which might be the most basic form of law. They work like this: "If you offend me in some way, I will try to kill you". A slightly more advanced version that takes account of possibly power differentials between offender and victim: "If you offend me in some way, everybody in my family will try to kill everybody in your family". This originally sounds unpromising, but it turns out that people really don't want their family members murdered. So we end up with an even more advanced version: "If you offend me in some way, we had better find some way to arbitrate our dispute, *or else* everybody in my family will try to kill everybody in your family".

The Somali system seems to be somewhere around here: if two people have a dispute, they find a mutually agreeable judge to arbitrate; the judge will decide who's in the wrong and what fine they need to pay to make it right. If someone refuses to go to the judge, or refuses to abide by the judge's decision, then it's family-member-killing time. Needless to say, Somali judges' services remain popular. And since judges gain status by arbitrating, and since only judges who make widely-regarded-as-good decisions get invited to keep doing so, there's economic pressure for the judges to make good decisions (which then go down as precedent and inspire future cases). It's easy to see how something like this can turn into a perfectly respectable legal system where people totally forget that killing each other's family members is even an option. Catch it at this last stage, and hear enough people admit they have no idea who "invented" their legal system, and it looks like it appeared by magic.

In fact, one of the most interesting things I got from this book is that all legal systems need a punishment of last resort – one that can be enforced whether or not the offender agrees with it – but these punishments practically never happen in real life. The Gypsies and Amish will ostracize members who defy the court – but since everyone lives in fear of ostracization, in real life they'll just pay the fine or make their public confession or whatever. The English will hang criminals at the drop of a hat – but since the threat of hanging incentivizes them to bribe prosecutors, in reality few people will need to be hanged. The Icelandic courts could declare offenders outlaws who can be killed without repercussion – but the threat encourages Icelanders to pay the wergeld, and nobody has to get outlawed. The Somalis are ready to have murderous family feuds – but the possibility of such a feud keeps people willing to go to arbitration. Even our own legal system works like this. The police can physically drag you to jail, kicking and screaming. But more likely you're going to plea bargain, or agree to community service, or at least be cooperative and polite while the police take you away. Plea bargains – which are easier for prosecutors, easier for defendants, and easier for taxpayers – seem like a good example of cultural evolution in action; once someone thought them up, there was no way they weren't going to take over everything despite their very serious costs[8].

III

Three other things worth noting about *Legal Systems Very Different From Ours*.

First, something kept seeming *off* about all the legal systems mentioned, which only clicked into place about halfway through: they really, really didn't seem prepared for crime. A lot of them worked on a principle like: "If there's a crime, we'll call together a court made of all the town elders, plus at least three different religious leaders, plus the heads of the families of everybody involved, plus a representative of the Great King, plus nine different jurists from nine different universities, and all of them will meet on the Field Of Meeting, and a great tent will be erected, and…" The whole thing sounded like it might work as long as there was like one crime a year. Any more than that and none of the society's officials would ever have time for anything else.

As weird as it is to punish murder with a fine, the fines these societies levied for murder sounded really high: the Islamic price was a hundred camels, the Irish price was seven female slaves. The average person wouldn't have that many slaves or camels, so people in Arabia or Ireland would band together into clan/family-based blood-money-paying-groups that acted kind of like insurance companies. If a member got convicted of a crime, everyone else would come together to help them pony up the money. I assume this helped incentivize people's families to discourage them from committing crimes. But it has the same feeling of nobody expecting very many crimes to be committed. How much of medieval Arabia's GDP consisted of transfers of 100 camels from murderers to victims' families?

One little-admitted but much-worried-about justification for mass incarceration in our society is the concern that some people are just so naturally violent that, left in the outside world, they would offend again and again until they died. The societies in this book didn't seem to worry about this. If someone killed, their family would give up the relevant number of camels, and then everyone would be on their way. As far as I can tell, the Amish have *no idea* what to do about any crime more dire than using a telephone. Nobody

---

[8] https://www.theatlantic.com/magazine/archive/2017/09/innocence-is-irrelevant/534171/

used anything at all like incarceration. 18th century England occasionally sent prisoners somewhere horrible like America, but once the colonies revolted they experimented with jails, found them too expensive, and just sort of flailed around punishment-less until they finally discovered Australia.

There's a lot of concern about police brutality, police racism, police failure-to-actually-control crime, et cetera. A few far-leftists have flirted with the idea of abolishing police, and the only way I can make sense of this is by analogy to something like Somali or Icelandic law. These were genuine community-based non-hierarchical legal systems. And, for the place and the time, they seem to have worked really well (Somaliland, which uses traditional Somali law, is doing way better than Somalia proper, whose law system is somewhat westernized). But I also know that it's weirdly hard to get a good picture of how modern crime rates compare to ancient ones. On the one hand are statistics like the ones saying crime has increased by an order of magnitude since 1900 or so; on the other are findings like Steven Pinker's that violence is constantly declining. Apply the "court made of town elders plus at least three different religious leaders plus..." to Baltimore, and the Field Of Meeting is going to get pretty crowded. On the other hand, in my past work with criminals I've been constantly surprised by how much role their families and their communities still play in their lives, and maybe a system that left legal enforcement up to them would do better than the overstretched and underperforming police.

(but what would the transfer process look like? Just cancel all funding for the Baltimore Police Department and hope for the best?)

Second, some complaints that are kind of unfair because they're along the lines of "this book is too good", but which probably need a mention.

Whenever I read a book by anyone other than David Friedman about a foreign culture, it sounds like "The X'wunda give their mother-in-law three cows every monsoon season, then pluck out their own eyes as a sacrifice to Humunga, the Volcano God".

And whenever I read David Friedman, it sounds like "The X'wunda ensure positive-sum intergenerational trade by a market system in which everyone pays the efficient price for continued economic relationships with their spouse's clan; they demonstrate their honesty with a costly signal of self-mutilation that creates common knowledge of belief in a faith whose priests are able to arbitrate financial disputes."

This is great, and it's important to fight the temptation to think of foreign cultures as completely ridiculous idiots who do stuff for no reason. But it all works out so neatly – and so much better than when anyone else treats the same topics – that I'm always nervous if I'm not familiar enough with the culture involved to know whether they're being shoehorned into a mold that's more rational-self-interest-maximizing than other anthropologists (or they themselves) would recognize.

And also, the cultural evolution idea is really optimistic. I've been trying to read a bit more about Marxism and Postmodernism lately, and they would be pretty skeptical about analyzing social systems by asking "What large-scale problem of human interaction is this system the exactly optimal solution for?"

Like, there's a perspective where lots of countries have a King, because societies that have a single central nexus to their coordination structure are able to coordinate better than ones that don't, and having them rule for life promotes long-term thinking, and them be hereditary provides a clear Schelling Point for secession disputes that prevents civil war *and* cleverly ensures that the previous ruler is incentivized to promote the peaceful transfer of power to the next one, and this is why constitutional monarchies have slightly higher yearly GDP growth[9] than other forms of government.

And there's another perspective where lots of countries have a King, because some guy seized so much power that he can live in a giant palace and order people around all day instead of doing work. And if anyone tries to prevent him from doing that, he can arrange to have that person beheaded. *Legal Systems Very Different From Ours* is very much part of the first perspective. It's a story of nations and legal systems evolving towards ever-more-optimal and ever-more-efficient institutions for the good of all, and it presents strong evidence supporting that story. I can't disagree with its evidence from within its narrative, but I still wonder how much to worry about this alternate way of looking at things.

Third, in all of the fretting about how terrible our government is, and trying to change our government to be less terrible, and trying to convince other people to go along with our terribleness-decreasing government change proposals – it's important to keep on remembering the degree to which you can still pretty much do whatever you want.

In New York, Orthodox Jews with business disputes still bring them before a tribunal of rabbis, who judge them based on Jewish law. In Pennsylvania, the Amish live their own lives in their own way pretty much completely

[9] http://fortune.com/2013/04/30/the-business-case-for-monarchies/

disconnected from US government decisions (although they needed a decent lobby group, the Amish Steering Committee, to work out a few special exemptions like from the draft). Socialists occasionally set up worker-owned companies run for the good of the proletariat, and they make products and earn money just like everyone else.

If you don't like the government, you're out of luck. But if you *and your whole community* don't like the government, you can organize your own internal relations however you want. You can't override existing laws – you'll still have to pay taxes, and you can't set up a bomb-making factory in your backyard. But you can add as many new laws as you want, enforced by threat of ostracism from your community, plus any other clever commitment mechanisms you can think of. There's nothing stopping communities – a broad term covering anything from villages to church congregations to cults to political organizations to online message boards – from creating internal welfare systems to help their poorer members, taking a say in when their members marry or divorce, making home schools that educated their members' children, demanding their members in business treat their employees or business partners a certain way, et cetera.

Right now doctors' services are super-bloated and expensive because if a patient sues them they can be held liable for not filling out any of seven zillion forms or following any of twenty zillion best practices. But if the doctor only saw patients in their own community, and everyone in the community had mutual arbitration methods that worked better than the courts, maybe they could charge of the current price. This might not be illegal, as long as the community wasn't based on a protected group like race or religion. There just aren't many existing communities strong enough to make it work.

But some small seeds are starting to sprout. Social justice communities have sexual harassment policies much stronger than those of the country at large, and enforce them by ostracism and public shaming. Christians are trying to build the Benedict Option[10], an embedded society that works on Christian norms and rules. And there's always the seasteading movement[11], currently led by – oh, that's interesting – David Friedman's son. *Legal Systems Very Different From Ours* hints that we could build something like

gradually, without anybody noticing. The Jews and Gypsies did something like it. So did the Amish. Maybe all we have to do is start threatening to feud against each other's families, and utopia is right around the corner.

---

[10] https://en.wikipedia.org/wiki/Rod_Dreher#Benedict_Option

[11] https://en.wikipedia.org/wiki/Seasteading

Legal Systems Very Different From Ours is available for free online at this *link*[12].

---

[12]http://www.daviddfriedman.com/Academic/Course_Pages/legal_systems_very_different
_12/LegalSystemsDraft.html

Index

$, 246
$999, 246
10000 hour rule, 389
10th through 13th century iceland, 456
18th century, 455, 462
19th century, 347, 381
23andme, 143
40 good data, 409
9/11, 278

10, 388
18, 330
1381, 333
1880, 382
1933, 378
1975, 222
1977, 188
2016, 188, 222
2026, 393
2050, 394
2060, 76
2062, 393, 394

a methodology, 54
aaron beck, 90, 91
ability to think probabil, 127
abolish police, 462
abomination, 112

abortion, 126
aboulomania, 202
absolute forecast error, 216
absolute risk, 118, 120
abstractions, 317
abu bakr, 151
academia, 216
accelerando, 174
accelerator, 316
accident risk, 316
accidents, 68, 277
accidents of, 35
accidents of birth, 35
acculturation, 368
accuracy, 327
ace inhibitors, 223, 225
acetylcholine, 193, 198
achievement, 135
acid, 167
action, 248, 421, 428, 436
active inference, 428
active listening, 25
activities, 148
actual, 399
ad-hoc, 295
adderall, 184
adjunct, 229
adjust, 432

administrative bloat, 232

administrative exercise, 334

ads, 19

advanced, 102

adversarial collaboration, 364

advertisement, 19

advertising, 18, 259, 260

advice, 26, 65

aei, 226

aerial dreadnaught, 115

africa, 325, 342, 344

afterword, 211

age of em, 169, 173, 175, 179, 183, 184, 188

agency, 432

aggression, 145

aging, 41

agitation, 406

agnotology, 356

agreement, 245

agricultural planners, 343

agriculture, 343, 344, 350

ai, 127, 169, 176, 186–188, 393–399

ai research, 394

ai risk, 399

akrasia, 320

al, 170

alarm, 420

alcatel-, 275

alchemist, 444, 448

alchemy, 299, 300, 444, 446, 449–451

alcoholic, 448

algeria, 346

algorithm, 182

ali, 151

aliens, 69, 74

alignment problem, 396

alignment research, 396

all, 119

alonzo de pinzon, 101

alpha, 65

alpha centauri, 63

alpha male, 66

alphabet, 334

alphago, 393

alston, 187

alternate timelines, 69

altruism, 18, 235, 245

alzheimer's disease, 297

amateur wasp farmer, 244

amazon death flu, 304, 305

america, 80, 134, 138, 143, 160, 290

  enterprise institute, 264

  exceptionalism, 273

  identity, 161

  sniper, 124

  undergraduate, 80

amish, 189, 454, 461, 462, 464, 465

amnesty, 250

amoebas, 94

ampa, 199, 200, 430

ampakine, 199

ampakines, 199

amtrak, 275

amy, 122

analysis, 91

anarchists, 278

anarcho-capitalism, 304, 452, 455

anarchy, 352, 458

ancestors, 180

ancient greece, 91

andromeda, 63

andy clark, 418

angle, 315

angry, 69
animal rights, 18
animals, 18, 96
anna, 205, 206
anomaly, 28
answer, 60
anthropology, 122, 463
anti-aging, 46
anti-body, 30
anti-communism, 30
anti-fasc, 29
anti-fascism, 30
anti-fascist, 365
anti-induction, 24
anti-inductive, 22, 28
anti-inductive culture, 25
anti-psychotics, 432
anti-semite, 380
anti-trump, 365
antifa, 365
ants, 96, 97, 365
anxiety, 85, 87, 90, 93
apex of the food chain, 62
app academy, 82
appearances, 115
apple, 275
approval, 25
aptitude, 42
aqua fortis, 451
aquaculture, 246, 247
arach, 24
arbitration, 460, 464
architects, 336, 448
architecture, 337, 338, 444–449
argument, 287, 362
art, 288, 341, 391, 448
art history, 82
artificial, 188
artificial intelligence, 395

artificial towns, 347
asch, 429
ashkenazi, 374–377, 379, 381, 383–
    385
assassins, 67
assimilation, 160
association, 245
astounding, 67
astral projection, 425
asymmetric weapons, 368
asymmetry, 253
asymptote, 450
atheism, 114, 115, 150, 158, 438,
    441, 442
    culture, 150
atheists, 115, 149, 150, 157, 362
atlantic cod, 247
atom, 437
attending, 202, 402
attention, 197, 267, 422, 423
attenuated priors, 199
aubrey de grey, 42
aud, 57
audit, 407, 410
autism, 152, 153, 196–198, 430,
    431
autist, 199
autocrats, 309
automakers, 278
automation, 395
autopsy consents, 207
avoid, 134
awareness, 210, 278
axe murderer, 70
ayahuasca, 60
ayn rand, 290

b. f. skinner, 322
baby, 109

bach, 371
backfire, 363
backfire effect, 355
bacon, 117–119
bacon sandwich, 120
bad, 162
bad guy bias, 304
baffler, 439
baker, 333
ban, 245
banalities, 440
bank, 66
banker, 376
banks, 182
bans, 250
basal ganglia, 319
basic, 433
basic sciences, 80
bat, 57, 59
batman, 70, 268
battlefield, 445
baumol effect, 228
bayes, 191
bayes' theorem, 191, 420
bayesian, 154, 194, 197, 418, 420,
　　　424
bayesian inference, 420
bears, 74
beating, 287
bee sting fallacy, 272
beershe, 331
bees, 96, 147
beethoven, 371
begrudge, 37
behavior: the control of, 315
behavioral economics, 215, 256
behavioral inhibition, 267
behaviorism, 322
bekka, 101, 106–109, 112–114

belgium, 147
belief, 369
bell curve, 217
bell labs, 275
ben carson, 161
ben franklin, 290
benedict option, 464
benefits, 262, 404
benjamin, 332
berkeley undergraduates, 218
berlin, 226
bernie sanders, 82, 83
beta cuck, 77
betrothal bond, 109
bf skinner, 314
bias, 186, 213
bible, 331
big business, 415
big crunch, 68
big fish, 363
big green bat, 60
binding oneself, 297
binocular rivalry, 432
biochemical, 198
biological, 44
biology, 34, 35, 42, 187
bipolar, 200, 403, 406, 407, 409,
　　　412, 413, 416
bipolar disorder, 44, 401, 404
birmingham jail, 290
black, 74, 108, 158, 284, 333
black belt, 73
black hole, 68, 77
black pill, 67, 69
blank slate, 426
blessings, 51
blind spot, 424
blindness, 195
blonde hair, 159

blood money, 461
blue eyes, 102, 104, 106, 112, 159
blue jeans, 145
bob, 304, 305
bobby fischer, 388
body, 293, 294
body politic, 207
body weight, 34
bohr, 382
book, 169
books, 445
boredom, 127
boss, 252, 253
bosses, 252
bost, 397
bostrom, 393, 395, 398
bottom up, 192, 197, 419, 423
bottom-, 196, 424
bottom-up, 193, 419, 422, 423, 425
boycot, 250
boycott, 249, 251
boycotts, 245
br, 337
brain, 174, 176, 185, 317, 318, 417, 421
brain emulation, 188
brain size, 217
brainpower, 250
brasilia, 339–341
brasilia-, 340
brasilite, 340
brave new world, 181
brayden, 122, 126
brazil, 339
bread, 341
breaks, 172
breeding, 95
brex, 357

brexit, 356
brian, 18
bribery, 455
bribes, 283, 458
brilliant scientists, 165
bring up genius, 386, 390
britain, 138
bro, 377
brother, 38, 40
brown eyes, 105
brute, 70
brute strength, 64–66, 69, 70, 76
bryan caplan, 131, 168, 256
bubbles, 22
budapest, 372, 374, 378
buddhism, 54
budget, 72
building, 447
buildings, 446
bullet, 69
bullet trains, 274
bullies, 31
bully, 31
bullying, 31, 254
burden, 45, 269
burden of proof, 45
bureaucracy, 209, 276, 335, 410, 413, 415
bureaucrat, 137
bureaucratic mishaps, 209
burns, 85, 90
bushel, 328
business, 22, 172, 250
business school, 218
buttress, 446

c, 65
c-, 37
cactus person, 60

cadastral map, 328
caesar, 445, 446
cahiers, 328
calculus, 36, 37
caldera, 114
calkas, 101, 102, 105, 107, 108, 110, 112–115
cambridge, 74
camels, 461
can never do anything right, 313
canada, 41, 42, 265, 279, 280
canadian fisheries, 247
canadian health care, 280
cancer, 94–96, 98, 99, 143, 279, 285, 356
cannes, 108
cannibalism, 101
canoe, 105, 108
canoes, 108
capital, 253
capital punishment, 308
capitalism, 246, 295, 296, 305
car, 59
carbon offsets, 17
cardinal, 269
cardinality, 269
carl rogers, 314
carl sagan, 354
casbah, 346
casebook, 172
castle, 444
castle of the winds, 444
castrated, 184
castration, 184
castration anxiety, 184
catholicism, 152
cato, 277
cause, 122, 198
cbt, 90–93

cell, 70
censorship, 413
census, 331, 332
censuses, 331
central coherence, 198, 430
central europe, 382
central european jews, 379, 380
central government, 349
centralised state, 326
centralized government, 224
cerebell, 427
certainty, 195, 242
cff, 193, 194
ch, 273
chanda, 161
chandigarh, 336, 338
change, 96
change culture, 363
change mind, 360
change minds, 360, 363
charity, 18, 51, 252, 306, 307, 359, 365
cherry picking, 279
chesley sullen, 177
chess, 386–392
chess champions, 377
chief of medicine, 207
child, 113, 287
child development, 123
child prodigies, 374
child prodigy, 391
childhood, 391
children, 51, 144, 262, 267, 276, 286, 287, 295
chimps, 97
china, 67, 79, 82, 384, 447
chinese, 64, 97, 135, 231, 301, 335, 367, 413
chocolate, 321

choctaw, 108
choice, 67, 222, 255, 285
choir, 38
christianity, 158, 265, 266
christians, 286
christmas, 22
church-goers, 443
cia, 67
cigarettes, 119
citations, 216
cities, 341
citizen, 416
city, 337
civil rights, 161
civil society, 349
civilization, 301, 302
claim, 294
class, 84, 285
classroom, 357
claveria, 334, 335
clever, 217
cliche, 23
cliches, 352
click, 421
climate change, 442
climate den, 443
clinical algorithm, 338
clinical research, 412
clinical standard, 297
clinical standards, 298
clinical trials, 412
clinton, 359, 361, 362
close, 108
clothing, 430
clubs, 232
co, 407
co-operation, 136
cochran, 374, 381
cod, 247

cogito ergo sum, 368
cognition, 417
cognitive, 24
cognitive ability, 44
cognitive behavioral therapy, 85, 90, 91
cognitive development, 121
cognitive difficulties, 44
cognitive dissonance, 360
cognitive layers, 436
cognitive psychotherapy, 360
cognitive science, 256
cognitive therapy, 127
coherent, 242
coincidence, 366
coke, 250
collaboration, 363
collaborative, 364
collage, 392
collapse, 247, 301
collective action, 249
collective bargaining, 254
collectivization, 344, 347
collectivized farms, 347
college, 21, 40, 82, 83, 124, 223, 227, 232, 235, 237, 264
college degree, 81, 84
college tuition, 232
colon cancer, 117, 118
colonialism, 333
colonization, 72
color, 104
colors, 424
coma, 206
comedy, 28
comment policy, 363
common, 343
commonalities, 162
commoners, 331

commune, 287

communism, 30, 259, 319–321, 437

community, 464

company, 251

comparative advantage, 45, 46

compassion, 209, 214

compassionate, 35

competition, 43, 348, 373, 412

competitive dictatorship, 454

complete argument, 281

complexity, 137

complicity, 42

component, 39

computational theory of identity, 49

computer, 275, 431

computers, 275

concave, 194

concluding, 440

concrete, 338

condescending, 441

conditions, 253

confidence, 196, 432

confidential, 406

confidentiality, 415

confirmation, 424

confirmation bias, 424

conflict, 460

conflict escalation, 432

conformity, 429

confusing, 341

congenital, 195

congress, 138, 371

conquer, 99

conquest, 95, 336

consciousness, 50, 196, 265, 317, 423

consent, 405, 408, 410, 411

consent form, 405

consent forms, 404, 409

consequences, 292, 297, 298, 307

consequentialism, 55, 287, 295–299

consequentialist, 295

conservatives, 22, 35, 261, 271

consistency, 168

conspiracy, 309

consultant, 64

consumer behavior, 260

consumer information, 257, 260

consumer protection, 272

consumer safety, 260

consumerism, 296

continued fraction, 40

control, 252, 253, 315

control systems, 315, 316, 319, 321, 323, 437

control theory, 320

controlled hallucination, 422

controversial, 134

convalescence, 228

conventional wisdom, 299

conversation, 21

convex, 194

convince, 360

cook the, 420

cookies, 117

cooperation, 95, 129, 130, 136, 137, 148

cooperative, 136

coordination, 244, 253, 287, 291, 319

coordination problem, 249, 251

coordination problems, 248, 252

copenhagen, 226

copy-, 175

cor, 442

coral reef, 96
corbusier, 339
corporate self-interest, 261
corporations, 275, 291, 310
correct position, 157
corruption, 132, 207, 274, 276
cost, 222, 223, 225, 227, 229, 237, 251
cost benefit analysis, 281
cost disease, 221, 228, 233, 237
cost effectiveness, 281
cost of health care, 223
cost of living, 238
cost overruns, 274
cost-benefit analysis, 282
cost-effectiveness, 282
costs, 262
counter-, 294
counter-object, 19
counterfactual, 224
countertherapeutic, 62
courage, 211
court, 458
cousin, 81
coworkers, 147
coziness, 341
cracked, 31, 32
crash, 22
creation, 441
credit, 37
crime, 20, 276, 452, 454, 455, 461
criminal, 290, 459
criminals, 283
crisis, 79
cropland, 329
crops, 345
cruel, 136
cruel and unusual punishment, 283
cruelty, 51

cthulhu, 95
cubic sun, 49
cul, 345
cult, 148, 154
cultural evolution, 459, 463
cultural genocide, 153
culture, 31, 123, 153, 158, 160, 266, 341, 443, 462
culture war, 363
cure, 152, 209, 281, 304
curiosity, 356
curiosity rover, 63
curriculum, 357
curtailing rights, 360
customary land tenure, 328
cute, 114
cvd, 303
cybernet, 320
cybernetics, 314

daath, 60
daffodils, 83
daho, 100, 102, 105, 108, 109, 113, 115
daily, 230
danger, 104
dangerous, 397
daniel kahneman, 356
dark knight, 70
darkness, 192
dashboard, 59
data, 403
dating, 148
david, 331, 332
david attenborough, 354
david chapman, 121, 123
david friedman, 452, 458, 462, 465
david hume, 168
david spiegelhalter, 118

de, 96, 98

deaf, 152

deaf community, 153

deaf culture, 153

deafness, 153

death, 41, 68, 206, 214

death flu, 304

death panels, 281

debate, 358, 359, 367

debating trump supporters, 358

debating trump supporters is point-
        less, 358

deborah, 344

debt, 80

deceiver, 51

decision theory, 68

decisions, 307

decree, 334

dectuple, 227

deep learning, 393

default therapist response, 25

defense, 307

deficit, 271, 272

degree, 82

delaware, 263

delhi, 342

delusion, 194, 367

delusions, 193, 195, 199

dementia, 205, 206

democracy, 250, 454, 463

democratic party, 156

dennis gabor, 374

depression, 33, 34, 89, 90, 92,
        141–143, 207, 234, 254,
        406, 416

deregulate, 233

desert, 63

deserve, 39, 307

desire, 315

desp, 299

despot, 337

despots, 299

destruction, 332

detective, 67

detroit, 45

deus vult, 439

developed countries, 262, 279

developing countries, 267

developing ethical, 121

development, 123, 135, 150

developmental psychology, 121

developmental stages, 122

developmental window, 390

deviation, 24

dew, 60

diagnosis, 209, 408, 412

diagnostic, 408

dictatorial, 17

dictators, 309, 336

dictatorship, 297, 308

die, 109, 113, 281

diet, 120

different existence, 95

dignity, 255

diminishing marginal returns, 268

disability, 152

disappear, 22

disaster prone third world country,
        23

discontinuity, 277

discovery, 448

discrimination, 84

disease, 279, 281

dishonorably, 137

dissolution, 150

ditch, 47

ditch-digging, 46

diversity, 132

divine command theory, 49
divine intervention, 417
dmt, 54, 55, 59, 60
doctor, 208, 212, 228, 232
doctor access, 280
doctor who, 274
doctors, 64, 80, 229, 230, 280, 409, 444, 464
documentaries, 365, 366
documentary, 356, 368
dollars, 223
domain generalist, 346
domain specific, 346
door-and-window tax, 330
dopamine, 193, 195, 198, 199, 430, 432
double standard technique, 88
douglas adams, 22
dr. w, 407, 409
dr. w, 403, 407, 408
dream, 95
dreams, 40, 425
dress of peacock feathers, 94
driving, 315
drug addicts, 256
drugs, 55, 195, 458
dsm, 401
dsm-5, 401
due, 413
dues, 245
dumping, 289
duping, 19
dutch, 78
dying, 206, 209, 444
dynamism, 237
dystop, 287
dystopia, 182, 297, 304

e, 218

eagleism, 146
eagles, 145, 146
early 1900s, 379
early psychedelic research, 165
earn, 225
easily prevent, 306
eastern europe, 381
eastern european jews, 379
easy job, 67
ecological zones, 330
economic and political conditions, 382
economic system, 182
economic theories, 257
economics, 78, 134, 218, 243, 344
economist, 169
economists, 133
economy, 66, 257, 270, 273
economy doubling times, 178
ecosystem, 95, 324
ecuador, 265, 266
eddie, 212
edge, 419
edges, 424
edit 2: paul crowley, 93
educated, 441
education, 29, 36, 79, 80, 82, 83, 131, 132, 135, 221–223, 227–229, 231–233, 237, 238, 260, 263, 264, 284–286, 305, 307, 357, 368, 372, 374, 382, 385–387, 390
effect, 134
effective altruism, 251
effectiveness, 241
efficacy, 258
efficiency, 182, 238, 273, 306
effort, 217

effusive, 25

egalitarian, 340

eggheads, 76

egocentrism, 127

egypt, 449

ehealthme, 141–143

el, 156

elaborate consent forms, 414

elasticity, 270

elderly, 235

elderly chess players, 389

election, 362

electrolyte balance, 205

eliezer, 148

eliezer yudk, 155

eliezer yudkowsky, 155, 310

elision, 39

elites, 138

elon musk, 42, 43, 177

em, 172, 174–180, 182, 183, 185, 186

em economy, 178

em era, 180, 181

em society, 180

em world, 178

emancipation, 381

embodied cognition, 433

embodiment, 418

emergency, 280

eminence, 33

emotional, 364

emotional appeal, 357

empathy, 125

emperor palpatine, 66

empiricism, 345

employee, 252, 253

ems, 174, 175, 179, 183, 185, 187, 189

emulation, 186

enactivism, 433

encoded knowledge, 341

encryption, 407

enemies, 208

enforcement, 245, 457

engage, 421

england, 330

english, 36, 82, 333, 452

english class, 37

enku, 102

enlightenment, 54–56, 92, 127, 324

ent, 68

entitlement, 261

entrepreneurship, 391

entropy, 69

entryism, 162

enuli, 104, 105

environment, 122, 247

environmental issues, 248

eotvos contests, 373

epa, 276

epicurus, 437, 438

epistem, 367

epistemic, 367

epistemology, 50, 58, 104, 369

equality, 252, 271, 285

equality of opportunity, 285, 286

equality of results, 285

equilibria, 348

ergonomics, 64

escape, 70

eschaton, 57

esperanto, 386

essential liberty, 290

ethical, 259

ethical theory, 295

ethics, 51, 109, 250, 295, 298, 301, 302, 400, 402, 410

ethics offset, 18
ethics offsets, 17, 20
ethiopia, 23
ethnicity, 122, 161
ethno-nationalism, 160, 161
ethnogenesis, 149
ethos, 168
etymology, 46
euorpean explorers, 101
europe, 115, 272
european geniuses, 382
european jewish population, 378
europeans, 102
evangelical christians, 156
everyone can contribute, 45
everything else, 94, 96
evidence, 61, 356
evidence-based, 338
evil, 94
evolution, 95, 137, 441
evolutionary, 148
evolutionary psychology, 304
exception, 301
exceptions, 294
excommunication, 454
excuses, 39
exit option, 453
expedited consent form, 406
experience, 223
experiment, 218, 402, 410
experimental design, 145
experimental procedure, 145
experimental proof, 260
experimental psychologists, 216
experimental results, 217
experiments, 130
expert, 219
expert advantage, 216
expert consensus, 399

expert predictions, 394, 398
expertise, 219
experts, 215–217, 219, 393, 397–400
extensional definition, 336
external, 177, 464
externalism, 58, 79, 95, 104, 135, 137, 289, 291, 293, 295, 350, 396, 400, 413
externalist, 225
externalist hypothesis, 250
externalists, 51, 88, 97, 146, 168, 186, 214, 231, 246, 263, 288, 301, 309, 325, 335, 346, 361, 362, 367, 371, 381, 383, 428, 450
externalities, 235, 244, 246
externality, 244
extinction, 96
eye color, 106
eye colors, 115
eyes, 104

faa, 277
facade, 340
facebook, 357
fact check, 360
fact checking, 260
fact-checking, 363
faction, 312
factorization, 53
factory, 336
facts, 354–357, 368
fagg, 30
faggot, 31
failure, 276, 326
failure modes, 346
fairness, 109, 261, 262, 267, 269
fallacy, 307

falls, 210
false, 327
family, 34, 148, 305, 392
family medicine, 23
famine, 325, 332, 344
fantasy, 417
farming, 344, 345
farming corporation, 344
fascism, 29, 30, 147
fasori gymnasium, 372
fast food, 83
fat, 34
fate, 69
fats, 203
fault, 265
favor, 21
fbi, 199
fda, 233
features, 424
feeling, 39, 197
fermi paradox, 71
ferrari, 174
festivals, 232
feud, 460, 465
feudalism, 327, 328
fhi, 399
field, 330
fields medal, 36
fifth tier, 317, 318
fight or flight, 73
figure ground inversion, 208
filipinos, 333, 335
filter, 246
final doom, 76
fine, 456
fines, 458
finite, 281
finland, 285
fire, 276, 292

firefighter, 81
firing, 253
first five, 347
first generation, 156
first hundred dollars, 269
first perspective, 463
first tier control, 316
first worlders, 306
fiscal, 333
fish farm, 246
fish farming, 291
fish farms, 246
fisheries, 247
five standards, 364
flat tax, 269
flax, 343
flight, 62
flightlessness, 62
florence, 333
flowers, 95
flu, 30
flying, 446
flynn effect, 132, 135, 138
flyvbjerg et al, 274
fog, 192
food, 259, 276, 345
foot, 185
football, 404
footnote, 45, 316
footnotes, 104
force, 286, 287, 291, 303, 369
force matching task, 428
forecasting, 170, 216
foreign, 303, 462
forest, 63, 294
forest ranger, 62
forgetting, 104
formal enumeration, 341
founded, 409

founding fathers, 159
four, 54, 149
fourth tier, 317
frameworks, 162
france, 279, 280, 326, 330, 331, 335, 346
fraud, 87
freddie deboer, 371
free college, 236, 237
free market, 242–244
free markets, 244
free rider, 249
free will, 68, 265
free will defense, 50
freedom, 287–290, 310, 463
freedom of religion, 298, 299
french, 335
freshness, 389
freud, 24, 87, 214
friedman, 459
friend, 88
friendly ai, 189
friends, 148, 288, 305
friendship, 147, 288
fruits, 120
fun home, 124
funding, 222
futarchy, 310, 311
future, 69, 170, 171, 180
future sight, 68
future values, 180
future-you, 72
futurism, 169, 170
futurolog, 173
futurology, 171

g, 102
g.k. chesterton, 324
gad, 332

galaxy, 71, 72
galleon, 100
game theory, 130, 137
gamer culture, 160
gamer girl, 160
gamergate, 159
gandhi, 368
garett jones, 128
garry kasparov, 386
gary kasparov, 387
gasoline, 267
gating, 429
gaucher's disease, 375, 376
gay, 88
gay couple, 30
gdp, 225, 238
geek, 26
gell-mann amnesia, 64
gender, 26, 44, 82, 135, 159, 389, 391, 400
gender roles, 65
gender studies, 82
general semantics, 124
generation, 225
genes, 264, 389
genetic diseases, 376
genetics, 35, 37, 38, 42, 264, 387
genius, 36, 383, 390, 446
genocide, 153
gent, 374
gentiles, 382
geologic phen, 114
george soros, 381
germany, 378, 380, 381
germs, 73, 107
give us, 73
givewell, 251
glad, 388
glenn hubbard, 264

global warming, 248, 309

globalization, 227, 228

glutamate, 193, 200

goal alignment, 396, 397

god, 46, 47, 51, 57, 74, 75, 157, 265, 292, 331, 332, 439, 450

goddess, 95–98

goddess of cancer, 94, 95, 97

goddess of everything else, 95, 96, 98, 99

gold, 444

gold standard, 297

golden, 336

goldman sachs, 23

gomer, 202, 211

gomer pyle, 210

good, 94

good faith, 363

government, 131, 207, 208, 222, 233, 236, 241, 242, 244, 245, 248, 249, 252, 260, 264, 272–278, 286, 287, 296, 301–303, 305–311, 313, 333, 410, 452, 463, 464

government aid, 266

government intrusion, 308

government programs, 222, 276, 312

government regulation, 247, 258, 288

government spending, 265

government-run health care, 280

government-sponsored, 284

grace, 209, 398

grades, 36

grain, 328

grains, 120

grandfather, 203

grandmother, 203

great filter, 398

great white shark, 62

greed, 261, 320

green, 57

green eyes, 112

grit, 42

grooming, 21

group, 438

groupies, 28

groups, 455

groupthink, 429

growth, 182

growth mindset, 33

guild, 450

guilt, 87, 114

gun, 67

gun control, 126, 242, 284

gun control laws, 284

gun laws, 284

guns, 73, 107, 364, 366

guns ger, 367

gut, 294

gypsies, 374, 453, 461, 465

gypsy, 453

hacking, 67

hadith, 144

haiti, 23

hallucination, 421, 422, 425

hallucinations, 194, 195, 199, 432

ham, 117

handout, 236, 237

hands off approach, 241

hanson, 171, 174, 175, 178, 180, 181, 183, 185–187, 189

hansonian, 187

happiness, 49, 148, 257, 287, 288, 404

har, 374

hard, 196, 265

hard takeoff, 395

hard work, 35, 39, 40, 43, 262–264

hard worker, 40

hardy, 374, 381

harebrained, 297

harford, 357, 364, 365

harm, 412

harsanyi, 372

harvard, 163, 265

harvesters, 77

hawaii, 83

hawk, 62

hawkins, 435

hayek, 348

headline, 276

health, 132, 223, 259, 273, 276, 288, 289, 356

health care, 80, 208, 221, 223–225, 227–229, 231–233, 235, 237, 238, 271, 272, 279–282

health insurance, 209, 223, 225, 227

health spending, 225

healthcare, 223

hearing voices, 193

heart, 302

heart attack, 234

heat death, 68, 69, 76

heaven, 265, 417

hedges' g, 91

hedonism, 50

hedonium, 185

hell, 182

hellish, 305

help, 59, 244

henry ford, 336

heritability, 33

herman cain, 161

heterochromia, 112

heterochromia irid, 112

heterozygote advantage, 376

heuristics, 256, 287, 298, 301, 303, 350

hidden book, 392

hierarchy, 288, 317, 318

hieroglyphs, 449

high iq, 131

high level systems, 437

high modern, 349

high modernism, 326, 335, 336, 340, 341, 348

high modernists, 326

high school, 36, 213

high-level systems, 426

high-scrupulosity, 41

hindu gods, 40

hip hop, 158

hipaa, 408

hippocrates, 23

history, 172

hitler, 309, 366

hive, 134

hive mind, 128, 134, 135

hobbes, 294

hole in, 56

holocaust, 153, 332

holography, 374

holy book, 157

holy books, 162

holy gra, 430

home schooling, 392

home-schooling, 392

homeless, 28, 30, 31, 45
homelessness, 80
homework, 392
homophobia, 31
homosexuality, 292
honesty, 319
honey, 96
hooked tuna, 206
hope, 69
hope for the, 410
horrible, 312
horribleness, 290
horror, 103
hospital, 228, 232, 410, 413
hospital administration, 405
hospitals, 233
hostile, 396
hot pussy, 77
hours worked, 238
house, 424
house call, 228
house of god, 201, 202, 204, 205,
        207–213
housing, 221, 226, 227, 238
huey long, 29
human, 148, 310
human being, 203
human beings, 203
human biodiversity, 161
human health care, 233
human intelligence, 33
human level ai, 394
human level intelligence, 394
human needs, 337
human pilots, 188
humane conditions, 283
humanities, 442
humanity, 72
humans, 97, 182

humor, 209
humphry osm, 164
hundert, 377
hungarian, 370, 371, 391
hungarian education, 386
hungarians, 380
hungary, 372–374, 378–383, 385,
        387, 392
hungry, 208
hunter-, 352
hunting lodge, 100
huppi, 273
hurricane, 369
hurting other people, 292
huxley, 299
hyperprior, 428
hyperpriors, 426
hypertext, 170
hypocrisy, 125
hypotheses, 421
hypothesis testing, 424
hypothetical, 310

i feel, 25
i-am-an-intellectual-imp, 43
ibm, 275
iceland, 456, 457, 461
icelanders, 458
id, 439
ideal world, 254
identity, 49, 156
ideology, 162
idiot, 232, 337
illness, 51
illusion, 56, 231
im, 57, 457
imaginary, 206
imaginary tests, 206
imagination, 72, 424

imbecile, 337
immigrants, 384
immigration, 132–134, 138
immortality, 76, 360, 449
immortality serum, 68
immune system, 30
implicit knowledge, 342
impossible, 88, 89, 311
inc, 187
incarceration, 283, 462
incentive, 218, 246
incentive systems, 207
incentives, 208, 215, 219, 260, 280
income, 134, 263, 264
income elasticity, 264
income tax, 270
incompetence, 264
incomprehensible, 22
inconvenience, 249
incrementalism, 311
independent culture, 157
indeterminate, 448
india, 342, 384
indigents, 455
individual, 134
individual differences, 129
individuals, 96
industrial methods, 343
inequality, 238, 268
infant mortality, 119, 279
inferiority, 87
inflation, 223, 225, 227, 231
informal systems, 342
information, 21, 106
infrastructure, 225
ingenuity, 273
ingroup, 153
initiation of force, 294
innate, 36, 39, 122, 426

innate ability, 36, 37, 43
innate aptitude, 42
inner critic, 93
innocent people, 283
inpatient, 412
insight, 92
institutional review, 402
institutions, 273
insults, 61
insurance, 232, 281, 282, 455, 461
intelligence, 34, 35, 37, 38, 44, 45,
        123, 183, 240, 262, 264,
        267, 365, 376, 381
intelligence explosion, 185, 186,
        398
intelligence test, 44
interests, 148
intergenerational income mobility,
        263, 264
intergroup relations, 145
intergroup rivalry, 145
internal, 212, 361, 396, 400, 464
internal medicine, 23
internalism, 58, 350, 424
internalists, 88, 214, 361
internet, 69, 275
internet flamewars, 262
interns, 212
internship, 202, 213
interruption, 444
interview, 403
intuition, 40, 368
intuitions, 34
intuitive, 448
inventions, 275
investors, 31
iq, 33, 34, 44–46, 128–132, 134–
        138, 154, 217, 218, 264,

267, 297, 375, 377, 379, 384, 387, 388, 391, 431
iq and the wealth of nations, 128
iq gap, 128
iq test, 44
iq tests, 375
ir, 412
iran, 67, 346
iraq, 302
irb, 402, 404–406, 408, 410–414, 416
irb review, 413
ireland, 79, 80
iridum, 112
irishmen, 80
irrational, 257
irrational consumers, 282
irrationality, 254, 256
irs, 291
is-ought dichotomy, 293
islam, 144, 151, 158, 266
israel, 331, 332, 383–385
italy, 73, 333, 379
iterated prisoner's, 132
iterated prisoner's dilemma, 137
iterated prisoners' dilemma, 136
ivy, 80

j, 422
j. p. morgan, 344
james scott, 324, 353
jane, 326
jane jacobs, 341
janitors, 407
japan, 82, 147
jared diamond, 73, 107, 135, 231, 250, 301, 335, 413
jayman, 161
jazz, 57

jean valjean, 300, 301
jean valjean's, 301
jeff kaufman, 18
jesus, 46
jewish, 376
jewish diseases, 379
jews, 134, 160, 374–378, 380–382, 465
jo, 205
joab, 331, 332
job, 21, 42, 51, 253, 254, 395
job interviews, 29, 68
jobs, 82, 83, 359, 395
john dewey, 436
john lilly, 164, 166
john maynard keynes, 238
john von neumann, 373, 382
johnson, 361
joker, 70
jokes played straight, 210
jones, 135
jones' paradox, 134
journalism, 364
judaism, 156
judges, 294
judgment under uncertainty, 256
junior, 211
jurisprudence, 144
justice, 267, 454, 455, 460
justify, 296

kaluhani, 102
kang, 273
kansas, 66
kary mullis, 164
ketamine, 194
keynes, 238
khan academy, 232
kids, 286

killing, 366
king, 64, 71, 77, 79, 290, 332, 444, 463
king abdullah, 64
king louis, 326
king of saudi arabia, 64
king william, 67, 71, 77
kings, 331
kleptocracies, 442
knee jerk, 312
knife, 67
knowledge, 68, 104, 107, 245, 369, 417, 445, 447, 448
korzybski, 124
kris, 453
kvithion, 57

la griffe du lion, 138
labor, 221, 243
labor market, 254
labor regulations, 254
labor unions, 254, 362
laborers, 182
lady in the corner office, 407
laffer curve, 270
lagos, 342
laisse, 241
lake, 246
land, 182, 328
laplace's, 107
large, 344
lark, 37
last names, 334
laszlo, 386
laszlo polgar, 386, 392
laszlo ratz, 371
late-night fights, 410
law, 251, 290, 454, 457, 460, 461
law of comparative advantage, 45

laws, 277
lawsuit, 143, 235
lawsuitphobia, 234
lawsuits, 234
lawyers, 335
layman, 219
laziest, 402
laziness, 39
le, 212
le corbusier, 326, 336–338, 350
lead, 132, 267, 299
lead poisoning, 267
leadership, 240
learned hyperpri, 426
learning, 322, 426, 447
learning experience, 213
left, 133, 366
legal, 62
legal system, 458, 461
legal systems, 459, 465
legal systems very different from ours, 463
legibility, 331–333, 349
legible, 326
leisure time, 183
lenin, 320, 321
leo szilard, 382
les miserables, 300, 347
less educated people, 260
less skilled, 134
less wrong, 154, 155, 310
lesswrong, 155
levels of the mind, 420
levi, 332
leviathan, 294
lew rockwell, 291
liability, 464
liberals, 35, 125, 261, 262, 266, 271

libertarian
  anti, 313
libertarianism, 236, 240–245, 247,
      248, 255, 257, 258, 269,
      286, 289, 292, 296, 300,
      304, 305, 307, 308, 311,
      313, 351
  critique, 242
  libertarians, 242, 262, 263, 271,
      277, 278, 287, 291, 292,
      294, 303, 307, 310–313
  of the poor, 351
  party, 311
library, 36
lie, 89
lies, 354
life, 71, 72, 117
life chances, 263
life expectancy, 118, 119, 223–
      225, 236, 279
lifespan, 119, 446, 450
ligands, 42
light, 315
limits of abilities, 65
limits of strength, 65
linguistic imperialism, 335
linguistic relativity, 329
link, 417
lions, 97
literacy, 284
lithium, 91
livable cities, 348
live, 89
lives saved, 278
lobbying, 283
lobotomized, 189
local conceptions, 327
local intelligence explosion, 185
locke, 293

locked room, 407
logic, 104, 121, 360, 368
logical debate, 365
logical fallacy, 365
logical program, 320
loneliness, 87
long run, 134
lopez, 364
loser, 361
love, 55, 65, 66, 437
lovecraft, 95
lower class, 263
lower levels, 427
lrf, 198
lsd, 164, 166, 167, 195
lucasian professor of mathematics,
      74
lucid dreaming, 425
luck, 35–37, 41, 43, 62, 66, 79, 97,
      265, 267, 268, 289, 366,
      464
luminance, 419
lump in throat, 203
lw sequences, 127

m, 167, 399
madman, 337
magical realism, 202, 204
magical thinking, 122
major depression, 141
malaria, 376
malcolm gladwell, 388, 389
malevolent force, 213
malleability, 390
malnutrition, 306
man, 72
man in black, 74
management, 64
managerial jobs, 377

mandarin, 64
mandatory, 278
manhattan project, 370, 378
mania, 195, 432
manic, 25, 199
marco rubio, 152
marginal utility, 268
marginal value, 268, 269
marijuana, 194, 350
marime, 453
market, 454
market failure, 244, 249, 257
marketing, 250, 259
markets, 232
marriage, 79, 137
mars, 63
martial arts, 73
martians, 370
martin luther king, 290, 366
marx, 299
marxism, 463
master, 447, 448
masters, 82
masturbation, 182
masturbatory, 182
materialism, 438
math, 36, 40, 46, 382
mathematical framework, 191
mathematics, 373, 391
matrix, the, 65
matzoh balls, 203
mayor, 337
me, 38
meaning, 148
measurement, 326, 327
meat, 18, 19, 117–120
mechanical turk, 217
medal, 371
media, 305

media bias, 276
median date, 394
medical, 86, 202, 207, 209
medical care, 205
medical education, 83
medical ethics, 208
medical internship, 201
medical malpractice, 234
medical practice, 210
medical research, 412
medical school, 23, 79, 80
medical screening, 409
medical treatment, 209
medication, 117, 143, 367
medicine, 46, 80, 81, 208–213, 230, 234, 304
medieval, 461
medieval history, 83
medieval ireland, 453
mediocrity, 41
medium, 24
meiji restorations, 351
memories, 213
memory, 104, 213, 422
men, 62
mental energy, 255
mental fatigue, 172
mental health, 148, 167, 361
mental illness, 34, 87, 411
mental performance, 172
mentally ill celebrities, 31
merchant, 376
merck, 415
mercury, 289
meritocracy, 261
mersenne primes, 102
mescaline, 165
mess, 326
meta-analysis, 91, 92

meta-baptist, 157
meta-levels, 210
metaphor, 59, 323
meteor, 424
meteorites, 369
meth, 235
metis, 349, 350, 352, 369, 459
metric system, 328
mib, 67
microeconomists, 216
microexpressions, 73
micropolitics, 327
middle, 144
middle ages, 326
middle class, 271, 272
middle east, 67
middlebury, 367
mike, 246
mike huben, 313
military, 271, 272, 307
milky way, 63
mind, 183, 265, 424
mind control, 74
mind reading, 74
minds, 61
minimal government, 311
minimum wage, 134, 313
mining, 250
ministry of chaos, 56
ministry of void, 56
minority, 222
minta, 373
misleading, 259
misreading, 433
mississippian, 263
mistakes, 302
mobile phone, 227
mobility, 263, 264
modafinil, 42, 184

models, 426
models of, 192
modern, 337
modernism, 340, 349
modernist cities, 348
modulor, 336, 337
mohammed, 151
moisture, 327
molesting, 28
molyneux's problem, 426
mom-and, 261
money, 268, 269, 281, 288
monitoring plan, 411
montana, 288, 343
mor karman, 373
moral, 287, 301
moral agent, 296
moral argument, 313
moral calculus, 36
moral circle, 19
moral decision, 296
moral epistemology, 299
moral goods, 296
moral gulf, 34
moral heuristics, 301
moral imperative, 41
moral issues, 243
moral luck, 18
moral parochial, 18
moral standards, 313
moral systems, 297
moral uncertainty, 18
morality, 250, 293, 296, 298, 301,
        302, 309
morally wrong-, 261
more obscure products, 260
more varied, 327
morgoth, 94
mortality, 119, 224

mortality statistics, 204
mortar and pestle, 103
mother of, 308
motivation, 392
motor cortex, 427
motor plant, 435
motor program, 427
motor system, 427, 433
mountain, 63
mouse, 275
move, 96
movement, 435
movie, 268
movie tickets, 227, 268, 269
movies, 268
mozart, 371
mp3 player, 275
mu, 145
murder, 20, 292, 456
muscle tension, 317
muscle tension control system, 316
muscles, 65, 316, 319
music, 38, 43
musical, 202
muslim, 359
muslims, 144
mutation, 30, 98
mutual protection, 455
mutual protection insurance groups,
    459
myers-briggs, 154
mysticism, 190

n=1 experiments, 391
narrative, 61, 350, 354, 357
nate, 85–87
nate silver, 86
nate the genius, 90
nathan robinson, 124, 125

nation, 134
national, 364
national differences, 129
national language, 335
national success, 128
nationalism, 161
nationality, 122, 162
native americans, 108
natural variations in ability, 42
nature, 62
nature vs, 391
nazi, 30, 402, 403
nazi germany, 403
nazi party, 403
nazi reg, 403
negative thoughts, 89, 90
negentropy, 77
negotiation, 253
negotiation partner, 253
neighborhood, 244, 245
neighborhood association, 245
neighborhoods, 341
neighbors, 244
neil degrasse tyson, 441
nejm, 225
neo-nazis, 29
neoliberal, 147
nerds, 147
netherlands, 78, 224
neuro, 167
neuronal, 418
neurons, 420
neuroscience, 190, 317, 318
neurosis, 207, 320
neurotransmitters, 430
neurotypical, 158, 431
never going to give you up, 422
never gonna give you up, 423
new athe, 441

new atheism, 439, 441–443

new atheists, 439–442

new economic policy, 347

new guinea, 79, 97, 112, 135, 231, 301, 335, 367, 413

new hampshire, 288

new study application, 403

new testament, 157

new world, 333

new york, 378

new york city subway, 225

new york times bestseller, 395

newbie, 408

newbies, 407, 408

newspapers, 276

next, 269

niceness, 136

nicholas kurti, 372

nick bostrom, 398

nick land, 181, 183

nickel, 227

niemey, 339

nigerian prince, 143

nih, 366

nitpicking, 410

njal's saga, 457

nmda, 194, 199, 430

no, 184, 294

no initiation of force, 294

nobel, 381, 383

nobel laureates, 371

nobel prize, 164, 372, 381, 383–385

nobel prizes, 377, 384

nobles, 331

nod, 25

noise, 196

noisy, 341

non-, 129

non-aggression principle, 294

non-libertarian, 240, 300, 313

non-libertarian faq, 240

non-libertarians, 312

nonlibertarian, 257

normal, 213, 391

norman borlaug, 42

north korea, 17

northern italy, 73

norway, 384

norway spru, 324

not, 335

nothing wrong, 21

now, 369

npr, 271

nsa, 67

nuclear physics, 299, 300

nuclear warhead, 295

number, 59

nurses, 229

nutrition, 132, 219

ny, 355

nyhan, 355

nyhan & reifler, 363

o-ring theory, 131

oak, 95

obama, 366

obelisks, 449

obese, 32

obesity, 31, 34, 321

object, 419

objectification, 362

objective time, 174

obsessive compulsive personality disorder, 403

ocd, 410

ocean, 63

oed, 24

oedipus, 24
office for human research protec-
        tions, 414
offsetting, 20
oil, 59
okcupid, 24, 391
oklahoma city, 144
olanz, 195
old school economics, 255
old testament, 157
oliver burkeman, 93
olson, 131
omnibenevolence, 49
omnipotence, 49
on the inside of the perimeter, 71
on-the-ground, 342
one shot, 136
online chart, 406
online social science journalism, 364
online wars, 157
open borders, 138
open letter, 133
open-mindedness, 180
openness, 166, 167
openness to experience, 166
oppression, 17
optical illusions, 417
optimist, 299
or, 94
orange, 74–76, 145
orchestra, 228
order, 341
ordinal, 269
oregon medicaid experiment, 209
organic, 119, 348
organicism, 325
orthodox jews, 464
orthop, 210
oscar niemeyer, 339

osha, 277
osmond, 165
ostracism, 453, 454
other path, 187
ouroboros, 449
outlaw, 456
outlaw cascades, 458
outrage, 276
outsiders, 450
outsourcing, 227
over correction, 318
overachieving jewish mothers, 38
overcoming bias, 169
overconfidence, 171
overhead, 307
overused, 23
overweight, 34
oxygen, 310
ozone, 248
ozy, 45

p-zombies, 50
pacifists, 291
pact, 246
pages, 445
pain, 429
pakistan, 160
pal, 271
pand, 276
panic attacks, 85
pants on, 360
paperwork, 413, 414
par, 194
parable, 46
paradigm, 314
paradox, 98, 104, 128
parent, 287
parents, 32, 36, 262, 286, 287, 295
paris, 226, 338, 347

parkinson's, 318, 430

parkinsonian tremor, 319

parliament, 79, 138

participant, 404

particle accelerator, 299

party, 242

pascal's wager, 114

passion, 374

past, 337

patents, 304

paternal, 255

paternalism, 255, 256, 291

patient, 25, 88, 202, 208, 367

patients, 91

patientsville, 143

patriotism, 161, 306, 360

pattern, 29, 57

pattern matching, 190

patterns, 23

paul, 87, 88, 292

paul erdos, 374

paul nemen, 388

paul's lover, 87

paxil, 184

pct, 320, 437

peace, 158, 273

peak productivity, 172

peasant, 324

peasant farmers, 346

peasant rising, 333

peasant villages, 352

peasants, 326, 333, 446

pelt, 369

pencil, 405, 411

penicillin, 143

pennsylvania, 464

pension plan, 255

pensions, 236

people, 296

pep rallies, 26

pepsi, 250

per capita, 238

per student spending, 221

percentile, 44

perception, 192, 194, 196, 197, 315, 368, 417, 421–423, 425, 428, 431, 433, 436

perceptual, 314

perceptual control theory, 315

perceptual handshaking failures, 193

perceptual processes, 426

perceptuocontrol theory, 322

perfect information, 257

perfect world, 310

perfectionism, 87

performance, 362

permanent hispanic surn, 333

perpetrator, 452

persecution, 376

person-by, 128

personal, 266

personal conversation, 22

personal self-determination, 295

personality, 166, 198, 266

perspective, 56

persuasion, 362

peru, 187

peter, 19, 292

pfizer, 415

phantom, 202

pharmaceuticals, 304

phatic, 25–27

phatic culture, 25

phatic therapy, 25

phd students, 216

phenomenal conservatism, 193

phenomenology, 321

philippines, 334

philosopher, 290
philosophers stone, 449
philosophy, 42, 50, 243, 302, 322, 400
philosophy of, 400
philosophy of math, 397
philosophy of mind, 196, 400, 437
philosophy of religion, 49
philosophy of science, 396, 397
phone calls, 22
physicalism, 437
physicists, 378, 379
physics, 68, 371, 381, 424
physiology, 40
piaget, 123
piano, 38–40
pills, 74
pink, 76
pinzon, 100, 102
placebo, 92
placebo effect, 92, 433
plague, 332
plan, 337
plane crashes, 276, 277
planets, 72
planned cities, 348
planned farms, 348
planning, 337, 445
platitudes, 442
playgrounds, 234
plea, 67
pleasure, 50
pleasure/perfection balance works, 86
poetry, 54
poland, 378, 379
polarization, 312
polgar, 386, 387, 390
polgar children, 391

polgar sisters, 387–389, 392
polgars, 388, 392
polgár, 392
police, 126, 294, 301, 307, 323
police brutality, 462
police racism, 462
policeman, 458
policy debates, 307
polio, 273
political bias, 131
political implications, 134
political pal, 311
politicians, 274, 291
politics, 157, 207, 236, 289, 303, 463
pollution, 246, 312
polyculture, 344
polygenic risk, 431
polymerase, 164
polynesia, 102
polynesian, 100
polynesians, 102
poor, 222, 236, 237, 261–263, 265, 266, 270, 271, 307, 351
poor children, 276
poor people, 79, 351
poor working conditions, 254
pope, 71, 74
pope, the, 73
population, 49
population growth, 100
pork, 207, 208
porter, 363
positive account of property rights, 458
positive proof, 241
post truth, 354
posterior, 429
postmodernism, 50, 463

potts, 204

poverty, 35, 36, 83, 251, 263, 272, 352

power, 69, 96, 252, 309, 446, 457

power law, 170

powerful ai, 400

powers, 316, 318, 320, 321, 436

powers et al, 436

pp, 432

pp model, 428

pr, 29

practical, 273

practical issues, 243

practical wisdom, 459

practice, 38, 39, 41, 251, 388, 389, 391

pragmatist, 436

praise, 36

pre-study training, 407, 412

precision, 196

predicament, 88

predict, 197

prediction, 30, 68, 170, 171, 198, 215, 217, 219, 319, 397, 419–423, 427, 431

prediction engines, 428

prediction error, 192, 198, 199, 427, 432

prediction machine, 419

prediction markets, 310, 311

predictions, 171, 217, 394, 420

predictive, 419

predictive coding, 417, 418

predictive model, 432

predictive processing, 417, 418, 421, 425, 433–437

pref, 178

preferences, 255–257

premod, 353

premodern states, 331

pressured speech, 25

prestige, 232

pretty, 65

prevention, 277

price, 227, 229, 235, 237

priests, 107

prime numbers, 53

priming, 425

priming effect, 425

primitive, 123

primitive cultures, 122

prince, 451

princes, 299

principle, 303

principles, 342

prior, 191, 429

priors, 194, 199

prison, 283

prisoner, 137

prisoner's dilemma, 129, 137, 249, 253

prisoners dilemma, 136

privacy, 341, 415

private, 273, 283, 307

private citizens, 307

private enforcement, 456

private health care, 280

private healthcare, 280

private police, 304

private prisons, 283

private property, 289

private prosecution, 456

private roads, 304

private schools, 285

privatization, 247

privilege, 37, 145, 400

privileges, 360

pro, 450

probability, 71, 107, 191
problem of evil, 50
problems, 25
procedure, 405
procedures, 301
processed meat, 119
prodigy, 38, 391
production, 270
productivity, 87, 246
professor, 229
profit, 46, 181, 281–283
profit motive, 282
programming, 164
progress, 180, 187
progressive, 35
progressive tax, 269
progressive taxation, 261, 269
progressives, 35, 262
progressivism, 442
promotion, 253
proper-, 146
property, 293, 295, 300, 456
property dualism, 437
proposal, 78
proprioception, 427, 428, 435
proprioceptive prediction error, 435
prosecutor, 456
prosocial, 148
prospectuses, 343
prosperity, 288
protect, 45, 185, 369, 424
protected health information, 408
protected health information con-
        sent, 409
protestant, 144
protestantism, 152
protocol, 411
prozac, 91
psil, 164

psilocybin, 163, 166, 167
psychedelia, 166
psychedelic, 164
psychedelics, 165–167
psychiatric, 406, 413
psychiatric evaluation, 44
psychiatric patients, 405
psychiatrist, 367, 405
psychiatrists, 91
psychiatry, 127, 165, 166, 200, 202,
        207, 212, 234, 350, 351,
        401, 405, 408, 412, 416,
        432, 440
psychoanalysis, 92, 214
psychological research, 404
psychology, 91, 217, 218, 256, 322,
        416
psychopathic solutions, 176
psychopaths, 175
psychosis, 194, 199
psychotherapy, 88, 92, 127
public education, 284
public good, 253
public goods, 452
public healthcare, 280
public school system, 392
public schools, 285
public system, 280
publication, 412
publications, 216
punch, 294
punching bag, 69
punching up, 31
punditry, 219
punishment, 322, 332, 452, 454,
        455
purely logical debate, 357, 358,
        365
purpose, 149

push, 410
putin, 67, 71

quack, 307
qualia, 196, 321
quality, 229
quirky, 24
quotas, 247
quran, 158

rabbi zusya, 47
race, 35, 135, 136, 145, 158, 161,
    285, 333, 379, 400
racism, 136, 161
radiation, 98
radical acceptance, 54
radio, 22
rain, 360
rallying flag, 149, 162
rallying flags, 162
ram dass, 164
ramanujan, 36, 40, 45
rand health insurance, 209
rand health insurance experiment,
    225
random, 217
rank-order correlation, 216
rap, 158, 159
rational, 218, 255, 256
rational design, 338
rational self interest, 463
rationalism, 325, 352
rationalist, 154
rationalist community, 41, 154, 155
rationalists, 147, 156, 324, 325
rationality, 127, 131, 137, 218,
    255, 256, 434
rationality community, 155
rationalization, 343

rationing, 281
rattlerism, 146
rattlers, 145, 146
ratz, 372
raw sparkroot, 103
ray kur, 398
re, 360
reaction, 169, 211
reading, 61, 125, 446
reading scores, 221
reagan, 359, 366
reality, 406, 433
reason for concern, 399
receptors, 42
recidivism, 283
records, 410
recycling, 248
red, 76
red meat, 119
red pill, 65, 67
red tape, 236
redaction, 448
redactor, 448
redistribution, 266, 267
reductio ad absurdum, 305
reformed, 157
refuting, 354
regression to the mean, 387
regulation, 185, 233, 241, 247–
    249, 264, 277, 278, 286,
    289, 307, 308, 312
regulations, 233
reifler, 355
reinforcement learning, 425
rejection, 88
relationship, 88, 89
relative risk, 118, 120
relative to other occupations, 229
relay, 68

religion, 30, 97, 114, 152, 156, 157, 298, 302, 441, 443
religious, 157
religious experience, 122
religious jews, 157
repetition compulsion, 440
replication, 416
replication crisis, 425
report card, 36
repression, 212
republicans, 359, 360
research, 42, 169, 404, 408, 412, 415
resettlement, 325
residency, 23, 207
resident doctors, 402
resources, 46
responsibility, 34, 35
restrictions, 284
results, 406
results log, 407, 410
retina, 419
retirement, 176
retirement fund, 255
retirement savings, 291
revealed preference, 255, 256
revenue, 270
reverse causation, 135
review, 390, 413, 414
review of a book that doesn't exist, 390
revolution, 328
revolutions, 299
reward, 322, 326
rhetoric, 364, 366
rhetorically, 357
rich, 261–263, 265, 270, 271
rich people, 159
richard alpert, 164

richard dawkins, 441
rick astley, 422
rick roll, 423
ridiculous, 410
right, 133, 300, 337, 366
rights, 287, 294, 295, 298–300, 305, 308, 463
rising costs, 228
risk, 118, 396
risk tolerance, 234, 235
risks, 395, 404, 405
ritual, 25, 102, 114
ritual needs, 345
road maintenance, 307
robbers cave, 145
robbers' cave, 149
robbers' cove, 148
robbing, 292
robert a. freitas jr., 180
robert howard, 388
robert kegan, 123
robin hanson, 168, 169, 173, 175, 179, 183, 185–189, 310
robinson, 364
rock star, 321
rokitansky, 204
role-playing, 88
romance, 177
romania, 378, 379
romans, 446
ron paul, 311
ronald fisher, 356
roof, 447
roommate, 232
rosa parks, 290
routine, 431
roy basch, 202
rsa, 53
rule, 282

rule codes, 342
rules, 245, 297
russia, 30, 67, 71, 346, 378, 380

sacred plant, 101
sacrifice, 37
sadness, 404, 417
safety, 258–260, 303
safety research, 399
sage, 59
sailor, 107
salary, 229
sales pitch, 29
salience, 192, 199
sally, 367
sam, 441
sanders, 83, 84
sanity, 286
sanity waterline, 369
sapir whorf hypothesis, 329
sarah, 93
sat, 217
satan, 331
satisfaction, 86, 87
saudi arabia, 64, 265, 266, 286
save, 69, 281
saving lives, 303
savings, 130
scale, 273
scandinavia, 302
scapegoat, 285
schelling fence, 20
schelling point, 463
schemes, 326
schisms, 151
schizophrenia, 44, 87, 167, 193–
        195, 199, 200, 431–433
schneider, 413
school, 222, 392

school choice, 222, 286
school spending, 221
schools, 222, 233, 286
science, 97, 134, 385, 402, 415,
        447
science fiction, 188
scientific, 363
scientific advances, 349
scientific forestry, 324
scientific impossibility, 76
scientific literature, 415
scientific omnipotence, 349
scientific training, 218
scientists, 413
scott, 21, 324, 326, 333, 344, 348–
        352, 459
scott alexander, 37, 349
screener, 403
screening, 406, 408, 409, 412, 413
screening test, 401
script, 25
scrubs, 201
sea, 109
seasteading, 464
seat belts, 278
seatbelt, 278
seatbelts, 278
secession disputes, 463
second generation, 156
second names, 333
secret, 67
secret code, 410
secret patient log, 407
secrets, 446
secularism, 156
secure, 406
security, 71
security theater, 413
sedition, 64

seduction, 70
seed capital, 46
seeing like a state, 353
seer, 332
selection bias, 371
self, 265, 266
self esteem, 34, 43
self evident, 242
self interest, 248
self ownership, 293
self-bl, 91
self-confidence, 195
self-control, 267
self-deception, 309
self-environment boundaries, 122
self-esteem, 34, 43, 85, 87, 91
self-interest, 246
self-knowledge, 72
self-mut, 462
self-ownership, 293
self-pred, 428
self-replicating, 178
self-worth, 44, 45
semantic stopsigns, 310
sense, 423
sense data, 419–421, 426
sense-data, 195, 420, 424
sensory, 197, 198, 419, 421, 426
sensory deprivation, 195
sensory integration, 197
sensory processing disorder, 197
seoul, 226
sequence, 317
serotonin, 193, 430
service, 98, 229
ses, 44
sesame street, 126
set, 436
set point, 321

sex, 62, 66, 175, 202, 379
sexual fantasies, 62
sexual harassment, 464
shadows, 419
shame, 87, 204
she, 99
shem, 212, 213
shergill, 428
shia, 151, 157
shia islam, 156
shortists, 240
shroud of turin, 74
sick, 281
sickle cell, 376, 377
side effects, 141–143
sidewalk, 339
sigm, 314
signal, 232, 369
signaling, 29
silicon valley, 442
simulation, 71, 424
sin, 78, 331
single, 350
single payer, 279
singularity, 169, 176, 182, 186, 394, 395, 398
siren, 96
skeptical, 149
skepticism, 277
skeptics, 149
skills, 198
skin, 197
skin problems, 285
skinner, 322
skittles, 126
slate, 233
slavery, 185, 259, 286, 287, 290
sleep, 67, 176
slippery slope, 301, 308

slow, 445
small business, 415
small farmers, 344
small talk, 21, 26
smallpox, 273
smart, 102, 131
smart fractions, 138
smoking, 117, 366
smooth, 196
snow, 74
soccer moms, 182
soccer practice, 181
social, 134, 156, 442
social and, 121
social change, 148
social class, 266
social conv, 339
social desir, 323, 437
social engineers, 343
social faux pas, 21
social grooming, 21
social interaction, 198
social justice, 442
social life, 156
social media, 357
social mobility, 264, 265
social norm, 278
social norms, 37, 278
social relations, 345
social safety net, 309
social security, 272
social status, 321
social workers, 287
socialism, 242
socialites, 31
society, 148, 266, 301
socioeconomic conditions, 264
soil conservation, 344
soldiers, 291

som, 461
somali, 452
somalia, 453, 460
something something true love some-
          thing the, 76
son, 444
soon, 397
soren kierkegaard, 440
sovereign citizens, 356
soviet collective farms, 347
soviet union, 290, 344, 347
space, 174
spaceship, 131
spaniards, 101, 333
spanish sailor, 103
spark, 104
sparkroot, 102, 110, 114, 115
sparrow, 62
special abilities, 71
special ed, 222
spectrum, 183
speculation, 78
speculative bubble, 78
speech, 367
speeches, 369
spending, 222, 264
spending cuts, 271
spherical sun, 49
sphingolipid, 376
spiritual chemistry, 449
spiritual enlightenment, 55
spiritual external, 55
spirituality, 54, 55
sportsmanship, 145
spring, 74
spur, 172
srinivasa ramanujan, 35, 47
ssc, 361, 363
st, 98

stable, 144
stages of moral, 123
stalin, 347, 366
stalinist, 211, 242
stalinists, 242
standardization, 335
standing ovation, 86
stanley milgram, 145
star wars, 188
starbucks, 229
stars, 76
start, 296
startups, 275
state, 326, 332, 335
state legislators, 311
state owned businesses, 272
state propaganda, 347
state-run, 274, 275
statewide competition, 37
stationary bandit, 131
statism, 260
statist, 240–242
statistics, 277, 364, 416
status, 25
status games, 43
status quo, 276
stealing, 289, 292
steel, 73
stein, 361
stem, 442
stereotypes, 146
steve, 246
steve jobs, 275
steward, 75
stickiness, 327
stifle research, 414
stigma, 34, 237
stimming, 197
stimulus, 436

stock market, 22, 23, 28
stone, 450
stone drawing, 109
stones, 108
stored, 77
stories, 34
storm, 108
straight, 88
strato-, 453
stream, 419, 422
street corner, 339
street corners, 339
stress, 253
strong ai, 394
stross, 174
structure, 448
stuart russell, 395, 397
student, 238, 447
students, 125, 357
studies, 265
study, 405, 406, 408–410
study binder, 410
study document, 410
stupid, 307
style, 168
subjective age, 172
subjective time, 174, 176
subsistence, 175, 176
subsistence levels, 175
subsistence wages, 175
suburb, 325
suburban mom, 181
suburbs, 341
subway, 226, 227
success, 262, 266, 267
suffering, 49, 50
suicidal, 316
suicide, 103, 104, 106, 109, 207, 234, 254

suicide note, 109
suicide pact, 109
sunni, 151, 157
super, 42, 404
super speed, 69
super villain comic, 185
super-, 262
superdense cities, 178
superforecasters, 216
supergenius, 370, 373
superintelligence, 393, 398
superintelligent, 397
supermarkets, 250
superpower, 66
superquadra, 340
superstition, 338, 453
superstitious, 337
superweapon, 72
supporter, 75
supportive, 24
suppresses, 304
surfing uncertainty, 427
surgeries, 280
surn, 384
surname, 335
surnames, 330, 333, 334
surprisal, 420, 432
surprise, 192, 420, 421, 423
survey, 44, 393, 399, 400
survival, 153
susan, 390
susan polgar, 389, 391
suspension, 301
swastika, 29
sweden, 279, 280
sympathetic, 35
sympathy, 26
systemic magic, 386
szent-györgyi, 373

t.s. elliot, 54
table, 102
tablets of enku, 108
taboo, 102, 106, 107
taboos, 110
tags, 430
tahiti, 105–110
taille, 328
tainted products, 261
talent, 46
talent searches, 382
talents, 47
tallists, 240
tanzan, 352
tanzania, 344, 345, 350
tanzanian peasants, 352
tatooine, 112
tattoo, 102
tax, 236, 291, 333, 444
tax and spend, 237
tax collectors, 330
tax cuts, 272
tax increases, 271
tax system, 262
taxable income, 270
taxation, 290, 331
taxation policy, 241
taxes, 252, 269–272, 302, 307, 328, 331
taxonomy, 333
tay, 376
taylor swift, 177
teacher, 82, 357, 451
teacher burnout, 230
teacher salaries, 229
teacher satisfaction, 230
teacher stress, 230
teacher training, 451
teachers, 229, 237, 285, 371

teaching, 82, 119
teaching of teaching, 449
team, 131
technocrats, 338, 342
technological sing, 179
technology, 66, 170, 227, 228
teller, 370
temporary security, 290
ten, 263
terence mckenna, 54
term, 96
terrain awareness systems, 277
terrorism, 303
test, 406, 413
test scores, 129, 221–223
textbook, 451
thank you cards, 27
theater, 256
theft, 20, 290, 291, 302
theist, 157
theodore, 372
theoretical psychologists, 216
theories, 322
theory, 22, 432
theory of mind, 122, 124, 125
therapist, 25, 62, 88, 89
therapists, 91
therapy, 24, 25, 87, 90, 92, 361
thermostat, 315, 318
third, 156
third world, 138, 325
thomas, 161
thomas campbell, 343
thomas hobbes, 294
thought experiments, 260
thought processes, 260
thoughts, 40
thousand, 246
three strikes law, 283

ticket, 268
tickets, 268
tiers, 320, 321
time, 56, 68, 389, 451
time dilation, 176
time discounting, 68
time machine, 266
time preference, 130
time travel, 69, 176, 417
timeline, 394
timelines, 395, 397
timothy leary, 163, 166
titan, 63
titanium, 70
title ix, 233
tobacco, 356, 366
tolerance, 132
tolkien, 94, 168
tooth, 203
toothless, 355
top, 431
top 5 %, 138
top 5%, 263
top down, 192, 197, 419, 423
top down processing, 192
top-down, 193, 419, 420, 422, 424,
        425
    model, 196
    stream, 423
torsion dy, 376
torture, 287
totalitarian, 326
tough-mindedness, 308
tourist, 63
town elders, 461
town hall, 337
toxic environments, 267
tracking, 67
trade, 244

trade-, 289

trade-off, 289

trade-offs, 289, 296

tradeoff, 235

traditionalism, 180

traitor, 290

transcription, 40

transfer, 456

transgender, 154, 417

transhumanism, 45

transhumanist, 154

transmission, 356, 357, 363

transmission mindset, 364

transmute, 299

treasury, 79, 270

treato, 143

tree, 192

tremor, 318

triangle shirtwaist factory fire, 254

tribalism, 147, 148, 161, 162

tribe, 148, 149, 162

tribes, 146–148, 159, 162

trickle down, 261, 271

tropical medicine, 29

true tutors, 450

trump, 359–362, 365

trump resistance, 442

trust fund, 36

truth, 211, 367–369

tulip, 78, 79

tulip mania, 78, 79

tulips, 79, 83

turf, 205, 211

turk, 215

turkers, 217

tuscan, 333

tweak, 183, 185

twenty-first-century, 66
    economy, 64

two hundred words a day, 39

tyler cowen, 221

tyranny, 308

tyrants, 309

uhuako, 102

uk, 279, 280, 384

umpteen, 421

uncaring government, 309

uncle tom's cabin, 210

undergrads, 216

unemployment, 83, 253

unethical, 250

unfair, 59

unfairness, 262

unions, 237

united, 279, 378

unity, 448

universal college, 236

universal free college tuition, 82

universalizability, 19, 302

universe, 22, 69, 77

university, 118, 222, 383

university of chicago booth school,
    218

unjust, 37

unknown, 72

unknown quantity, 261

unprofitable, 275

unsupervised learning, 425

uploading, 184, 188

uploads, 174, 186

upper class, 263

upper story, 344

urban liberals, 441

urban planning, 64, 325, 338, 341

us, 273, 284, 325, 385

usaz, 384

ussr, 325

usufruct, 329
utilitarianism, 50, 281, 297
utility, 268, 269
utopia, 238

vacation, 176
vaccine denialists, 356
vaccines, 356
vague, 401
vague memories, 401
value, 117, 223, 287, 289, 293, 451
values, 160
variance, 362
vegan, 119
vegetables, 120
vegetarianism, 18, 19, 119
verbruggen, 364
vermin, 402
vermont, 22
veterinary care, 233
victim, 452, 456
video games, 159
vile offspring, 174
village, 109, 329, 330
violence, 96, 158, 297, 364, 365, 367, 406, 462
violin, 38
virginity, 31
virgins, 32
virgo superconfederation, 76
virtual, 174
virtue, 37, 209, 287
vision, 424
visual system, 419
vitruvius, 445, 446
vlach rom, 453
void, 98
volcano, 115

voluntary, 34, 243, 244, 246
von neumann, 370
voodoo psychology, 433
voting, 131, 249
vouchers, 286
vox, 441
voxsplainer, 364
voxsplaining, 441
vulnerable group, 411
vulnerable subgroups, 414

wages, 229
waiting lists, 280
wal, 261
wal-mart, 261
walking, 317
wall street journal, 230
walter, 87–90
wanda, 249
wanda's acts, 249
wanda's widgets, 248
war, 98, 303
war in iraq, 302
war movies, 201
washington, 137
washington post, 126
wasp, 134, 244
wasp farmer, 244
wastefulness, 264
watchable films, 268
water, 63, 237, 289
water board, 276
watkins, 170, 171
wayland, 249
weak central coherence, 430
wealth, 262, 266
weasel words, 142
weaving, 327
weight, 34

weinryb, 377

weirdness, 166, 167

welfare, 296, 464

well, 409

wergeld, 456, 457

western european jews, 379

what the bleep, 433

wheat, 343

white, 108, 222, 284

who, 30

widget factory, 244

wife, 22, 69

wigner, 370

wikipedia, 374

wildflowers, 74

will powers, 314, 437

willam, 67

william t. powers, 315

willpower, 34, 39

wireheading, 185

wisdom, 365, 369, 445

wisdom of crowds, 216

witchdoctors, 453

within the world, 262

wolves, 96, 97

woman, 72

woman in blue, 73

woman in pink, 74

women, 62, 391

wondering, 74

work, 176, 254

work week, 238

worker, 253, 464

workers, 252

workplace accidents, 277

world, 265

world hunger, 251

worm, 77

writing, 39, 41, 445

writing advice, 40

x, 80

x-men, 268

x-wings, 188

xanadu, 170

xerox, 275

xolair, 141–143

xwunda, 462

y, 155

yachts, 182

yale, 265

yamaha, 38

yearly, 463

yellow, 75

yield, 330

yields, 344

yokels, 338

young, 264

young adult dystopia, 336

yud, 395

zack, 180

zoning, 226

CPSIA information can be obtained
at www.ICGtesting.com
Printed in the USA
LVHW092321291020
670156LV00010B/239